Also by Laura J. Stevens and Rosemary B. Stoner

HOW TO FEED YOUR HYPERACTIVE CHILD
(*with George E. Stevens*)

How to Improve Your Child's Behavior Through Diet

LAURA J. STEVENS
and
ROSEMARY B. STONER

Foreword by John F. O'Brian, M.D.

Illustrations by Anthony F. Holtgrefe

DOUBLEDAY & COMPANY, INC.
GARDEN CITY, NEW YORK
1979

Library of Congress Cataloging in Publication Data

Stevens, Laura J, 1945–
  How to Improve Your Child's Behavior Through Diet
  Bibliography.
  Includes index.
  1. Food allergy in children—Psychological aspects. 2. Emotional problems
of children—Nutritional aspects. 3. Cookery for allergics. I. Stoner, Rose-
mary B., 1941–   joint author. II. Title.
RJ386.5.S73 613.2
ISBN: 0-385-14820-8
Library of Congress Catalog Card Number 78-22649

For
Jack, Jeff, Diane, Rob,
Billy, Danny, Dale, Cory,
Nicki, Michael, Rick, Matthew,
Jonathan, Heidi, Scott,
David, and . . .

FOREWORD

Nutrition remains a stepchild of American medicine. It has been much slower evolving into a practical science than other branches of the medical field. It is only now gradually becoming the important part of medical education that it should have been long ago. Less than half of the medical schools today have a department or chairman of nutrition. In other schools nutrition is taught as an individual or integrated part of each separate department; that is, surgery, medicine, pediatrics, etc.

Nutrition has two important subdivisions, analytical and biological. In the earlier days of medicine both of these were used equally by the practicing physician. With the advent of the colorimeter in the mid 1800s, the science of measuring the various components of foods was developed. At this point the study of nutrition branched into the two major subdivisions. In analytical dietetics, all of our foods were analyzed in thorough detail, and various graphs and charts illustrated our deficiencies, excesses, and apparent average needs. Because of the scientific basis and reproducibility of these results, analytical dietetics has overshadowed biological dietetics, which studies the effect of a given food upon the human organism. This has been largely ignored since it is not easily measured and depends by definition on history and less scientific observations. As it cannot be conveniently catalogued into graphs, the science of biological dietetics has not progressed as rapidly or as thoroughly as analytical dietetics. And yet, to the people who are bothered by the food that they eat directly or indirectly, biological dietetics is the more important aspect of nutrition.

Dietetics at present has also been concerned with *adequate* nutrition so that the body organs can function efficiently; but little has been said about *optimal* nutrition, enabling the individual to interact in his environment comfortably and, in turn, to receive and relate stimuli adding to his intellectual and emotional growth. In the case of the hyperactive or chronically ill child where factors such as exposure to some foods and chemicals are blocking his ability to respond and to catalogue new experiences, the child's development is correspondingly slow and his ability to cope with everyday stresses such as family conflicts, school pressures, peer pressures, and illness is less. The same is true in the chronically ill adult who suffers from his environmental exposure and whom medical science seems unable to help toward better health. Application of the principles of biological dietetics may greatly enhance the optimal nutrition that these people need to enjoy better health.

In the allergic or hypersensitive person the two major sources of harmful substances or stress factors are the air we breathe and the food we eat. The air can be partially controlled, purified, conditioned, filtered, and otherwise altered. We can satisfactorily use allergy skin tests and allergy injections to alter a person's response to airborne contamination by pollen, dust, or molds. But due to its nature, the food we eat is not as easily treated. Food is considered by some allergists to play a very significant part in the major stresses encountered in daily living by the highly sensitive or allergic person. Since eating is a mandatory daily activity, exposure is difficult to avoid. Also the foods we eat most frequently are the ones most likely to be offenders. With increased food commercialization and greater use of additives to preserve that food, it has become more difficult to identify the food or substance that is causing the symptoms and to demonstrate the effect of a specific food biologically on a given person.

Since there are no satisfactory blood tests or even allergic skin tests that reliably indicate the effect of a food upon a person, the physician must depend upon the history and observations of the individual patient. These very often are influenced or clouded by emotional or nervous problems in the individual's life at that time. This is why so many physicians very blithely blame it all on nerves, not taking the time to separate the food allergic reactions from the emotional symptoms. Using the presently available guides, outlines, and informational literature, food allergies can be more correctly identified and subsequently treated. In this way, bi-

ological dietetics is used to improve the nutritional effect on the
whole person.

Fortunately for the parents of children bothered by the foods
and liquids they ingest, the authors of this book have gathered,
distilled, summarized, and very capably presented a method of
using biological dietetic principles to identify the problem and
solve it. They are to be congratulated on the scope of their work.
The conscientious study of this material will be quite rewarding to
the parents of hypersensitive children.

JOHN F. O'BRIAN, M.D.
November 1978

ACKNOWLEDGMENTS

We wish to thank our husbands and families for their encouragement, enthusiasm, and endurance. Thanks go to the following special people: to Jack, Jeff, Diane, Rob, and David for their patience while we were busy writing and cooking. To George Stevens for his encouragement, sense of humor, editing, and insightful suggestions. To Flo Stoner for her commitment to the idea and for her tireless efforts in the kitchen testing recipes. To Anthony Holtgrefe for his skillful illustrations. To Dr. John O'Brian and Dorothy Boyce, R.N., for their enthusiasm, support, and expert advice. Lastly, thanks and best wishes go to all the heroic, dedicated parents who have shared their experiences with us.

CONTENTS

NOTE: Recipes indicated by an asterisk (*) may be
located by consulting the Index.

INTRODUCTION

Every child misbehaves. Most of the time the child behaves reasonably, but parents wish they could do something about those "impossible" times.

Then there are children who are even harder to raise. These children have more than their share of problems. Since no two children are alike, their physical, behavioral, and learning problems are varied. Success and happiness at school, home, or with peers often are impossible. In recent years, "experts" have blamed problem behavior on poor environment and improper parenting, so parents have been made to feel responsible. Even though they may have successfully raised other children, for some "psychological reason" they act differently toward one child causing him*
to have many more problems than any other sibling. On top of the difficult task of managing the child, the heavy burden of guilt is added.

If the child has significant problems, everyone offers the parents lots of suggestions. Professionals may advise that the child will outgrow the problem, just be patient and try to ignore it. They may insinuate that somehow it's all the parents' fault. Parents blame each other. Mothers claim dads don't spend enough time at home with the child. Dads hide at work because they can't manage the child either and insist that Mom just isn't firm enough and the child needs more discipline. Often it's tough for Dad even to admit there might be something wrong with his child, especially a son. Grandparents offer advice on how they raised their children or tell the parents how the grandchild reminds them of their son

* "He," "him," and "his" are used for the sake of simplicity in this book.

or daughter. Neighbors and friends ask why you can't control the little monster and suggest everything from a good beating to extra doses of love and attention. So the parents get lots of advice (most of which they've already tried to no avail) and the child remains a constant problem.

One concerned father of five remarked about his last child, "If Jim had been our first, he would have been our last. He's more difficult to raise than our other four put together. What are we doing wrong?" Another mother of five with three overactive and allergic children commented, "I didn't realize there was anything wrong with my children, I was so used to erratic behavior. When people used to tell me that these were the best years of my life, I dreaded the future." Another couple, parents of four grown children, were faced with raising an aggressive, violent grandchild. They felt totally unprepared for the experience. Like parents of children born late in life, they felt they were too old to cope with such a difficult child. Likewise, young parents of problem children have blamed their inexperience as one cause of the problem behavior. Whether young or old, new parents or experienced parents, couples with a child who is hard to raise face frustration, despair, exhaustion, and criticism by relatives, friends, and professionals. Life can be hell not only for the child but for those close to him.

But there is new hope for every child, whether his problems are few or many, thanks to a growing number of physicians who have been promoting the idea that poor diets and/or specific sensitivities to foods and food additives can cause, in some individuals, a wide range of behavior and physical problems. In turn, parents are becoming more and more aware that what they feed their children affects not only their growth but also their behavioral, emotional, mental, and physical development and health. In fact, many doctors and parents feel every child could benefit from a better diet. So even if you don't consider your child to be a problem, he may behave better if he has a better diet.

For example, one mother couldn't understand why her toddler had such dramatic swings in his behavior. A real Dr. Jekyll and Mr. Hyde, he would be happy and delightful one moment, impossible the next. Since her pediatrician only saw the child when he was calm and quiet, he could not understand her problems. He suggested that having another baby might help. The observant mother noticed that every time her son had an ear infection and received artificially colored and flavored antibiotics, he would become a terror. So she started watching his diet and soon realized that her son became highly irritable every time he ate anything artificially colored or high in sugar. Bacon, luncheon meats, and hot dogs would also set him off, so she now avoids any food to which sodium nitrite has been added. As long as her son sticks to his diet, his behavior is just fine.

Another mother was surprised to learn from her nutritionally oriented doctor that her toddler was physically hooked on sugar. She had already noticed that artificial colors and flavors made him quite irritable and had substituted 7-Up for other colored soft drinks. However, during the day her son was increasingly demanding more and more 7-Up and had begun to waken in the middle of the night screaming for more. She related her problem to her doctor, who informed her that the child was really hooked on sugar and "needed a fix" in the middle of the night. He instructed her to mix sugar-free 7-Up with the regular half and half and gradually wean the child off sugar. When she had switched the child totally to the sugar-free 7-Up, her son easily accepted the change to pure unsweetened fruit juices. He stopped waking in the night and his disposition became sunny.

One learning disabled child was so hooked on sugar that every time he passed the sugar canister he would lick his hand, dip it in the sugar, and then lick it off. He had found his own way to get his needed "fix." Some children will even steal candy to satisfy their sugar craving.

Another perceptive mother suspected that her seven-year-old daughter was having trouble in school due to some food sensitivity. The teacher had reported that the girl seemed too tired all the time to be interested in reading and her other schoolwork. Once the mother learned that chocolate is a common food causing behavior problems, she stopped giving her daughter chocolate milk for breakfast and lunch. The teacher couldn't believe the change in the girl was due to diet, but she became a firm believer after the child had a piece of chocolate candy and was listless the rest of the afternoon. Now the mother uses carob, a delicious natural chocolate substitute, and everyone is happy.

Parents of three allergic children were concerned particularly about their seven-year-old son, who was asthmatic and also a bed-wetter. Although his asthma was under control, he wet the bed three or four times a night. Not only was he miserable and embarrassed, but changing his clothes and bed so many times each night interfered with a good night's sleep. After carefully ruling out any physical problems like a urinary infection, his doctor put him on an elimination diet. Milk was found to be the culprit. As long as he avoided it, he remained dry at night, a great relief for the whole family.

Another family had a very disgruntled, irritable daughter every morning. She could hardly get out of bed and was unpleasant to everyone and refused to eat any breakfast. Once she finally ate some food, her mood would improve and she would be fine until the next morning. Her doctor suggested banning sugary bedtime snacks and substituting instead high protein snacks like peanut butter and cheese so that the girl's blood sugar would not fall so drastically at night. The girl's disposition greatly improved and she happily ate her protein snacks. Her family was equally delighted to see a smiling face at breakfast.

Like these families, my husband and I have also seen dramatic changes in behavior in both our children after changing their diets.

Our older son, Jack, had severe colic for nine months as a baby. He continued to be overly sensitive to his environment. By the time he was six months old and sitting up, he had learned to rock back and forth and continued this constant motion as he learned to walk and stand. He also learned to bounce and bounced his way through two crib mattresses. As a toddler he was fussy, irritable, and had frequent temper tantrums. Our first pediatrician always insinuated that somehow we were to blame for Jack's poor behavior. If we would be calmer, Jack would be calmer.

By the time Jack was three and a half, his problems were multiplying and we began to seek other help. Finally we consulted a pediatric neurologist. From Jack's history, physical exam, and abnormal brain wave test, the neurologist concluded that Jack was severely hyperactive. He predicted learning problems once Jack reached school. Although he rarely prescribed medication for preschoolers, he decided to try Jack on Ritalin. But Jack never responded the same way to the medicine, sometimes looking like a zombie and other times being completely out of control.

In desperation we read Dr. Ben Feingold's book, *Why Your Child Is Hyperactive,* and immediately put Jack on the additive and salicylate-free diet. In five days we had a dramatically different child. He was calm and reasonable for the first time ever, a real delight. His temper tantrums and behavior problems disappeared and his body was calm. He obviously felt good about himself and us and was full of hugs and kisses. His speech slowed down and could be understood.

Several months later we discovered by accident that Jack could react to perfectly natural foods too. Chocolate was the first culprit. Homemade natural chocolate pudding made him fussy and impossible for twenty-four hours. Next, adding soybean powder to his homemade bread caused him to become extremely hyperactive. After a number of months, the list of foods that bothered him began to grow. It seemed impossible to feed him. Finally we consulted Dr. John F. O'Brian, of Fort Wayne, Indiana, who is doing special allergy testing and is having success testing and treating children with behavior problems using elimination diets, rotation diets, and sublingual (under the tongue) provocative food testing and treatment drops (see next chapter).

Jack has responded very well to his food drops and diet and as long as he sticks to both, he is calm, reasonable, happy, and a joy to have around. He's in second grade now and shows no signs of any learning problems. In fact, he's among the best readers, excels in math, has neat printing, is a very hard worker, and has lots of friends. Although he enjoys treats from time to time, he knows he feels best on his diet and can't understand why other kids eat so much junk.

Our second son, Jeff, has had an entirely different set of problems due to food sensitivities and has made us aware that it's not just the hyperactive child who is bothered by his diet. Much to our dismay, Jeff also had colic as a baby. He also had trouble tolerating any formula without projectile vomiting, and surgery was finally performed when he was ten weeks old. After his colic passed, however, he became a model baby—happy and placid— almost too placid. Since we were in the middle of Jack's problems, my husband and I were content with the doctor's reassurance that Jeff was fine.

By the time he was eighteen months, however, Jeff had no speech at all. Although he was usually bright and happy, too often he looked like a zombie and was too tired to play. We had his speech and hearing tested and were advised to have him rechecked every six months just in case there was a problem. A year later he had made little progress in his speech and his gross motor development was found to be at least a year delayed.

Jeff began to waken at night having what the doctor called "night terrors." He would tear around the house trying to destroy everything in sight. To our horror, he started having the same type of behavior during the day. He became easily frustrated over everything. We'd already noticed that artificial colors and flavors made him very irritable. Then one night we were all eating plain popcorn, and we noticed Jeff's tummy getting larger and harder by the minute. He started tearing around the house banging his head against the wall. But we had our answer: he was allergic to corn and maybe other foods. So we took him to Dr. O'Brian, who was successfully treating Jack, and Jeff was found to be just as sensitive. His worst food problems were milk, sugar, corn, and soy. Once he received his food drops and stayed on his diet, his terrors disappeared, his legs stopped aching, his speech began to develop, and he became a happy, delightful child with lots of constructive energy. At age five, he still receives speech therapy but is catching up. He loves nursery school and gets along fine. Like Jack, Jeff knows his diet makes him feel better and is very good about not cheating.

While we were learning first hand how diet affects behavior, we were also reading what various doctors have written. As mentioned, the first book we read was *Why Your Child Is Hyperactive* (Random House, 1974) by California allergist Ben F. Feingold. Dr. Feingold has made the idea popular that food additives, particularly artificial colors, flavors, and preservatives, plus a group of natural foods containing an aspirin-like compound known as salicylate, could cause hyperactivity in some children. He has found that 50 to 75 per cent of the hyperactive children he's seen improved on this additive and salicylate-free diet. Jack's behavior had dramatically changed on this program (see also *How to Feed*

Your Hyperactive Child, Doubleday, 1977, for our experiences with Jack plus 400 salicylate- and additive-free recipes).

We later read another super guide for parents of hyperactive and/or learning disabled children (*Can Your Child Read? Is He Hyperactive?* Professional Books, 1975) by pediatrician William Crook. Dr. Crook has found through elimination diets and sublingual provocative food testing that many children with learning and behavior problems are sensitive to one or more natural foods, the most common problems being sugar and milk. His *Tracking Down Hidden Food Allergy* (Professional Books, 1978) is a great help to any mother trying to discover which foods bother her child.

Another interesting book written in a colorful style is pediatrician Lendon Smith's *Improving Your Child's Behavior Chemistry* (Prentice-Hall, 1976). Any parent of a problem child will identify with the characters in his book. Dr. Smith has found that sugar and refined white flour can interfere with normal blood sugar levels causing behavior problems. He advises that milk is also a very common food causing both physical and behavior problems in many individuals. He uses large doses of vitamins B and C and calcium to help calm many problem children.

One of the pioneers is Dr. Theron Randolph, Chicago, author of *Human Ecology and Susceptibility to the Chemical Environment* (Charles C. Thomas, 1970). He has been working for over thirty years on the relationship of food and chemical sensitivities to physical and emotional problems. If he suspects a patient has a rather widespread or complex problem with allergies, he hospitalizes the patient in his ecological environment (allergy-free) unit. After a four-to-seven-day fast, foods and other chemicals are reintroduced one at a time and symptoms noted.

Other professionals are also finding that diet affects behavior. In Cuyahoga Falls, Ohio, probation officer Barbara Reed has found that many criminal offenders eat very poor diets. She insists that her parolees change their diets by eating natural foods and avoiding all refined sugar and flour, artificial colors, flavors, and preservatives. She finds that people don't get into trouble if they feel well and the rate of return of her parolees to prison has drastically dropped (see *Prevention* magazine, Vol. 30, No. 5, May 1978).

Many others have also written about the relationship of diet to behavior (see Appendix J). There seems to be a general consensus that sugar, additives, refined foods, and food allergies are causing behavior, learning, and physical problems in many children and adults. Changing diets and controlling allergies relieve the problems. Some doctors are having success using large doses of vitamins and minerals. Others feel the value of this approach is scientifically unproven as yet.

Although diet is not the only cause of the following symptoms and other causes must be *carefully* ruled out, these doctors have traced the following variety of problems to food intolerances and/or poor diets in children and adults:

Physical Problems:
  Colic, formula problems, frequent spitting up, projectile vomiting
  Rash, eczema
  Runny nose, stuffy nose, itchy nose
  Frequent colds, ear infections, infected tonsils
  Urinary problems, bladder infections, bed-wetting
  Stomach-aches, indigestion, diarrhea, constipation
  Headaches, migraines, dizziness
  Leg aches, muscle aches, joint pain
  Puffy eyes, dark circles under eyes, water retention, puffiness, pale color
  Convulsions, epileptic seizures
  Chills, flushing
Behavior and Nervous System Symptoms:
  Irritability, whining, fussing
  Hyperactivity, overactivity, can't sit still, short attention span, constant motion, talks too much, impulsive behavior
  Hypoactivity, fatigue, listlessness, drowsiness, weakness, sleeps too much, always tired
  Depression
  Paranoia, "everyone hates me"
  Mental confusion, spaciness, feeling of unreality
  Insomnia, can't sleep, up and down all night
  Anxiety, restlessness, jitteriness, nervousness, overly sensitive
  No sense of danger, fear of everything

Clumsiness, lack of co-ordination
Oversensitivity to odors, noise, hot, cold, light, touch, tick-
    lishness
Specific learning problems like dyslexia
School phobia

None of these experts claim to have all the answers for every
problem child, nor do they believe that environmental influences
aren't important too. But they do believe that many children can
be helped or improved by changing their diets. The mechanism of
why food additives and natural foods cause problem behavior is
not known. Some doctors use the term "allergy"; others are quite
adamant that "allergy" is the wrong word and instead use "food
sensitivity" or "intolerance." Other doctors remain skeptical that
there is any relationship between diet and behavior. But is the idea
that diet affects behavior really so radical considering the vast
number of different chemicals that make up the human body
which must interact with all the chemicals (foods, food additives,
and environmental chemicals) taken into the body? Many parents
who have witnessed first hand a change in a child after changing
his diet are firm believers that diet affects behavior. Studies are
now underway in several universities.

From personal experience I know how hard it is for parents
who are already exhausted and harassed to try different diets for
their children. Eliminating things like additives, sugar, and milk,
very common culprits, seems an impossible task and likely to
cause a revolt at home. So I enlisted the help of my sister-in-law,
Rosemary Stoner, who co-authored with me *How to Feed Your
Hyperactive Child.* She is an experienced cook for her allergic
family. It is the purpose of our book to provide helpful information, needed recipes, menus, and suggestions for successfully carrying out these diets to see if food is the cause of your child's
problem behavior.

LAURA J. STEVENS

CHAPTER ONE

HOW FOOD AFFECTS BEHAVIOR

If your child has not had a recent physical exam, now is a good time for one. You don't want to overlook any possible clues to his problems, nor do you want to blame diet if other causes are at work. Some routine tests might include a urine specimen to rule out urinary tract infection, especially important if your child is a bed-wetter. A complete blood count will indicate if your child is anemic or has some chronic infection. Lead poisoning should be ruled out. Other blood tests may be indicated depending on your child's symptoms. A five-hour glucose tolerance test will show if your child has a blood sugar problem. But you should know that there is considerable controversy over how to interpret the results. Some doctors believe hypoglycemia or low blood sugar is very rare. Others feel it's very common. In some cases, the doctor may order an electroencephalogram (brain wave test). Allergy is one often overlooked factor that may cause an abnormal brain wave test. Pinworms should be ruled out since they can make children highly irritable and restless. If your child has not had his hearing checked recently, a hearing test may be indicated. Same for vision. A child who can't hear or see properly is naturally going to have problems.

Unless you have a nutritionally oriented doctor to work with you, your doctor may be most skeptical (perhaps even hostile) to the idea that diet affects behavior. So you may be on your own, trying to put all the clues together to figure out what's bothering your child. At least you can reassure yourself that providing a more nutritious diet or trying various elimination diets can't possibly hurt your child. In a few cases, the solution may be as easy as providing better, more nutritious meals or discovering that your child is sensitive to chocolate and removing chocolate from the diet. Unfortunately, it isn't always that easy and you will have times when both you and your child are discouraged and ready to quit. Don't! Hang in until you're positive that you've ruled out diet as the cause of the poor behavior. The right discovery can make such a difference in both your child's life and your own. Here are some information and clues that will make your search easier.

You're going to be investigating three different but related diet problems that can affect behavior adversely. Sometimes only one is a problem, but often it's a combination. One cause of behavior problems due to diet is low blood sugar (hypoglycemia), where the blood sugar falls too low and/or too quickly so that the brain can't function properly. While it would seem that an easy solution to low blood sugar is to increase one's sugar intake, the opposite is true. When sugar or a refined food like white flour is eaten, too much insulin may be secreted by the pancreas, causing the blood sugar to plunge rapidly. Eating more sugar temporarily increases the blood sugar and makes the person feel better, but more insulin is secreted which causes the blood sugar to drop again. So it becomes a vicious cycle. A diet high in protein and low in refined carbohydrates and sugar will keep the blood sugar at the proper level. Then the brain has the right amount of fuel to function properly.

Another cause of behavior problems is a diet without adequate nutrients. Americans think of themselves as a well-fed population but how many of us really get a balanced diet with all our daily requirements met? Most of us lead more sedentary lives than our ancestors, so we consume fewer calories (if we want to remain thin) and therefore have fewer opportunities to consume all the necessary nutrients for good health. Our foods are often high in sugar and refined carbohydrates but lacking in protein, vitamins, and minerals. So if you've often promised yourself to offer your family a better diet, your problem child should give you an extra incentive. Some doctors also feel that these children's nutritional requirements are far greater than average and therefore they need certain extra vitamins and minerals.

A third cause of behavior problems is a specific sensitivity or intolerance to a food or food additive. Although any food has the potential for causing problems in any given person, people tend to be sensitive to those things they consume most frequently. So it's no wonder that many problem children are bothered by all the artificial colors, flavors, and preservatives so prevalent in our food supply. Of the natural foods, milk and sugar seem to be the most common culprits. Sugar is very cheap and who doesn't like the taste? Consequently it is added to many, many foods as an inexpensive filler. Early exposure to cow's milk in the form of infant formulas (which also contain sugar) makes milk a very common food causing both behavior and physical problems. Other foods commonly causing problems are chocolate and cola, wheat, corn, egg, and citrus. But you should keep in mind that "one man's meat is another man's poison"—any food or food additive can be the troublemaker in a given person. No food or food additive is safe for everyone.

Substances other than foods and food additives which enter the body can also cause behavior and/or physical problems. Man-made substances derived from coal, oil, or gas are a common problem for the chemically sensitive person. Jack can get just as hyperactive and Jeff just as irritable from gasoline fumes, dust, chlorine, and paint fumes as from foods and food additives. The following is a partial list of environmental substances that can cause problems:

Gas fumes, gas stoves and appliances
Dyes, paints, turpentine, varnish
Synthetic fabrics, polyester, nylon, rayon
Chlorine in swimming pools
Christmas trees, pine scent
Cleaning agents, fabric softeners, detergents, waxes, oven cleaners, alcohol
Perfumes, deodorants, soaps, after-shave lotion, hair spray, bubble bath

Chalk, pencil shavings, carbon paper, Xerox fumes, newsprint,
    felt-tip pens, glue, finger paints
Dust, molds, fungus, grasses, trees, ragweed
Tobacco smoke
Plastics, rubber sheeting, foam rubber
Dog, cat, animal fur

So you might ask yourself some questions like, "Is my child
better during some seasons of the year than others?" Seasonal airborne allergies may be affecting him. Hives, runny nose, wheezing,
sneezing, and itchy eyes also point to airborne allergies. "Is my
child worse when I'm cleaning the house?" Maybe he's sensitive to
dust or your cleaning products. "Does he have more problems
after swimming?" Chlorine may be the culprit. "Does my child
have more problems around exhaust fumes, for instance, in a gas
station or riding in the car?" He may be affected by gas fumes.
You might get your car and furnace (if gas) inspected for gas
leaks. Gas stoves are a problem for many individuals. "Is my child
worse at school?" Chalk dust, cleaning agents, or some other
chemicals may bother him. Older children may react to chemicals
used in science classes. Some doctors have found that fluorescent
lighting makes some children hyperactive. At times it's difficult to
do much about some of these environmental problems. Avoid-
ance, trying other brands of cleaning agents, keeping the house
cleaner (especially the child's bedroom), allergy desensitization
shots, and allergy medications are some alternatives.

How do you find out if your child's problems are due to diet?
Unfortunately, no one diet solves the problems for every child and
unless you are working with a doctor who prescribes a specific diet
based on what he feels your child's problems might be, you can
try the following steps. How vigorously you pursue them will depend on your child and what problems he's having.

Begin by keeping for seven days a careful food diary of every
food and beverage your child eats, plus comments on any physical
or behavior problems. Also record any medications, toothpaste, or
mouthwash used. Include environmental exposures like gas fumes,
paints, chlorine, etc. After a week has passed, look at the diary.
What types of problems is your child having? How frequently do
they occur? Is your child's diet high in sugar? That sugar may be

hidden in soft drinks, puddings, cereals, pies, cakes, etc. Is your child getting lots of artificial colors and flavors? If his sugar intake is high, then he's undoubtedly getting those additives. Does he consume caffeine in chocolate, cola drinks, coffee, or tea? Does he fill up on so much milk that he doesn't have room for anything else? Does your child receive adequate nutrition? If you're not sure, consult Appendix H.

The next thing to do is to switch your child (and the whole family when possible) over to a nutritious diet which we're going to call the Basic Diet (see Appendix A). Refined foods and sugar are out. You will want to use unbleached flour at least and whole wheat flour when possible. Or try mixing together unbleached and whole wheat flours. Bleached flour is out for several reasons. First, the bleaching and maturing agents can cause problems in some sensitive persons. Second, although several vitamins that are lost in the milling are re-added to "enriched flour," many important nutrients are not and are lost completely. You can further enrich unbleached flour by using a method developed at Cornell University called the "Cornell Triple Rich Formula" (see Appendix I).

You will want to eliminate all cane and beet sugar and sugary products. Brown sugar, confectioners' sugar, and molasses are out. So is raw sugar. Although raw sugar has a few nutrients, the amounts are small and can still affect blood sugar levels and also cause problems if the person is sensitive to cane. Some parents think they're providing nutritious snacks by serving granola bars made with brown sugar. Sugar is sugar and is to be avoided in all forms. Don't we need sugar in our diet, you may ask? The answer is an emphatic "no." It's true that the body needs fuel in the form of glucose, a simple sugar, but the body can convert proteins, complex carbohydrates, and fats into all the simple sugar it needs without adding extra sugar to foods.

It's quite possible to be physically hooked on sugar and to feel terrible if it's withdrawn suddenly, so such a gradual program might be easier on everyone. Eventually your aim is not to use any sugar and instead use small amounts of maple syrup and honey. However, if you start substituting lots of honey and maple syrup for all the sugar your child was consuming you're not going to be any farther ahead. People can be sensitive to honey and maple syrup, although these sweeteners usually seem to be tolerated better than cane and beet sugars. Don't forget that the nutrients in honey and maple syrup are minimal. Both are high in calories, can affect blood sugar levels, and can cause tooth decay, so they're not magical even though they're natural and unrefined. But honey and pure maple syrup if used sparingly will help make the transition easier from highly sugary foods to natural foods without added sugar.

Chocolate is eliminated on the Basic Diet because it's usually found with lots of sugar and artificial colors and flavors. It also contains caffeine, which adversely affects blood sugar levels. Likewise, avoid coffee, tea, and all cola drinks (diet and regular) as these too contain caffeine.

On the Basic Diet you should limit your child's consumption of milk to two glasses (sixteen ounces) a day. Milk is very filling and will kill his appetite for other foods he needs if he overdoes it. While milk is rich in calcium, vitamins A and D, and vitamin B_{12}, it lacks iron, vitamin C, and other B vitamins. Milk is not the perfect food, in fact no food is. Nutrition is best guaranteed through a variety of foods. Don't overlook water as a beverage. It's not very popular these days, but it's time to revive the habit of drinking lots of water. Try serving it with ice cubes in a fancy cup or glass.

You will also want to watch which additives you use. The term "additive" applies to a wide variety of foods and chemicals added to other foods. Not all additives are bad and need to be avoided. But here you should particularly avoid products with artificial colors and flavors, and preservatives (like BHA and BHT). Start substituting natural products. Nitrites found in luncheon meats, hot dogs, and ham seem to cause physical and behavioral problems in some persons so avoid them. For further information on which additives to avoid, see Appendix G.

Certainly there are some other very good reasons for living on this type diet. The U. S. Senate Select Committee on Nutrition and Human Needs has recommended that Americans decrease their consumption of sugar, saturated fats, and food additives while increasing consumption of fresh fruits, vegetables, and whole grains. If yours is an average American family, each member is eating over a hundred pounds of sugar each year and consuming some five pounds of other various additives. Many researchers feel that all this sugar is contributing to the increase in heart disease, diabetes, and cancer. At least, it's well known that sugar helps cause the high incidence of tooth decay, the most prevalent disease in the United States. Certainly sugar helps add excess pounds that many Americans are eternally trying to lose. Refined sugar adds lots of calories and no nutrients. In the case of additives, many researchers are concerned that these chemicals have not been sufficiently tested for safety. Many related chemicals used as additives have been removed from the market because they cause cancer and birth defects in test animals. If you use a lot of salt in cooking or at the table, you should work on cutting down the amount. Salt may not affect behavior, but too much salt may contribute to high blood pressure. So even if your child's behavior does not change or improve on this diet, you should adopt it as a way of life anyhow. Your child will grow up accustomed to and preferring food that is good for him.

These are difficult steps to take in the average family and a gradual change may work out best in some families. If the only way you can get your child and family to tolerate this diet is to serve sweetened foods, you might consider artificial sweeteners as a temporary measure, keeping in mind that some people are sensitive to them and that they also may be dangerous to your health. But if using these sweeteners determines whether you stay on the diet or not, use them for now.

If possible, all family members should live on the Basic Diet for two reasons. First, it will be easier for the child with problems if he sees everyone else eating the same foods. Second, if the problem child is the way he is due to a poor diet or low blood sugar or allergies, frequently other members of the family have the very same problems and all will benefit from a better diet. The tendency toward allergy is an inherited trait. While the child's problems may be blamed for the parents' short fuses and exhaustion, the underlying cause of the child's problems may also be affecting the behavior of the parents and other family members. It's common to find parents who are as hooked as their children on soft drinks, liquor, coffee, and other sources of sugar and caffeine. Sometimes it's hard to convince them to change. Some families have discovered that it's far easier for the kids to kick the sugar habit than for Dad or Mom. But many parents have found after changing their diets that their fatigue, joint pain, indigestion, sinus, etc., disappear. So if possible, try to get all family members on the diet so that everyone's nerves will have a chance to settle down.

If your child has symptoms of low blood sugar (worse before meals, better after, Dr. Jekyll-Mr. Hyde type of behavior, weakness, fatigue), you will want to eliminate honey and maple syrup, limit pasta products like rice, noodles, and spaghetti, give him lots of protein snacks to nibble on (peanut butter on whole wheat toast, cheese and crackers, cottage cheese, nuts, a piece of meat, etc.), and feed him frequently—three meals and three small high protein snacks a day. You may find that such natural fruits as raisins, dates, dried fruits, grapes, plums, and prunes contain enough natural sweetener (fructose) to cause symptoms. If eating these foods causes problems, they should be eliminated or perhaps eaten in small amounts with some protein.

Parents always want to know how long a child has to stay on this diet. The answer is, for a lifetime! Don't panic. You will discover many delicious, sugar-free treats the whole family will enjoy. Once your child has improved, he may tolerate a sugary treat on special occasions. We all cheat on our diets from time to time, but the children understand that the diet starts again the next day. We do try to limit treats to Friday nights so the effects will wear off before a school day.

Will you have to spend hours preparing snacks and meals? Absolutely not. Snacks can be as simple as nuts and seeds served with juice, or fresh fruits and vegetables with peanut butter or a dip. A "peanut butter lollipop"—peanut butter on a spoon—is a snack. How much time you will have to spend preparing foods depends on you and how much you enjoy cooking. Once you learn what foods you should be feeding your child, it's just a matter of making sure they're always available. You may be surprised how easy it is to prepare cakes, breads, puddings, and so on from scratch. Many of us have been brainwashed by TV commercials into thinking mixes save lots of time. Convenience foods certainly cost more.

So at this point you have your child and, we hope, the whole family living on the Basic Diet. Everyone will enjoy lots of whole grains, fresh vegetables, fruits, and good protein. Milk should be limited to two glasses a day. Unless your child shows signs of low blood sugar, you should use just a little honey and maple syrup as sweeteners. This step probably won't be achieved overnight and without some strong objections. Soon your child should lose his sugar craving and his behavior should improve. This may take anywhere from a few days to several weeks or months. Don't quit!

CHAPTER TWO

SEARCHING FOR SPECIFIC FOOD SENSITIVITIES

What if your child is still having problems after a few weeks on the Basic Diet? How do you determine if there is a specific food that's bothering him? If you want to play detective, here are some clues. You should suspect any food that your child craves or any food he dislikes. Frequently, a child is sensitive to his favorite food and keeps eating it because his body is hooked on it. So if your child craves chocolate, you'll particularly want to try him on a chocolate-free diet. If he hates milk and won't drink it unless forced or craves milk and drinks it in large quantities, you should definitely try a milk elimination diet. Here are some other reasons to suspect milk: if other family members cannot drink milk because it makes them sick, if the child had colic, frequent spitting up, and/or formula problems as a baby, if he was bothered by skin rashes and eczema as a baby, if the child has frequent ear infections. Milk allergy seems to be the only specific food allergy that runs in families.

Keep a careful diet diary for a week, as you did before trying the Basic Diet. Are there days when he's good and days when he's bad? What is *different* on the bad days? What did he eat then that he didn't eat on the good days? One problem is determining if the child reacts immediately to a food, several hours later, or even longer. The reaction time varies with the child. Jack and Jeff react immediately, which makes it easier to track down the problem. Their reactions generally last twelve to twenty-four hours before subsiding. It takes some children, however, several days to recover. But an accurate diet diary is essential in determining these reactions and their patterns.

Keep in mind that any food substance with the exceptions of pure salt and water can bother a given person, but the most likely culprits for children in the United States seem to be cow's milk, chocolate and cola, corn, eggs, citrus, sugar, wheat, and food additives such as artificial colors, flavors, and preservatives like BHA and BHT. Tomato, legumes, apple, pork, white potato, and cinnamon are other common problems.

Approximately 80 per cent of food allergies are unfixed, meaning that if you eliminate that food for a certain length of time (one or two months) then reintroduce it on a rotation basis of once every four or five days, your child will be able to tolerate that food. A fixed food allergy (20 per cent of all food allergies) always produces symptoms and cannot be reintroduced. So first you have to discover which foods cause problems. Then you have to determine how much food, if any, can be tolerated. Foods that cause extreme reactions like swollen tongue, hives, collapse, or shock should *never* be reintroduced unless advised differently by your doctor.

If you can't pinpoint one suspicious food, you may want to try each of the following elimination diets, which exclude a given food or foods from the diet for seven to eight days or until the child's symptoms have improved for two days. The child may not be completely symptom-free but should be improved. Don't keep the food out of the diet longer than ten days. Then each food in pure form, one food at a time, is reintroduced and the child's behavior is observed. How do you know which food is the cause of the problems? If your child's behavior is worse or he develops some physical symptoms, that food becomes a number-one suspect. By allowing that space of a week between eating the food and then reintroducing it, the reaction will be more exaggerated than if he ate the food every day. *However, if the food is withheld too long, the child may develop some tolerance to it and not react to it the first few times it's eaten.* So then the food is included in the diet, the child is resensitized, and the food is not suspected since he did well initially on its reintroduction. So the timing on these elimination diets is very important.

It's possible to eliminate all these foods at one time and reintroduce them one at a time. This Common Foods Elimination Diet, which eliminates milk, chocolate and cola, corn, eggs, citrus, sugar, wheat, rye, and additives, is outlined with menus and recipe suggestions in Appendix B. Such a plan saves time but you may find the diet too overwhelming and too hard to follow. So you may want to try only one food or a few foods at a time.

For example, suppose you're trying an elimination diet for milk, sugar, and chocolate. First you serve your child all three foods— maybe homemade chocolate milk made from milk, cocoa, and sugar. Then you don't serve milk, sugar, or chocolate again for seven days. At first your child seems worse but by the end of the week his symptoms have largely disappeared. He's calmer and happier. He hasn't wet the bed during the diet. His legs have stopped aching. On the eighth day you test for milk by giving him pure milk as often as he will drink it, starting at breakfast. By lunch time his nose is running, he's fussy, irritable, and acts very tired. Milk becomes a number-one suspect and again you stop serving it. That night he wets the bed, which suggests further that milk is the culprit.

Then wait until the milk reaction subsides (twenty-four to forty-eight hours) before testing for sugar. On the tenth day your child is better again so you offer him some pure sugar cubes or add sugar to unsweetened pineapple juice. By midmorning he's very hyperactive and can't sit still. Sugar is added to your list of very suspicious foods. Again wait until the sugar reaction subsides. By the twelfth day he is better so you return pure chocolate, using bars of Bakers' Unsweetened Chocolate or Hershey's Cocoa. You are still avoiding milk and sugar. By midmorning your child complains of leg aches, has dark circles under his eyes, and is fussy. Chocolate is added to the suspicious foods list. So you avoid milk, sugar, and chocolate for one to two months. Then see if he tolerates a small amount. If he does tolerate a little sugar and chocolate, you will still want to save these foods for very special occasions.

Keep in mind, however, that your child may have several food allergies, say to milk and citrus. So if you eliminate only milk, your child may drink more orange juice, causing symptoms. Then on the citrus-free diet, he consumes more milk, believing the milk to be okay and so he still has symptoms. Then the wrong conclusion is drawn that neither milk nor citrus is a problem.

Here are some other guidelines to follow when using an elimination diet. Don't be discouraged if you find the instructions confusing the first time you read them. Everyone feels that way. Appendix C may help you understand all the steps involved. Read every label carefully. The food to be eliminated is frequently found in food mixtures, so if the contents of the package are not listed, don't buy it. Be sure to plan your menus prior to starting the diet. You don't want to discover when you go to fix dinner that you don't have the necessary supplies to stay on the diet. If you break the diet, you have to start all over again, so you'll want to do it right the first time. Even one little bite or swallow of the forbidden food during the diet may foul up the whole thing. So don't cheat or you may not learn anything.

Here is a step-by-step outline for the Common Foods Elimination Diet. The principles apply to any elimination diet.

1. Serve the foods before starting the diet. This is critical. Your child's body must be exposed to each food before the foods are withdrawn.
2. Diet trials should last seven to eight days or until the symptoms have subsided or disappeared for two days. During this time avoid the food or foods you're testing for completely.
3. Then return the foods to the diet one at a time in pure form starting at breakfast. Here are some suggestions for serving a pure form of each food:

   Milk: a glass of milk

   Cane sugar: sugar cubes, or sugar in unsweetened pineapple juice

   Citrus: a fresh orange sectioned or fresh-squeezed orange juice

   Egg: a hard- or soft-cooked egg or scrambled eggs (without milk) in pure safflower or sunflower oil

   Wheat: Cream of Wheat, using no milk or sugar

   Rye: Ry-Krisp crackers (plain)

   Artificial colors: mix together equal amounts of McCor-

mick's or French's food colors, then add ½ teaspoon of
that mixture to unsweetened pineapple or grape juice

Corn: corn on the cob with safflower margarine, plain popcorn cooked in pure oil

In other words, you don't want to serve several foods that
have been mixed together, for example, ice cream (milk,
sugar, artificial colors and flavor, egg, etc.) or scrambled eggs
(eggs and milk). If you return more than one food at a time,
you won't know which food causes the reaction.

4. Return the foods to the diet starting with the food you least
suspect. Since your child may be sensitive to his favorite
foods, save those for last.

5. If you don't get a reaction the first time the food is served,
give the food again at a midmorning snack or lunch, still in
pure form. Keep serving this food all day, if your child will
eat it, until symptoms develop. Once you observe symptoms,
stop serving the food. If no symptoms are provoked by bedtime, and you've followed the diet carefully, you can assume
your child is not sensitive to that food. Keep that food out of
his diet, however, while you test the other foods.

6. If your child reacts to a food, you should wait until the reaction subsides (twenty-four to forty-eight hours) before reintroducing the next food. If there is no reaction you can return another food the next day. But only add the foods being
tested one at a time on the day of challenge.

Your child's symptoms may become worse during the first few
days of the diet. This is a favorable sign and you shouldn't be discouraged. His body is missing the food.

If your child does not improve on the elimination diet after ten
days, you may return in excess at one time all the foods being
tested. If his symptoms then become worse, you should repeat the
elimination diet and add the foods one at a time. If his symptoms
don't become worse, he's probably not sensitive to those particular
foods being tested.

If your child becomes worse on the elimination diet, you should
suspect foods you're substituting for the ones eliminated. For instance, a child on a milk-free and citrus-free diet may suddenly

drink lots of apple juice. If he is sensitive to apples, his symptoms may become worse.

Be sure to keep a careful diet diary listing both the foods eaten and any symptoms observed. What symptoms should you watch for? Here are some common examples: headache, runny nose, dark circles under the eyes, rash, stomach-ache, muscle aches, bed-wetting, overactivity, irritability, poor co-ordination, sleep problems. These symptoms can be confusing. For instance, if hyperactivity is the major problem, you may be surprised when your child wets the bed after a food is returned to his diet. Even if he doesn't become more hyperactive, you should regard the bed-wetting as a sign that the food bothers him and contributes to the hyperactivity. Avoid the food.

If you're not sure about a food after going through an elimination diet, then try it over again. You don't want to eliminate a nutritious food if your child isn't sensitive to it, but you don't want to overlook any problem either. If your child reacts to a food, remove the food from his diet totally for one to two months. Then reintroduce it once a week and see if he tolerates small amounts. If he still reacts to it, you'll have to avoid it again for several months. It's possible he'll always be sensitive to that food no matter how infrequently he eats it. The kinds of symptoms may change too. For instance, milk may have given your child colic as a baby, caused him to wet the bed at age four, but may make his nose run when he's ten.

If you don't use the Common Foods Elimination Diet, you can try the following elimination diets in any order. Here are some suggestions for each diet.

Chocolate, Cocoa, and Cola

This elimination diet is one of the easiest to follow. It's really included in the Basic Diet since chocolate is such a common problem and contains caffeine. If you really want to see if your child is allergic to chocolate, serve the chocolate in some pure form (like Baker's Unsweetened Chocolate or Hershey's Cocoa) without all the sugar, artificial colors and flavors. Then remove chocolate totally from the diet for seven to eight days or until your child has been improved for two days. Then reintroduce the chocolate, being careful to use pure chocolate. Watch for any physical or behavioral change. Cola and diet cola drinks are excluded too, as they're close relatives of chocolate and people are often sensitive to both. Again, the cola is found with lots of sugar and additives and contains caffeine, so you should be avoiding it anyhow.

There is a delicious chocolate substitute available called carob. You may be able to find it in your regular grocery store. If not, it will be at your health foods store. You can use it measure for measure for cocoa and substitute 2 to 3 tablespoons carob powder for each 2 ounces of chocolate. A carob drink mix is also available but contains sugar. Some commercial carob powder contains citrus flavorings, so use plain carob powder during the elimination diet and if your child is sensitive to chocolate, carob will continue to work well as a substitute. However, children sensitive to members of the legume family (peas, peanuts, beans) may be sensitive to carob.

Cane and Beet Sugars

If you haven't totally eliminated all your child's sugar as recommended in the Basic Diet, now is the time to see if there's a specific sensitivity to cane and/or beet sugars. Although it is possible to be sensitive to one and not the other, generally people are often sensitive to both. Even labels on bags of sugar often don't say whether it's cane or beet sugar and which one is used will depend on your area of the country and the current price of each sugar. If you use both cane and beet sugar, you should test each one.

Remember you must eliminate cane and beet sugar entirely during the diet trial or you won't learn anything. Beets should also be avoided during this diet. It's tough to avoid all sugars since they're found everywhere, it seems. Catsup, barbecue sauce, pickles, mayonnaise, hot dogs, table salt, Karo syrup, and maple syrup are some of the less obvious places. Be sure to read all labels carefully. Other words on labels that may mean cane or beet sugar are: sucrose, natural sweetener, confectioners' sugar, turbinado sugar, brown sugar, molasses, and cane. You may substitute honey and *pure* maple syrup for sugar in recipes, using about half as much honey or maple syrup as the recommended sugar and decreasing liquids if necessary.

To see if your child is sensitive to sugar, give him some, then eliminate it for seven to eight days or until his symptoms subside for two days. Then reintroduce the sugar in pure form (sugar cubes or sugar added to unsweetened pineapple or grape juice). Be careful not to add artificial colors and flavors which might confuse the results. Watch for any physical and/or behavior changes. Remember, even if your child doesn't show a specific sensitivity to sugar, you will still want to avoid it.

Artificial Colors

If you really want to check to see if your child is sensitive to artificial colors, first give him several drops of each food color (McCormick's or French's), available in the spice section of the grocery. Then remove all artificial colors for seven to eight days or until he's better for two days. Mix equal amounts of the dyes together and reintroduce the food dyes by giving him ½ teaspoon of the mixed dyes in water or unsweetened allowed juice. If he reacts adversely with either physical or behavior symptoms, you know he's sensitive to one or more of those colors. If he doesn't react, then you can assume only that he isn't sensitive to those particular colors but could be bothered by other dyes and artificial flavors. You can easily make your own homemade dyes for icings and Easter eggs by following the recipes in Chapter Six.

Milk

Cow's milk is the most common food allergy in the United States. On this elimination diet, cow's milk and goat's milk (if used) should be avoided in all forms. When reading labels, look for the following terms, which may mean milk: non-fat dried milk solids, evaporated milk, condensed milk, lactose, whey, cream, cheese, butter, margarine, casein, calcium caseinate, sodium caseinate, caseinate, lactalbumin, curds, yogurt, and lactate. These

items are often found in breads, soups, margarines, powdered
artificial sweeteners, so-called non-dairy creamers, which usually
contain milk, cereals, luncheon meats, vegetables with butter or
milk sauces, and dessert mixes, to name a few. So you will have to
prepare most foods from scratch. There are several milk-free margarines available, so consult Appendix F.

Soybean milk may be used as a substitute in cooking, although
your child probably won't drink it like cow's milk. However, many
soy formulas contain sugar and corn so read all labels carefully.
(CHO-FREE® [Syntex Laboratories, Inc.] is made without
corn, milk, or sugar.) In cooking, try substituting water or allowed
fruit juice for milk, adding an extra tablespoon of shortening for
each cup of milk called for. Later on you can try goat's milk to
see if it's tolerated.

Mothers often panic at the idea of avoiding milk for seven or
eight days and if the child is sensitive to milk and must avoid it for
several months, they become terror-stricken. Children really can
survive quite well without milk. In addition to calcium, milk supplies protein, phosphorus, vitamins A and D, and vitamin B_{12}.
These nutrients are available in other foods that your child should
be eating anyhow—meats, eggs, beans, fish, nuts, whole grains,
vegetables, and fruits. However, if your child must avoid milk,
you should check with your doctor about a calcium and vitamin
supplement. You'll want to locate one that is uncolored,
unflavored, sugar-free, and without a milk powder filler! So don't
panic. If your child is sensitive to milk, he will really be much
healthier avoiding milk.

Corn

Corn is a very common allergy-causing food. If your child
doesn't like corn, you may think that he rarely eats any, but corn
is widely used in many forms. Ingredients like syrup, cornstarch,
starch, corn sugar, hominy, grits, corn sweeteners, dextrose, malt,
dextrin, dexin, fructose, shortening, glucose, maize, and vegetable
oil indicate or may indicate the presence of corn. These are found,
for example, in table salt, confectioners' sugar, chewing gum, baking powder, margarine, catsup, pickles, cereals, sweetened fruit

juices, fruits packed in syrups, luncheon meats, and mixed vegetables. The glucose used in the five-hour glucose tolerance test is a corn base, so a sensitivity to corn may confuse the test results. Corn may also be found in non-food items like toothpaste, aspirin, many medications, cough syrup, bath powders, stamps, gummed labels, envelopes, and paper cups, just to name a few!

You will need to locate a brand of baking powder that is corn-free or you can easily make your own (see Chapter Six). You will need to use pure vegetable oil, like safflower or sunflower, for cooking and locate a corn-free margarine that is also milk and color-free. You will probably have to prepare most foods from scratch.

When trying a corn-free diet, be sure to serve corn first. Then remove it for seven to eight days or until the child is better for two days. Return corn to the diet in pure form, like corn on the cob with allowed soy or safflower margarines, or popcorn popped in pure corn, safflower, or sunflower oil.

Wheat and Rye

Living on a wheat-free or grain-free diet is hard. Some people are sensitive to all grains (wheat, rye, oats, barley, rice), but sometimes if one grain isn't tolerated others can be. On this diet, you will need to avoid wheat, barley, and rye but may serve oats and rice. Oat flour can easily be made by pulverizing rolled oats in a blender or food processor. Since most crackers, breads, and baked goods must be avoided, fresh fruits and vegetables will help fill your child up during the seven or eight days on the diet or you can try some of the all oat or rice recipes in this book. Don't expect them to taste just like wheat. Their taste and texture are different, but they may help your child stay on this diet. After the diet trial of seven to eight days, reintroduce wheat and rye in pure form on separate days and watch for symptoms.

If your child is sensitive to one or more of the grains, you will want to use the others sparingly (once every four days) so that the child doesn't become allergic to those too. This happened to Jack. He was hyperactive on wheat, so in ignorance and desperation we substituted lots of rye, which he tolerated for a brief time. Next we substituted lots of oats, which he was able to eat for several weeks. Finally we used rice, which lasted several more weeks before he was bothered by that too. You may also need to try an oats and rice elimination diet for seven to eight days if symptoms still persist after eliminating wheat and rye.

It's possible to make rice, oat, and potato starch cookies and muffins (see Contents), but these don't work too well in yeast breads, although we're providing a recipe for an all oat yeast bread. If your child is sensitive to wheat, you may find if you wait several months he will regain some tolerance and be able to eat small amounts once a week or so. You'll have to experiment.

If your child should improve on this wheat and rye elimination diet but doesn't get worse when you return the grains one at a time in pure form (Cream of Wheat, Ry-Krisp), he might be sensitive to yeast and not the grains. To test for yeast, keep it out of the diet for one week, then reintroduce it in pure form by dissolving it in allowed juice. Watch for symptoms. Bakers' yeast is used for leavening, brewers' yeast for enriching products with B vitamins.

When reading labels, watch for flour, wheat flour, gluten flour, graham, enriched flour, wheat germ, bran, durum flour, seminola, and monosodium glutamate (MSG). Commercial rye, potato, and oat breads almost always contain wheat flour. Adults may be bothered by grain-distilled liquors. You can substitute tapioca, rice, potato starch, soy, arrowroot, or pure buckwheat (sometimes contains wheat) flours for thickening agents (see Appendix I) or in some baked goods recipes. Also look for available mixes (potato mix, rice mix) in your health foods store. These mixes come with lots of recipes. They work best if you can use eggs, but you can also try using an egg-free egg replacer.

Eggs

Avoid both egg whites and egg yolks on an egg elimination diet. Some terms that indicate the presence of eggs in a product are egg yolks, vitellin, globulin, ovomucoid, obomucin, egg whites, powdered eggs, dried eggs, whole eggs, and albumin. Eggs are found in baked goods, clarified coffee, noodles, root beer, some breads, mayonnaise, tartar sauce, some egg substitution products, such as

Egg Beaters, and ice creams. Egg is also found in live virus vaccines, like polio, mumps, and measles.

Cooking without eggs can be a problem, as it's hard to make the ingredients bind together. In other recipes eggs act as a leavening agent. You can try a commercial egg replacer product from your health foods store. Read the label carefully. Or you can try the Soy Egg Yolk Substitute or the Apricot Egg Replacer, both found in Chapter Six. You can also try substituting 2 tablespoons allowed flour, ½ teaspoon allowed shortening, ½ teaspoon baking powder plus 2 tablespoons water, milk, or allowed juice for each egg in appropriate recipes. Greasing and lightly flouring cookie sheets help eggless cookies stay together. You may find later on that your child tolerates small amounts of eggs in cooking.

To try an egg-free diet, first serve your child some eggs. Next, remove eggs completely from the diet for seven to eight days or until the child is better for two days. Then give the child eggs in pure form, like a hard-cooked egg or scrambled eggs (made without milk) cooked in a little safflower or sunflower oil. Watch for changes in behavior or any physical problems. If your child is sensitive to eggs, you will want to be sure he gets other good sources of protein and iron.

Citrus

Fruits to avoid on this diet are oranges, grapefruit, lemons, limes, kumquats, and tangerines. You do not need to eliminate citric acid on a citrus-free diet. Sometimes if one citrus fruit is not tolerated, others might be. Serve citrus fruits to your child before the diet. Then avoid citrus in all forms for seven to eight days or until the child is without symptoms for two days. Give the citrus fruits back one each day in pure raw form and note reactions. Some children tolerate pure orange juice but not the rind, which is frequently dyed orange.

If all citrus fruits must be avoided, you will want to see that your child is getting enough vitamin C, as this vitamin is required daily and is easily obtained from eating citrus fruits. Other good sources of vitamin C are cantaloupe, tomato juice, guava, mango, papaya, broccoli, Brussels sprouts, and green pepper. Or you may have to give him vitamin C tablets or pure powder that is uncolored, unflavored, sugar-free, and without preservatives from your health foods store. Check with your doctor on the dosage.

Other Common Problems

You should try on your own any other elimination diet indicated by your child's craving for specific foods. Tomato is a common problem and if your child loves spaghetti, pizza, and catsup, you should be very suspicious and try a tomato-free diet. Conduct the diet just like those above. We're providing several good recipes for tomato substitutes—catsup, chili, pesto pizza, and pesto spaghetti, all made without tomatoes. If your child is bothered by tomatoes, he may also be sensitive to eggplant.

Another common problem is a sensitivity to one or more members of the legume family—peas, green beans, soybeans, and peanuts. If your child lives on peanut butter, you should try this legume-free diet and substitute cashew butter. Cashews, walnuts, and pecans are not related to peanuts. If your child didn't tolerate soy formula as a baby, you should also try this diet. Soy is another hard food to avoid as it's found everywhere—shortening, baked goods, vitamins, breads, mayonnaise, salad dressings, etc. Lecithin and food "extenders" are a soy derivative. Honey should also be avoided on this legume-free diet, as clover is a member of this family.

Apples are another common problem and if applesauce, raw apples, and apple pie are favorites at your house, you should try an apple elimination diet. Pears are members of the same family, so if your child is sensitive to apples he may be sensitive to pears too.

Cinnamon is a common troublemaker and is widely used in many baked goods. When trying a cinnamon-free diet avoid any product that just lists "spices" on the label. If your child is bothered by cinnamon, you might try substituting allspice, which is not related but tastes similar. Bay leaf is related to cinnamon, however, and may cause problems if cinnamon is a problem.

Other common problem foods are white potato, pork, beef, and chicken. Lamb is usually tolerated. Another clue is to suspect members of the same food family that share chemical similarities. If one member of such a family causes problems, other members may too. See Appendix D for some of the common food families or ask your librarian for a complete list of food families (plant and animal taxonomies).

If hyperactivity is the major problem with your child, you might consider removing all the salicylate fruits and vegetables (see Appendix E) along with the artificial colors and flavors and preservatives. This diet is referred to as the Kaiser-Permanente or K-P diet and is recommended by allergist Dr. Ben Feingold. However, other doctors have found that hyperactive children more frequently seem to be bothered by all the additives, milk, and sugar than by the natural salicylate-containing fruits. You should try this salicylate-free diet if your child is worse after taking plain white aspirin, which is also a salicylate compound. Often parents can't evaluate this factor since the child has only had colored baby aspirin and other colored medications when taking the aspirin. If the child improves on the salicylate-free diet, return these foods one at a time every three or four days and watch for new symptoms.

By now you may be shaking your head in total confusion and wondering what you'll ever be able to serve. Take heart. You don't have to do all these elimination diets at one time and once you've tried an elimination diet you'll find they're not all that difficult. But don't expect to accomplish all this overnight. It takes a while to track down problem foods.

What if your child seems sensitive to so many foods you can't avoid all of them? This happened to Jack and it became more difficult to feed him anything. One thing to try is a rotated diet (see Appendix D). On a rotated diet if your child consumes beef one day, he should not have beef again for five days. If he eats apples one day, he doesn't get them again for four days. Every part of his diet should be rotated this way to allow his body time to recover and tolerate eating the food again. This will not only help your child tolerate the foods he's sensitive to, but will help prevent further food sensitivities. It takes a while to adjust to a rotated diet. Planning menus is essential.

What if you are still having trouble or suspect that your child has a food-related problem but you haven't been able to determine just what the problem is? Your best bet is to try to locate a doctor who is nutritionally oriented and doing specific testing for food sensitivities. This can be tricky. The traditional allergist often does not recognize that foods can cause behavior problems and may not be doing food testing. Other doctors have found that traditional scratch tests for foods may not be very reliable. So you should find out in advance, if possible, if that doctor is doing the kind of work you need.

This doctor will have several ways of helping you. First, he may be able to tell from examining your child whether or not he thinks the child has allergies. He'll notice clues in his mouth, throat, eyes, chest, and skin that will suggest the presence of possible allergies. He will take a careful history which will give him clues as to what substances your child may be sensitive to and whether other family members have a history of allergy. He may want to see any food diaries you've kept. He may order some specific blood tests for allergies. The RAST (radioallergosorbent) test can be used for both food and inhalant allergies (dust, mold, pollens). However, it is quite expensive at this time. Another expensive test is the cytotoxic test for food allergies.

This doctor may do either intradermal (under the skin) or sublingual (under the tongue) provocative food testing. Here a small amount of food extract (working with various dilutions, one at a time) is either injected under the skin or dropped under the tongue. Both physical and behavioral reactions are noted, and in the case of intradermal testing, the skin reaction is also measured. In ten minutes another dilution is administered and this process is repeated until the person doing the testing is sure no symptoms have been provoked (indicating the patient is not sensitive to that food) or reaches a dose that neutralizes any reaction. This is the treatment dose and may be administered every day to the child under his tongue at home and enables him to eat one serving of that food each day. But this kind of testing is also expensive, quite time consuming, and depends on the skill of the person administering the drops or shots. Sublingual food drops have worked out very well for both Jack and Jeff.

The doctor may also recommend antihistamine medications. Frequently if one medicine doesn't work or causes side effects, another one will be okay. These drugs help the child's body tolerate whatever substance is bothering him. They are not habit forming and are safe when used as your doctor directs. If artificial colors and flavors are a problem, your doctor should be able to locate an antihistamine that's white. For instance, Benadryl® liquid for children is colored, but Benadryl® capsules contain a white powder. Optimine®, Tavist®, and Periactin® are all white antihistamine tablets. For the hyperactive child, the doctor may recommend a temporary trial of stimulant drugs like Ritalin® or Cylert®.

CHAPTER THREE

GETTING STARTED

Trying an elimination diet can be a frustrating experience, so a good start is important. You may not be getting much support. Your doctor may say you're wasting your time. Grandparents may find the idea that food can affect behavior ridiculous. How awful that you're going to deprive your child of sweets and goodies! Your spouse may be hostile to the whole idea and may not want to give up his or her treats. Your child may be planning a revolt and you're wondering if it could really be worth all the time and trouble. It is! You won't know if your child is affected by what he eats until you try these diets. What you don't look for you won't find!

It's impossible to predict which children will respond to a change in diet, but any one of the following factors suggests that your child may be bothered by what he eats: a family history of allergy, diabetes, low blood sugar, alcoholism, mental illness, or obesity; strong food cravings on the part of the problem child; if the child has allergies himself or suffers from constant runny nose or frequent colds; if the child had formula problems as a baby. Another clue is if your child's behavior problems improve or disappear when he's sick and can't eat anything for a day or so. Some parents have reported how they've regretted seeing their children get better from an illness when their bad behavior returns. Other parents whose children have been taking colored medications complain how much worse their behavior is at those times, but everyone blames the behavior on the illness. Stress of the illness may cause behavior to worsen too, so don't stop any prescribed medications unless your doctor approves. It's hard to forecast which child will improve on a change in diet, but you have nothing to lose and everything to gain by trying this approach.

If you're like most parents of these hard-to-raise children, you probably feel harassed enough caring for the child, other children, household chores, an outside job, or whatever. Like many parents in this boat, you too may have related food problems, so you will want to try these diets yourself. You may be surprised how much better you can feel and how well you can cope fed the proper foods. After reading the last chapter you may have thrown up your hands and declared "impossible." It's not impossible and you can do it! Like any new diet it will require a period of adjustment for both you and your family. The first few days and weeks are the hardest; after that, grocery shopping and cooking become routine, your family adjusts to different meals, and hopefully your child is responding and his behavior is improved. As his problems decrease, the emotional and physical strain on you will also decrease. So hang in! In our suggested menus for the Common Foods Elimination Diet we have purposely chosen recipes that are easily prepared. You can adapt these to your family's likes and dislikes.

You'll want to choose a time that's good for both you and your child to try these diets. Don't choose a hectic time when you're busy with extra activities, planning a trip, or expecting guests. Instead, pick a relatively peaceful time. Some parents find summer vacation an ideal time as they feel they have more control over what their children eat. Fresh fruits and vegetables fill in for all the missed goodies. Other parents feel just the opposite way and find vacation time too hectic.

Now that you're determined to give these diets a good try and are fired with enthusiasm and determination, you need to enlist the support of your child. Stress what he can eat, not what he can't. Approach the subject in a positive manner and expect co-operation. He may surprise you. Many parents have been amazed by the child's willingness to help. Jack, who had rarely had a reasonable day in his life prior to the diet, shocked us completely with his attitude. Unfortunately, he had long been accustomed to drinking cola drinks as he pleased, and we expected a terrible uproar when he learned he couldn't have them. Instead, he accepted this change matter-of-factly. A year later when he had to give up 7-Up due to the sugar, he announced that he didn't really like it anyhow, it didn't make him grow, and it didn't have any protein in it! So your child may very well surprise you. He probably doesn't like his present behavior any more than you do and will appreciate that you're trying to help him have happier days.

Choose a quiet, peaceful time to discuss the diet with your child, a time when his attention span is long enough for you to tell him briefly what's going to happen and why. Stress what he can eat that he likes. Eventually he will have to learn what he can't have but you can downplay that for now. Enlist his help in planning the meals and picking out recipes. If appropriate, explain that the Basic Diet will probably become a permanent way of life at your house, but the Common Foods Elimination Diet will only be temporary and some of the foods he'll be able to eat again soon.

This is an age of diets so you may want to explain your child's new diet in reference to other people he may know who have to live on diets. Grandparents may be on low-fat diets or salt-free diets; parents may be trying to lose a few pounds; relatives may have a food allergy; a friend or relative may be diabetic. Explain that his diet will help him have happy days. Explaining that his diet will help him grow faster to be big and strong like Daddy may appeal.

You may want to set up a reward system where the child receives stars or check marks every meal he sticks to his diet. At the end if he's been good about the diet, then he can have a special treat—a toy he's been wanting, a trip to the park or zoo that you've been putting off, or some other special occasion that your child would enjoy. You know your child better than anyone, so you'll know best what will appeal to him. But set down the ground rules beforehand and make sure he understands them. Older children in particular have so many opportunities to have snacks away from home that you can't possibly police them and will have to depend on their own self-interest. Remember that your child's food cravings may be *extremely* strong and it may really seem impossible to him to deny what his body is needing. So you have to provide some extra incentive for him. Try not to be angry if your child cheats and encourage him to tell you when and if he does because one slip could affect the elimination diets. Even though you may feel like wringing his neck, thank him for telling you, let him know you appreciate his help and co-operation, that you know the diet isn't easy. But don't blow your stack or you'll discourage him from telling you another time.

Hopefully the whole family will stick to the Basic Diet and even try the Common Foods Elimination Diet. However, if that's impossible and you have a rebellion on your hands, insist that other family members eat forbidden foods away from home. In time they will realize that the meals you are serving are just as delicious as before. No one need suffer on these diets. You can still have goodies. They'll just be made differently.

You'll want to make it clear to other children in the family that you won't tolerate any teasing connected with the diet. Once you've gotten into the diet, it's best not to discuss it very much. Treat the subject matter-of-factly. Put the food on the table and don't discuss anything that is missing. If your child rebels and doesn't want to eat, don't force the issue. Have him leave the table and find something else to do. Don't keep his food around and don't beg him to eat. He'll eat when he's hungry. The bigger the deal that's made, the harder the diet becomes for everyone. As your problem child gets better (and other family members too), life will be more peaceful for everyone.

Label Reading

While you're preparing yourself, your child, and the rest of the family for the diet psychologically, you'll also need to start becoming a label reader. You need to know the ingredients in every food you will feed your child. If the container doesn't list the ingredients or you are not sure what a particular item means, don't use it. If that food is important to your family, contact the manufacturer for further information.

There are several problems with current food labels. First, there may not be full disclosure of the ingredients. The manufacturer may list "vegetable oil" without disclosing the fact that the oil he purchased contains BHA/BHT. Or the term "butter" does not state that the butter used was already colored. So ingredients of ingredients are very often not listed. Sometimes the packaging material is treated with preservatives that leech into the food, but preservatives are not listed on the label.

Second, products often flaunt the terms "pure," "natural," "100 per cent natural," or "all natural," but careful reading of the fine print on the label reveals artificial ingredients like artificial colors, flavors, and preservatives. So don't be deceived by the large print.

Third, some products do not have to list ingredients, as they have a "standard of identity" set by the government. So dairy products like ice cream, cheese, and butter do not have to list ingredients.

About all you, the consumer, can do is to read all labels carefully. When in doubt, contact the manufacturer. Many companies are very helpful, only a few are hostile. If still in doubt after corresponding with them, avoid the product. Checking with other mothers in your area may reveal that their children are bothered by the product, which may suggest "hidden" ingredients.

Start by reading labels of foods in your own cupboards that your family eats most often. Are they artificially colored? Such terms as "color added," "artificial color," "U.S. Certified Colors," "tartrazine," and "yellow Dye No. 5" all mean that artificial color has been added. If the label says "naturally colored with carotene" the product may be okay. Carotene, saffron, tumeric, and annatto are all natural dyes and not chemically related to the coal tar dyes.

Do the products in your cupboards contain preservatives? Remember you are looking for such chemicals as BHA (butylated hydroxyanisole), BHT (butylated hydroxytoluene), sodium nitrite, and sodium nitrate. Avoid products with monosodium glutamate (MSG).

If a product is artificially flavored, the label should say "artificial flavoring." If it's artificial vanilla that's used, the label may say "vanillin." If the label says "natural flavoring," it may be okay but you should check with the manufacturer to find out just what flavoring is used if you suspect a problem. Citrus oils and cinnamon are natural flavors. See Appendix G for further information about common additives.

Which products contain sugar? If you're already discouraged by how many products contain additives you can't use, wait till you read labels for sugar. Staples like catsup, table salt, mayonnaise, pickles, bread, jams, jellies, and many others all commonly contain sugar or corn sweetener. The label may read "dextrose," "glucose," "sugar," "natural sweetener," "molasses," or "sucrose." These are all to be avoided. But don't be discouraged. Chapter Six has lots of easy recipes for all the staples you'll need. You'll also have to know which products contain the natural foods you will be eliminating on the Common Foods Elimination Diet— milk, egg, corn, wheat, rye, chocolate, cola, sugar, and citrus. In the recipe chapters you'll find you can really make spaghetti, chili, and pizza without tomato, mayonnaise without eggs, chocolate cake without sugar and chocolate, and bread without wheat. You'll soon learn from experience how to change many of your family's favorite recipes so that they can still enjoy them.

What should you do with all the products you have in the house that your child can't eat now? Hopefully, the whole family will be living on the diet, so it's best not to have any of those products in the house. Most families can't afford just to discard these items, and maybe you can find a neighbor or relative who is willing to buy them. Otherwise, before starting the diet use them up but replace them with brands or other foods that will be okay on the diet. For instance, after using up a colored margarine that contains milk, coloring, and corn, replace it with one that is milk-free, corn-free, and with natural coloring. In other words, get all of the foods not permitted out of your cupboards and refrigerator. Cravings for forbidden foods can be very, very strong and it's easier if these tempting foods aren't around.

Now is a good time to start keeping a detailed daily record of all food and beverages consumed. This diet and behavior diary will be extremely important to you. Keep a special notebook in the kitchen and get in the habit of writing down after each meal or snack what your child has eaten. If he's eaten away from home, be sure to ask what he's had. If he's old enough and can co-operate, get him to write it down. You'll also want to write down comments on his behavior plus any physical symptoms. You may want to keep exact count of how many times a day he displays some behavior problem—temper tantrums, crying, fighting with siblings, etc. This way you will know for sure if he's better on the diets because you will know if the number of specific behavior problems decreases. It's best during elimination diets to have your child at home, particularly on the days you return foods to his diet, but this isn't always possible. Obviously, you'll have to pack a lunch for him. You will want to keep track of his papers from school to see if his work is affected by the diet. Perhaps his teacher can also keep a daily record of how he's performing both in the morning after breakfast and in the afternoon after lunch, and can encourage your child to put the date and time of day on each paper.

You also need to record other environmental factors. On the food diary, write down any medications taken. Try to obtain color-free and flavor-free drugs if any need to be taken. Instead of toothpaste, which may contain colors, artificial flavors, and corn, have your child brush with baking soda and salt. If he rebels at this as our children did, have them brush with just water. Jack and Jeff have never used any toothpaste in the last three years and neither has ever had a cavity, probably due to their good diets. Avoid mouthwash. If your child goes swimming in a pool, he's been exposed to chlorine so record that in your diary. Watch for any reactions to paint, varnishes, sprays, perfumes, dust, etc. You should avoid perfumes or after-shave lotions for now.

As you look for "safe" brands to replace those you've been using, you may find the list of products (see Appendix F) we've compiled helpful. If you can't find these particular brands, you may find similar local brands, but you should write or call the manufacturer if you have any questions. Fortunately, stores seem to be stocking many more natural food items these days. So it's easier than it was several years ago to find products you can use. If your store doesn't carry the kinds of products you need and want, tell the manager so he can order what you will buy. You will probably have to visit your local health foods store for some items.

You need to start planning your menus now before you start any elimination diet. You don't want to be in the middle of the Common Foods Elimination Diet at dinnertime one night with nothing to serve. If you break the diet, you have to start all over. Good planning will save you much time and effort.

You'll also want to start looking for or making staples you'll need, like catsup, mayonnaise, mustard, etc. (see Chapter Six). You'll also need to buy sugar-free and corn-free salt, corn-free baking powder, rice and oats flour, honey, etc.

Now let's go grocery shopping for a minute. Actually, when you do go, plan to spend some time reading labels and getting ideas. These diets and the shopping necessary can be overwhelming at first. Later on, you will find shopping a breeze as you automatically by-pass most items. Shop without your children if possible. Otherwise, it will take twice as long and your concentration will be interrupted. After your child has been on his diet awhile and has lost his sugar craving and is more reasonable, you can take him shopping and help him to become a careful label reader. After all, someday he will be on his own and shopping will be his responsibility. If he's used to treats when you go shopping, take along some carrots, nuts, or a piece of cheese if necessary.

Okay, let's go shopping. We're going to go row by row as our own supermarket is laid out. First we come to the packaged, processed luncheon meats. These may contain artificial colors and flavors, preservatives (sodium nitrite), sugar, corn, and milk. There will probably be nothing that you can purchase from that array. You may be able to find additive- and filler-free hot dogs and bologna at your health foods store. Hot dogs are dear to many children's hearts and unfortunately there's no practical way to duplicate them at home. Canned hams are out too (nitrites, color, corn syrup, and sugar). Don't buy self-basting turkeys (coloring, butter), but you should be able to find frozen turkeys that are okay. Read the labels. Read the labels on frozen fish. Try to find brands without additives. Don't buy breaded fish (wheat, egg, sugar, color).

Over to the fresh meat department. Fresh meat and poultry are fine. Choose what you want. However, note the purple stamping on the outside of some of the meat cuts. This dye really bothers Jack. Unfortunately, this stamping is often ground right into hamburger. Explain this problem to your butcher and ask him to grind your meat without any stamping. Our store has been most helpful with this problem. There's no extra charge. On your other meat cuts, trim away the stamping before cooking.

By-pass the deli section of your store. Unless you have some inside information and can find specific items that are okay, you'll run into lots of preservatives, colors, wheat, egg, milk, etc. Our next aisle has candy on one side, pasta products on the other. Forget the candy and gum. Even some marshmallows are dyed to make them look whiter, not to mention all the sugar and other junk. Chapter Seventeen has some candy recipes using honey, pure maple syrup, or sweet fruits, but you'll want to keep *all* sweets to a minimum, including these. We've tried to make these treats more nutritious than usual by adding extra nuts, milk powder, wheat germ, and nutritious fruits.

You don't want to overdo pasta products either, as they contain lots of starch and may affect sensitive people with sugar metabolism problems. You may want to buy these products at the health foods store where you can find them made from whole grains. Buy only those products which list ingredients you can use. As far as pasta sauces are concerned, almost all contain sugar or corn syrup so you'll have to make your own. Chapter Ten has some tomato-free recipes too, since many people are sensitive to tomatoes. Make your own macaroni and cheese; don't use a prepared mix. Buy only brown, unprocessed rice. Avoid rice mixes (MSG, sugar, corn).

Next come canned meats, fish, and soups. Many brands of tuna and salmon are fine. Choose brands packed in just water or oil if the type of oil is listed. Forget the hash, meat spreads, stews, etc. (colors, nitrites, corn, sugar). You'll want to make your own soups as the canned and powdered soups are a disaster (MSG, colors, sugar, corn, etc.). You'll find homemade soups delicious and easily prepared. On the other side of the aisle are crackers and cookies. If you look carefully, you may be able to find some whole grain crackers (see Appendix F for some safe brands) that are free of sugar, colors, and preservatives. Most are made of wheat or rye, which you'll be avoiding on the Common Foods Elimination Diet. You should be able to find all-rice crackers or rice cakes at your health foods store. Chapter Sixteen has some suggestions for making these more appealing.

As we go down the next aisle, there are beverages like coffee, tea, and cocoa. Although some parents report that coffee seems to calm their hyperactive child, it's best for the whole family to avoid products with caffeine. Remember that coffee, chocolate, cocoa, and cola are all related and are common allergy-causing foods. You may be able to find some herb teas that everyone enjoys which do not contain caffeine. Don't buy cocoa or chocolate drinks; even the carob drink has sugar added. Farther down the aisle are the soft drinks which you'll obviously avoid. See how fast and easy your shopping has become? Think of the money you're saving!

On the other side of this aisle are the condiments. All catsup seems to contain sugar and/or corn sweeteners, but Chapter Six has some good recipes you can try. Same for the barbecue sauces. Worcestershire sauce contains sugar. You may find a Tabasco and a soy sauce that are okay. Pickles will probably be out (color, sugar, corn syrup), but you can make your own from the recipes in Chapter Six. You may be able to locate some capers, which substitute well for chopped pickles. These may be located in the gourmet or foreign foods section. Several brands of mustard should be okay. Some vinegars contain corn. Anyone sensitive to apples shouldn't use cider vinegar; anyone bothered by grapes shouldn't use wine vinegar. All the mayonnaise has sugar and eggs so Chapter Six has recipes for both a regular mayonnaise and an egg-free one. Ditto for salad dressings—sugar, colors, egg, corn, stabilizers, etc. Making your own is easy and economical.

Now we come to the canned fruits and vegetables. Read your labels. Many canned vegetables contain colors, corn sweeteners, and sugars. Some beans are dyed. Look for fruit packed in its own juice and not in light or heavy syrups (sugar, corn). Fruit cocktail usually has colored maraschino cherries. Some persons even react to the lining of some cans. Your best bet is to use fresh fruits and vegetables whenever possible. Fresh produce tastes better and is better nutritionally. When choosing dried fruits, look for sun-dried products and avoid sulphur dioxide. If you can't get sun-dried fruits in your grocery, look for some at the health foods store. Many of the bottled fruit drinks and juices are a disaster (color, sugar, corn syrup). Choose only unsweetened pure juices like pineapple, grape, grapefruit, tomato, prune, etc. Cranberry juice cocktail has corn sweeteners. Don't overlook good old plain tap water as the best, cheapest beverage around. Add a few ice cubes and use freely!

Cereals are a real problem for many kids. Most of the popular ones have coloring, flavoring, and preservatives, not to mention tons of sugar. Even the natural cereals have lots of brown sugar. Of course, most contain wheat. Oatmeal, homemade granola, and cream of rice are about all you can use on the Common Foods Elimination Diet. Later, if your child isn't sensitive to grains, you might see what your health foods store offers. Read all labels. Even their corn flakes may contain added sugar. Of course, instant breakfast drinks are out.

You'll by-pass all the cake mixes, prepared icings, piecrusts, gelatin mixes, puddings, etc., for obvious reasons. Do look for some unflavored gelatin and some pure maple syrup, which will be expensive. Remember raw sugar, brown sugar, and molasses are out. In the flour line, buy unbleached white or, better yet, stone-ground whole wheat, which is much more nutritious. Some wheat flour has barley added. You may want to mix whole wheat with unbleached so the texture won't be quite so coarse. Look for some raw or toasted wheat germ. You may be able to find rye, oat, potato, and rice flours in your grocery or you may have to go to the health foods store. Instant dry milk is a good buy or look for the non-instant dry milk powder (it's very smooth, not gritty) at your health foods store. Evaporated milk often has stabilizers added. Condensed sweetened milk contains sugar. Some grocery stores are starting to carry brands of pure vegetable oil. Be sure the label tells you just what oils are present and that there are no added preservatives. You may have to purchase these at your health foods store.

Read labels on any spices you buy. Most will be fine but occasionally you'll find MSG, colors, or dextrose added. Buy only pure extracts—vanilla, orange, lemon, lime, peppermint, and almond. Obviously, no food colorings. You can make your own if needed. Shredded coconut often has added sugar and artificial flavor, so you need to buy only unsweetened pure coconut, probably at the health foods store. Forget all the chocolate and look for some carob powder. Commercial carob powder may contain cinnamon and citrus oils marked only "natural flavoring." Choose only nuts without preservatives, oils, and sugar. Raw unprocessed nuts are best for you. You'll have to locate sugar-free salt and cereal-free baking powder or you can make your own baking powder.

Choose fresh vegetables and fruits liberally, keeping in mind that you need to avoid corn and citrus fruits on the Common Foods Elimination Diet and thereafter if your child is sensitive to them. Just a few words of caution. Occasionally sweet potatoes are dyed. Vegetables like zucchini, rutabagas, squash, parsnips, cucumbers, and green peppers are often waxed and should then be avoided as the chemicals are not water-soluble and can't be washed away. Or peel away the shiny waxed portions and discard. Lemons and apples are sometimes waxed. Either choose dull, un-waxed-looking lemons and apples or don't use any lemon rind and peel your apples before eating. Oranges may be dyed orange on the outside, so choose those that don't look so perfect. Then you know they haven't been dyed. "Color added" is often but not always stamped on the skin. We have been told that oranges from California are not dyed. Occasionally some citrus fruits are injected with preservatives, but that information should be stated. Limes may be dyed on the outside, so don't use the rind. This is a good time to choose fruits and vegetables you seldom use, like papayas, honeydew melons, sweet potatoes, squash, etc., as your child is much less likely to be sensitive to foods he's rarely eaten.

Most foods from the dairy case will be off limits during the Common Foods Elimination Diet (milk products, cheeses, and eggs). If your child is not sensitive to milk, use only white milk, not chocolate. If milk is okay, buttermilk is fine but don't buy the kind with butterflakes (color may be added). Margarines and butter are a problem. During the Common Foods Elimination Diet you will want to locate a margarine (butter is a milk product) with a soy or safflower base that is naturally colored with carotene (see Appendix F for several brands). You may have to get that at the health foods store. Most margarines contain milk, corn oil, and coloring of unknown origin. If your child isn't sensitive to milk, there are a few brands of uncolored butter available. Manufacturers add coloring to butter to standardize the yellow shade as the color of butter varies with the time of year and whether the cows are grazing in the pastures or eating in the barn. Dairies are not required by law to list whether butter, ice cream, and cheese contain coloring or not. You might talk to your local dairy. Perhaps they can sell you some butter, margarine, or cheese before the dyes go in. When buying sour cream, whipping cream, cottage cheese, and yogurt remember you are buying milk products and you should choose brands with the fewest additives. Gums are often added as stabilizers and some people are sensitive to these. Choose only plain yogurt as fruited varieties unfortunately contain sugar. Add honey to sweeten if necessary. Or make your own yogurt at home, which is cheaper and tastier. You'll also find yeast cakes or dry yeast packages in the refrigerator case. Buy a brand without preservatives. Of course, all the ready-to-eat type of items, like potato salad, gelatins, cole slaw, and similar foods, are out.

In the non-food aisle of cleaning products, just remember that the perfumes and sprays can bother sensitive individuals and the fewer products (especially aerosols which are easily inhaled) used around your child and home, the better.

You will probably have to bake your own bread, rolls, buns, etc. Some breads contain dye to make them look richer in whole wheat and rye flour. Or yellow dye is added to make you think the product contains eggs. Most of the bread is made with bleached flour and lots of sugar. Of course, there's the basic problem of wheat itself. Oat, barley, and rye commercial breads always have wheat added. The shortening may be corn oil. Preservatives are commonly used. Making baked goods without wheat and rye can be difficult but Chapter Seven has some recipes for oat and rice breads. As mentioned earlier, don't expect cooking with rice and oats to be exactly like wheat. If your child is sensitive to wheat and rye, you will want to try eliminating the other grains too. If he's okay on them, use them moderately (once every four days) or they'll become a problem too.

If your child can eat wheat, you'll still have to bake all your own bread. The super-easy, fail-safe recipes in Chapter Seven should help if you're not an experienced baker. You may decide to invest in an electric mixer with a dough hook, which does all your kneading for you. Or consider buying a bread maker, which is cheaper. It looks like a bucket and has a handle you turn with a dough hook attached that easily kneads the dough as you turn the crank. Kids love to help.

Jams and jellies all contain sugar or corn syrup. By choosing naturally sweet fruits, you can make some delicious jams, jellies, and fruit butters without using any additional sweeteners, so consult Chapter Six for some ideas. Choose peanut butter made of only peanuts and salt. Several brands are available now in our supermarket. Some honey manufacturers have been accused of watering down their honey with sugar water and corn syrup or feeding the bees on sugar water. Perhaps you have a local beekeeper who can assure you his products are pure honey.

In the freezer case, choose unbuttered vegetables and non-sweetened fruits. Frozen vegetables and fruits are preferable to canned but not as tasty and usually not as nutritious as fresh produce. You may be able to locate an ice cream made with honey at the health foods store or try one of the recipes in Chapter Fifteen. There are some milkless ices there. Popsicles are out of course (sugar, color, flavor), but it's a breeze to make your own. Avoid frozen or other prepared whipped toppings. You can easily prepare them yourself. Read all labels on frozen fruit juices. Many contain sugar or corn syrup and a few, like lime juice, contain dye.

You'll soon find that your grocery shopping goes quickly. You'll automatically pass by many areas and know exactly what brands you're looking for. It's not a bad idea to keep reading labels from time to time as manufacturers do change their products. You'll probably have to shop at a health foods store also. Some health foods stores do carry items containing artificial colors and flavors, preservatives, and lots of sugar, which may be labeled "raw sugar," "brown sugar," or "turbinado sugar." Avoid these products and be sure to read all labels carefully. When in doubt, don't buy the product and contact the manufacturer for further information.

What about cost? This will really depend on your family and how you presently live. Grocery bills do seem to go up at the beginning as you replace many staple items. Items like pure maple syrup, rice flour, and oat flour are more expensive. Some products like the old-fashioned peanut butter seem to run a few pennies more than the other brands. In the long run, however, your bills should decrease as you make more things from scratch, use few prepared convenience items, and avoid the costly junk-type foods. As you learn what your family likes and what they can eat, you'll be able to buy fruits and vegetables in season and items on sale. A large freezer is helpful but by no means a necessity.

You may find *The Supermarket Handbook* by Nikki and David Goldbeck (Harper and Row, 1973) a helpful guide. It's interesting reading and gives considerable information on various brands of just about everything.

Sticking with the Diet

Once your child's problems have improved, you will want to stick with the diet. What this diet is will vary from family to family depending on the specific foods you have found that bother your child. You should stick with the Basic Diet of no sugars, a little honey or maple syrup if tolerated, no artificial colors, flavors, or preservatives, no more than sixteen ounces of milk a day, no refined flour or rice, serving smaller meals and frequent high protein snacks. Variety of food is important. This is a good diet for almost anyone and should encourage good health throughout a lifetime.

In addition to the Basic Diet you will need to eliminate any foods that you have found bother your child. If you're not sure, you may want to try that particular food elimination diet again. Once you're sure, keep the food out of the diet for a month or two. Then see if your child tolerates it served just once a week. If he doesn't, eliminate it for a longer period of time and then try it again. If he still doesn't tolerate it, it's possible he never will. For the child who's allergic to several foods, you should try to rotate his diet as explained in the last chapter so that more foods aren't added to the list of troublemakers.

Your child probably realizes himself how much better he feels and that will be an incentive to stay on his diet. Although Jeff was given permission to enjoy a special trip to the ice cream store on the last day of nursery school, he told the teacher he didn't want an ice cream cone because he knew it would make him feel bad! Jack keeps special cupcakes and cookies made with a little honey in the nurse's freezer at school and helps himself on special days. When candy is handed out, he brings it home and exchanges it for a penny a piece. He's very interested in saving his money, so he's delighted by this arrangement. However, both boys were started on their diets at early ages so they don't really remember living any other way and their craving for sweets has subsided. More difficult days may lie ahead as they grow older.

Do expect some times of rebellion. Especially if they've been off their diets, these children may be less reasonable. A vicious cycle develops when the more your child is off his diet, the more he will crave forbidden foods. The more forbidden foods he eats, the more he'll want. You can see that if your child is off his diet just a little all the time, it's more difficult for him to stick with his diet and he may always be a little high and unreasonable. When your child comes in angry and announces that he's tired of the diet and is going to eat everything in sight, don't lose your cool. Instead use some psychology. Don't react by saying "Don't you dare do that again or I'll . . ." whatever you might feel like threatening. Instead, say something like, "You must be very tired of the diet. I know you miss many of the foods. I wish you could have them too." This type of response shows your child you understand how he feels and will likely calm him down. If you have to watch your diet too, he'll know you really do understand how tough it is to have food cravings and not give in to them.

There may be occasions when you feel it's worth the price you may all have to pay to let him go ahead and eat what he wants on a special day—a birthday, Easter, Halloween, or whatever. However, do consult Chapter Eighteen, which gives you lots of holiday suggestions, so that you can plan special days for him without a lot of work and still stick to his diet. Whether you break the diet or not may also depend on the severity of the problems. If it really makes him totally out of control or physically quite sick, it wouldn't be worth it. In Jack and Jeff's case, we do break our diets on special occasions and they do realize they're going to feel bad. We find using an antihistamine at such a time makes the reaction less severe, so you might check with your doctor about that. We also use Alka Seltzer Gold® in the gold packets without aspirin, which lessens the allergic reactions. Some kids don't like the fizz and some people are sensitive to the citric acid in it.

What about snacks and treats in school? Seek your child's teacher's help. She may welcome an excuse to limit all the junk that's handed out. Jack used to take his own snack for kindergarten and, as just mentioned, he keeps special cupcakes and cookies in the nurse's freezer. Jeff also takes his snack to nursery school and no one makes a big deal out of it. If your child's class has a party to celebrate a holiday, you might offer to supply some of the food, choosing items your child can eat.

Another problem is after-school snacks at a friend's house. Try to encourage your child to bring his friends home for snacks and then provide them with nutritious treats. Chapter Sixteen has some ideas for snacks that don't take much work but would be allowed on the diet.

Undoubtedly, you will have to send a lunch box to school. A very few school districts have started to serve natural foods instead of the usual starchy, sugary lunches that most school children must eat. If your child is bothered by one or more food sensitivities, it's even more vital that you pack his lunch.

Your child may be much healthier on his new diet and not require any medications. Most pediatric medicines are full of artificial colors, flavors, preservatives, and sugar. However, several drug companies are test marketing some new prescription drugs for some common illnesses free of those chemicals. Or your doctor can choose an all-white pill or suggest transferring the white contents of a colored capsule to an uncolored plain gelatin capsule provided by your pharmacist. The contents of some capsules may be dissolved in juice, but you should check with your doctor or pharmacist. The Feingold Association of New York publishes a list of uncolored, unflavored medicines (see Appendix J for address). Of course, some doctors don't believe that children are bothered by these substances and will only prescribe the usual pediatric drugs.

You will want to be sure that your child is getting all his necessary nutrients, which shouldn't be hard on the type of diet he's on. Adequate vitamins and minerals seem super-important with these children who are under stress (and you too) and some doctors feel that the minimum daily requirement is not nearly enough and must be supplemented with extra vitamins and minerals. Other doctors feel this is unproven and warn that too much vitamin A and D can be toxic. Natural vitamin supplements can be quite expensive and you can waste your money if you don't give the right amounts of the right vitamins and minerals. Each child is different and has his own individual needs. So it's best if your doctor will guide you. Some children are bothered by the vitamins themselves and others by the fillers in the tablets. On your own, however, you can make sure your child gets nutritious meals. See Appendix H for a nutrition review. Keep an eye on your child's weight. If you are unsure whether he is getting adequate nutrition in his diet, or if his weight changes very much either way, consult your physician or his nurse.

What about eating out? This can be a problem when you visit grandparents or other relatives who may not understand or are hooked themselves on sweets. They may tell you how awful it is to deprive your child of all the goodies, that every child needs lots of milk, and how foolish to think that food could cause behavior problems. You will just have to be firm and encourage them to serve what your child can eat. If they've seen much of him and can now see a change in his behavior, they'll be more inclined to go along with the diet. Do try to avoid a fuss about it or much discussion of the diet with your child present as it may just make things harder for him.

Eating in restaurants is another problem since you can't possibly see what goes on in the kitchen. Try to order plain items like chopped steak, roast beef, lamb chops, baked potato, cottage cheese, or fresh fruits. It's harder at a hamburger stand—a plain hamburger is about the best you can do, with French fries and white milk or water. However, that won't work for the child sensitive to wheat, corn, or milk.

If your child has been receiving professional counseling, special education, reading therapy, speech therapy, or whatever, don't stop until you're sure your child is coping well and overcoming his previous problems. Seek your doctor's advice or a professional's opinion who has been working with your child. He may need some time to mature and catch up with his peers. This can take more time for the older child whose problems have gone on longer. Diet therapy is not the magical solution for all problems, but it should help your child cope better with his world. Don't forget to use lots of "psychological" vitamins too. This means treating your child in a positive manner and using praise as much as possible. Make an effort to offer positive comments much more often than negative criticism. Your child needs to learn to feel good about himself and to know that you feel good about him too.

If your child improves on this diet, perhaps you can help other parents in your community try a diet change for their problem children. By now you know well how elimination diets work and where in your area you can purchase all the supplies needed. Sharing your experiences and offering moral support will be welcomed by other bewildered parents who suspect that diet affects their child's behavior but don't really know how to zero in on the culprits.

If your child does not respond to the diet at all, at least you gave it a good try and hopefully the whole family will stay on the Basic Diet. Your child will grow up wanting and demanding good, nutritious food, which is bound to have dividends. Research continues into the relationship between diet and behavior, a new concept in its earliest stages with much to be learned. So one day there may be an answer for your child too; soon, we hope.

Do let us know how your child is getting along. You can write to us in care of our publisher, Doubleday & Company, Inc., 245 Park Avenue, New York, New York 10017.

CHAPTER FOUR

AN OUNCE OF PREVENTION

If you're expecting a baby or are planning to have one, you may worry that the newest addition to the family will also be another difficult child to raise and have either the same set of problems or entirely different ones. Your next child may be just fine, but there are some sensible steps you can easily take now to ensure his future and your own too.

Of course, there are no guarantees against future problems, but doctors who work with allergic families believe that the severity of future allergic problems of new babies can be significantly reduced. Whether allergies are involved or not, doctors believe that all children can benefit from proper nutrition both prenatally and during the early years.

Ideally, good nutrition starts years before conception on the parts of both the mother and father, but it's never too late to start. Presumably your whole family is living on the Basic Diet and enjoying good, nutritious meals. Once the mother is pregnant she really needs to watch her diet closely. What she eats during pregnancy will affect the emotional, mental, and physical development of her child.

This prenatal time is the most important period nutritionally in the development of the new child. The mother will be eating for two and needs to be sure that both the baby and herself are getting what they need. It's an old wives' tale that the baby just takes from the mother what it needs and therefore can't suffer from malnourishment. Besides, the mother needs to remain in optimal condition not only for her own sake, but also for the rest of the family and the new baby. After all the mother may suffer from some of the same problems as her problem child (allergies, low blood sugar), which can be made worse by the extra stress of pregnancy.

Eating a well-balanced diet, avoiding lots of sugar, caffeine, salt, and additives, taking vitamin and mineral supplements as prescribed by her doctor (it would be great if she could locate uncolored, unflavored prenatal vitamin and mineral supplements), and avoiding any foods to which she knows she is sensitive, will help her feel better and benefit the unborn child. If allergies are a family problem, some doctors advise staying away from or cutting down on milk and eggs. They also recommend that the mother vary her diet as much as possible and avoid eating large quantities of any one food. She should avoid stress when possible because it's thought that stress before birth, during birth, or after can increase the likelihood that allergies will develop in the baby. She should avoid all unnecessary medications unless prescribed by her doctor. If possible she should give up smoking and limit any alcoholic beverages.

If you didn't breast-feed your other children, you should really think twice about it this time. Besides other advantages, your child will have a much better chance of escaping allergies or not having them as severely. Do go to the store and read the labels on the baby formulas. They are full of cow's milk, sugar, and corn. Such early exposures to these foods make them prime candidates for causing allergy. Even soy milk formulas contain sugar and corn besides soy. Unfortunately, we didn't know how important it was to breast-feed and thought formula feeding would be easier, just as nutritious, and, more convenient. Consequently Jack and Jeff had severe colic and are very sensitive to cow's milk, sugar, and soybeans.

If at all possible you should plan to breast-feed for at least four to six months. Even a few weeks is beneficial to the child. Continue to watch your diet closely as you are still eating for two. What you eat affects your baby. If he develops colic or spits up a lot, you should keep a diet diary of what you eat and drink and see if there is some relationship. You should first suspect cow's milk. Other common foods causing problems are eggs, chocolate, citrus, and wheat. You should also suspect the baby's vitamin drops. Some babies are sensitive to the fillers (some drops are artificially colored and flavored and contain sugar) and other babies are bothered by the cod liver oil itself. You should think twice before switching your baby off breast milk if he isn't doing well. The very babies who are fussy and irritable on breast milk may do worse on formula.

You should also keep the baby's room as clean and free of allergens as possible. A stripped room with all washable items and no rugs may help. One doctor found that installing an electronic air cleaner in his grandchild's house promptly brought an end to the child's colic.

Some doctors may disagree with the following recommendations but generally speaking your baby won't need any other food but breast milk until three or four months of age. The longer you wait, the better the chances the child won't become sensitive to the new foods. This may make you feel uneasy and you may get a lot of criticism from family and friends who all started solids early. Your baby doesn't need these foods in the early months. Not knowing why the boys were screaming with colic, we used to hope that a little cereal would make them feel better and help them go longer between feedings. It didn't and it just exposed them unnecessarily to the cereal grains at an early age. Hopefully your doctor will be helpful and encourage you to breast-feed and start solids late.

When you do start solids you should begin with rice or oat cereals. Read the labels carefully and avoid those with barley, at least for now. Mix these with either breast milk or water, not formula or cow's milk. Leave wheat until at least nine months. Fruits may be started at four months or preferably six, but apples, peaches, citrus fruits, and berries should be withheld longer. Leave raw fruit till twelve months (except bananas), citrus fruits until eighteen months, and berries until twenty-four months. Bananas, pears, plums, and apricots are least likely to cause problems. Vegetables may be started next, beginning with carrots. Beets, squash, asparagus, sweet potato, and white potato are likely to be well tolerated. Don't offer peas, beans, or spinach until the child is a year old and wait another six months before adding tomatoes, leaving corn until age two. Between six months and nine months strained meats like lamb and veal, then pork and beef, can be started. Leave liver and chicken until last. Don't introduce eggs until at least nine months and preferably a year. Then start with small amounts of hard-cooked egg yolk, adding a little hard-cooked white if the yolks are tolerated. Chocolate, nuts, and nut butters should be withheld until two to three years of age.

Give the baby only a teaspoon of a new food at a time, doubling the amount each day until a full serving is given. Don't introduce a new food more often than once every three days. Some symptoms to watch for are increased fussiness, sneezing, diarrhea, rash, vomiting, "cold," and coughing. Of course, these problems can have other causes too. Keep a careful food diary of baby's age, food given, and any reaction. Don't use food mixtures since you won't know which ingredient caused problems. Don't give any one food too often or in extra-large helpings. Try to rotate the baby's foods to avoid sensitizing him to any one particular food.

If you are tempted to go faster than the above schedule, here is what the Allergy Information Association of Canada advises:

The baby doesn't need it. It is you that needs the variety. Fast feeding is beneficial to the baby food companies, not to your baby. Fast feeding is a symptom of our hurry, hurry, world. Above all, remember that how you feed the baby in the first year will affect him all his life. He will be what he eats.

Should you buy your baby food or make your own? There are pros and cons both ways and you'll have to decide what's best for you, your life style, and your baby. If you do buy baby foods, be careful to read all labels. Fortunately, the baby food companies have made an effort to improve their products by removing salt, preservatives, artificial colors and flavors, and reducing or eliminating sugar. But many products still contain sugar, so you'll have to read labels carefully. Avoid mixtures like mixed vegetables, cereals, dinners, and desserts. If you buy bananas, you may find other ingredients like orange juice added, which you'll want to avoid using for a while. Teething biscuits and crackers all contain bleached flour, corn syrup, and sugar. Juices may contain sugar or corn sweetener. Be sure not to use a bottle of milk or juice as a pacifier at bedtimes or nap times as the natural sugars will help cause tooth decay.

If your baby is weaned from the breast before a year, you might consider using soy milk instead of cow's milk for a while, especially if there is a family history of cow's milk allergy.

Once the child is old enough to eat what the rest of the family is eating, be sure to keep him on the Basic Diet and away from sugary, empty snacks. Finger foods like raw carrots, celery, slices of fruit, cheese, and bits of meat should be encouraged at the appropriate age. Use nut butters after age three. If your child starts life on the best foods and continues on them in his early years, he won't crave sweets and junk and will grow up demanding good, nutritious food.

CHAPTER FIVE

USING THE RECIPES
IN THIS BOOK

We've gathered together several hundred recipes that will help you live on the Basic Diet, on any one or more elimination diets, or on the Common Foods Elimination Diet. All the recipes are sugar-free, chocolate-free, and use ingredients without artificial colors and flavors.

We've tried to make the recipes as nutritious as possible. For instance, carrots and pumpkin are added to cookies, cakes, bread, and ice cream for extra nutrients. Non-instant dry milk powder (if milk is tolerated) may be added to some recipes for extra protein and calcium. If wheat is tolerated, nutritious wheat germ may be added to many recipes. Try adding brewers' yeast for extra protein, B vitamins, and iron. Nuts used in cookies, breads, and cakes provide extra protein, minerals, and vitamins.

The recipes aim to use as little honey or maple syrup as possible and depend instead on the natural sweetness of dates, raisins, pineapple, oranges, apples, and peaches where possible. If you find you can decrease the amounts of sweeteners called for, by all means try it. We have included after many recipes how many teaspoons of maple syrup or honey are present per serving or cookie or piece.

Under the title of each recipe is a list of the common allergy-causing foods and natural salicylates that the recipe does *not* contain. For instance, this list may state "No milk, egg, corn, wheat, rye, or citrus" and you know that you can use that recipe on the Common Foods Elimination Diet. In some recipes, where alternative ingredients are listed such as "egg or egg replacer" or "milk or soy milk" or "allowed unsweetened fruit juice," the recipe is still listed as "no egg, no milk" since it can be prepared without eggs or milk.

Here are a few other ingredients that may need some explanation. If you are following a corn-free diet, you'll need to locate or make a corn-free baking powder. Only the term "baking powder" is used in the recipes. "Uncolored butter or allowed margarine" means if milk is allowed, locate an uncolored butter. If your butter is unsalted, you may want to add one-half teaspoon salt per stick of butter. That salt is not included in the recipes. Otherwise, locate a margarine that is colored with one of the vegetable dyes like carotene and does not contain any milk. If your diet is corn-free, you'll need to locate a naturally colored all-soybean or -safflower oil margarine. Similarly, you will need to use a pure (without added preservatives), corn-free vegetable oil such as safflower, soy, or sunflower oil. If you are following the Common Foods Elimination Diet, you may need to toast your own carob powder, as the commercial brands may contain citrus oils.

We hope from this core of recipes, you can choose foods that will delight your family and child while adhering to his particular diet. Hopefully you will then be able to adapt many favorite family recipes so that they are as nutritious as possible while observing the limits of your child's diet.

CHAPTER SIX

MAKING YOUR OWN STAPLES

You should be able to locate "safe" brands of many staples, but if you can't or aren't sure about the ingredients, this chapter should help.

Homemade Butters

HOMEMADE SALTED BUTTER

No egg, corn, wheat, rye, citrus, or salicylates

Makes 8 ounces

1½ pints pure whipping cream, chilled
1 teaspoon salt

Using an electric mixer on high speed, beat the chilled cream until it passes the foamy stage and begins to look like corn meal mush. Continue beating until lumps are corn-kernel size.

Drain off the liquid (buttermilk). Run very cold water over the remaining butter and press with a wooden spoon, squeezing out more buttermilk. Discard the liquid and repeat procedure until the buttermilk is completely gone.

Add salt and mix thoroughly. Pack into containers and store in the refrigerator. Butter may be frozen up to 6 months.

WHIPPED BUTTER

No egg, corn, wheat, rye, citrus, or salicylates

Makes 1½ cups

2 sticks uncolored butter, softened
¼ cup pure whipping cream
1 teaspoon salt (if butter is unsalted)

Beat softened butter with mixer on high speed until smooth. Slowly add the cream and continue to beat until well mixed and very light. Add salt and mix well. This stretches the butter and also makes it easier to spread.

APPLE BUTTER

No milk, egg, corn, wheat, rye, or citrus

Makes 1½ cups

1 pound apples (peeled, if waxed)
1 cup unsweetened apple juice or apple cider
1 teaspoon cinnamon (optional)

Wash, quarter, and core apples. In a heavy saucepan cook apples in apple juice or cider until soft. Put through a strainer or food mill. Add cinnamon. Return to heat. Simmer until desired thickness is reached.

HONEY OR MAPLE BUTTER

No milk, egg, corn, wheat, rye, citrus, or salicylates

Makes about ⅔ cup

½ cup uncolored butter or allowed margarine, softened
¼ cup pure honey or pure maple syrup

½ teaspoon salt (if using unsalted butter)
¼ teaspoon cinnamon (optional)
¼ teaspoon nutmeg (optional)

When butter is soft, beat in honey or maple syrup and spices and whip until fluffy. Refrigerate and use as a spread on toast or biscuits, or melt and pour over hot pancakes, waffles, or French toast.

PEACH BUTTER

No milk, egg, corn, wheat, rye, or citrus

Makes 1 cup

4 cups (about 2 pounds or 8 peaches) sliced peaches
½ cup water
1 teaspoon pure lemon juice (optional)
⅛ teaspoon allspice or cinnamon (optional)

In a heavy saucepan cover sliced peaches with water. Bring to a boil. Cover, reduce heat, and simmer until peaches are soft. Pour peaches and liquid in a blender. Chop. Return peaches to saucepan. Bring to a boil again. Reduce heat and simmer slowly until peach butter is thick. Add lemon juice and spices, if desired, and simmer 5 more minutes. Pour boiling hot into sterilized canning jars, leaving ½-inch headspace. Seal. Or cool and refrigerate in a covered container. Delicious on toast, muffins, pancakes, etc.

Basic White Sauces

THIN WHITE SAUCE

No milk, egg, corn, wheat, rye, citrus, or salicylates

Makes 1 cup

For vegetables, soup, or macaroni.

1 tablespoon pure allowed vegetable oil or uncolored butter or allowed margarine, melted
1 tablespoon unbleached flour or rice flour or potato starch flour

½ teaspoon salt
Dash of pepper
1 cup milk or Chicken Stock*

(See cooking directions under Thick White Sauce below.)*

MEDIUM WHITE SAUCE

No milk, egg, corn, wheat, rye, citrus, or salicylates

Makes 1 cup

For meats, eggs, noodles, fish, scalloped dishes.

2 tablespoons pure allowed vegetable oil or un-colored butter or allowed margarine, melted

2 tablespoons unbleached flour or rice flour or potato starch flour

½ teaspoon salt
Dash of pepper
1 cup milk or Chicken Stock*

(See cooking directions under Thick White Sauce below.)*

THICK WHITE SAUCE

No milk, egg, corn, wheat, rye, citrus, or salicylates

Makes 1 cup

For soufflés or thick cheese sauces.

3 tablespoons pure allowed vegetable oil or un-colored butter or allowed margarine, melted

4 tablespoons unbleached flour or rice flour or potato starch flour

¼ teaspoon salt
Dash of pepper
1 cup milk or Chicken Stock*

Blend shortening with flour and seasonings in a heavy saucepan. Add liquid gradually. Cook quickly, stirring constantly, until mixture thickens and bubbles.

Condiments

CATSUP I (TOMATOLESS)

No milk, egg, corn, wheat, rye, or citrus

Makes 2 cups

1 quart (4 cups) fresh or
   frozen (thawed)
   chopped rhubarb
½ cup water
¼ cup chopped onion or 1
   tablespoon dried minced
   onion

½ cup honey
½ teaspoon salt
¼ cup apple cider vinegar
¾ teaspoon cinnamon
½ teaspoon ginger
¼ teaspoon nutmeg

Combine rhubarb, water, onion, honey, salt, and vinegar in a heavy 2-quart saucepan. Over medium heat, boil slowly until thick, stirring occasionally. Add spices, cook 5 more minutes. Cool. If too lumpy, put in blender until consistency is equivalent to that of tomato catsup.

Refrigerate in covered container. Use as needed, or pour boiling hot into sterilized canning jars, leaving ⅛-inch headspace at the top. Adjust lids. Process in boiling water bath for 5 minutes.

CATSUP II (TOMATOLESS)

No milk, egg, corn, wheat, rye, or citrus

Makes 3 cups

1 8-ounce can sliced beets,
   undrained
⅔ cup apple cider vinegar
⅓ cup water
½ cup pure maple syrup
¼ cup coarsely chopped
   onion

½ teaspoon cinnamon
½ teaspoon nutmeg
1 teaspoon salt
1 teaspoon Tabasco sauce
1 1-pound can pumpkin

Combine all ingredients except pumpkin in a blender. Blend

until smooth. Add pumpkin and mix thoroughly. Simmer for 20 to 30 minutes. Cool and store in refrigerator.

TOMATO CATSUP

No milk, egg, corn, wheat, rye, or citrus

Makes about 2 cups

½ cup apple cider vinegar
½ teaspoon whole cloves
1 2-inch stick cinnamon
½ teaspoon celery seed
4 pounds (about 12 medium) tomatoes, washed and quartered

¼ cup water
2 tablespoons dried minced onion or ½ onion, finely chopped
⅛ teaspoon black pepper
¼ cup honey
2 teaspoons salt

Combine vinegar, cloves, cinnamon, and celery seed in a small covered saucepan. Bring to a boil. Remove from heat. Let stand.

In a large kettle or Dutch oven cook tomatoes, water, onion, and pepper over medium heat until tomatoes are quite soft. Put tomato mixture through sieve or food mill. Return juice to stove. Add honey and salt. Bring to a boil. Reduce heat and simmer until volume has been reduced by half. Strain vinegar into tomato mixture, discarding spices. Continue simmering until desired consistency is reached, stirring frequently. Pour into sterilized canning jars leaving ½-inch headspace. Seal. Process in boiling water bath for 5 minutes. Or cool and refrigerate in a covered container.

HORSERADISH

No milk, egg, corn, wheat, rye, or citrus

Horseradish roots
Apple cider vinegar

Wash, scrape, and grate fresh horseradish roots. Fill sterilized canning jars two-thirds full with grated roots. Cover roots with vinegar. Seal. Store in cool, dry place.

HORSERADISH SAUCE I

No egg, corn, wheat, rye, or citrus

Makes 8 ounces

1 cup sour cream
2 tablespoons drained Horse-
    radish*

½ teaspoon dry mustard
¼ teaspoon salt
Dash of paprika

Combine all ingredients and mix well. Chill.

HORSERADISH SAUCE II

No egg, corn, wheat, or rye

Makes 8 ounces

8 ounces softened cream cheese
3 tablespoons drained Horseradish*
1 tablespoon pure lemon juice

Whip cheese. Add horseradish and lemon juice. Mix well and chill.

MAYONNAISE

No milk, corn, wheat, rye, or citrus

Makes 16 to 18 ounces

2 egg yolks
3 tablespoons apple cider
    vinegar
½ teaspoon honey
1 teaspoon salt

Dash of pepper
1 teaspoon dry mustard
½ teaspoon paprika
2 cups pure allowed vegetable
    oil

Place egg yolks with 1 tablespoon vinegar in mixing bowl and whip with electric mixer. Continue beating and add honey, salt, pepper, mustard, and paprika. Add oil a tablespoon at a time, beating continuously until mixture is very thick. Beat in remaining vinegar. Gradually add remaining oil and beat until the mayonnaise is thick and well blended. Refrigerate.

EGGLESS MAYONNAISE

No milk, egg, corn, wheat, rye, or citrus

Makes 1 cup

1½ tablespoons rice flour or
   2 tablespoons unbleached
   flour
½ teaspoon salt
¼ teaspoon dry mustard
¼ cup cold water
¾ cup boiling water

1 tablespoon apple cider
   vinegar
½ cup pure allowed vege-
   table oil
⅛ teaspoon paprika
Salt and pepper

Combine flour, salt, dry mustard, and cold water. Stir well. Add boiling water. Stir constantly over medium heat until mixture thickens and comes to a boil.

Cool until lukewarm. Combine vinegar and ½ cup pure vegetable oil. Add the vinegar and oil very slowly to the mixture, beating constantly. When it is well blended, beat in paprika. Salt and pepper to taste. Refrigerate in a covered container.

HOT MUSTARD

No milk, corn, wheat, rye, or citrus

Makes 2 cups

1 cup apple cider vinegar
1 cup dry mustard
2 eggs
½ cup honey

Add vinegar to dry mustard and stir until lumps disappear. Cover and let sit overnight.

Pour the mustard mixture into the top of a double boiler. Beat eggs, add honey. Slowly add the egg and honey mixture to the mustard. Cook over boiling water, stirring to avoid lumps, for about 12 minutes until thickened. Pour into covered container and refrigerate. Keeps for months.

MILD MUSTARD

No milk, corn, wheat, rye, or citrus

1 part Mayonnaise*
1 part Hot Mustard*

Mix equal parts mayonnaise and hot mustard recipes. Refrigerate.

Main Dish Sauces

EGG SAUCE FOR FISH

No milk, corn, wheat, rye, citrus, or salicylates

Serves 4

2 tablespoons pure allowed vegetable oil
2 tablespoons unbleached flour or rice flour
1 cup Chicken Stock*

½ teaspoon salt
¼ teaspoon dried minced onion
Dash of pepper
1 hard-cooked egg, chopped

In a saucepan combine oil and flour. Add stock. Stir constantly over medium heat until sauce boils. Add salt, onion, and pepper. Remove from heat and stir in chopped egg. Serve in gravy bowl so the sauce may be poured over the fish as needed.

TARTAR SAUCE

No milk, egg, corn, wheat, rye, or citrus

Makes 1 cup

1 cup Mayonnaise* or Eggless Mayonnaise*
1 teaspoon grated onion
2 tablespoons capers, slightly mashed, or chopped Sweet Pickles*

1 teaspoon dried minced parsley
¼ teaspoon dry mustard

Mix all ingredients thoroughly and chill. Serve over fish.

APPLE BUTTER BARBECUE SAUCE

No milk, corn, wheat, rye, or citrus

Makes 1½ cups or enough for 12 chicken pieces

1 cup Apple Butter*
2 tablespoons Hot Mustard*
1 teaspoon celery seed
½ cup apple cider vinegar
¼ cup uncolored butter or allowed margarine or pure allowed vegetable oil
¼ cup honey
2 tablespoons dried minced onion
½ teaspoon salt

Combine all ingredients in a saucepan. Bring to a boil. Remove from stove. Cool. Use as a marinade and barbecue sauce for chicken.

TOMATO BARBECUE SAUCE

No milk, egg, corn, wheat, rye, or citrus

Makes 1 cup

1 cup Tomato Catsup*
2 tablespoons pure allowed vegetable oil

Mix catsup and oil together and use as a meat marinade and barbecue sauce.

PESTO SAUCE

No egg, corn, wheat, rye, citrus, or salicylates

Makes ¾ cup

2 to 4 tablespoons dried sweet basil
2 cloves garlic
½ cup grated Parmesan cheese
1 teaspoon salt
1 teaspoon black pepper
½ cup pure allowed vegetable oil

Combine all dry ingredients in a blender. Add half the vegetable oil. Blend on high speed. Add remaining oil and blend until thoroughly mixed.

Refrigerate leftover sauce in a covered container.

TOMATO SPAGHETTI SAUCE

No milk, egg, corn, wheat, rye, or citrus

Makes 8 cups

1½ pounds lean ground beef
3 cloves garlic, minced
1 large onion, minced
1 1-pound, 12-ounce can whole tomatoes, undrained and slightly chopped
2 6-ounce cans tomato paste
1½ teaspoons oregano

1 teaspoon dried sweet basil
½ teaspoon thyme
1 bay leaf
1 teaspoon salt
¼ teaspoon pepper
1 cup water
2 4-ounce cans chopped mushrooms, drained (optional)

Brown the ground beef in a large saucepan. Add garlic and onion and cook slightly. Add all other ingredients and bring to a boil. Cover, reduce heat, and simmer for approximately 1 hour. Add more water if necessary.

Use immediately or store in freezer for future use.

TOMATOLESS SPAGHETTI SAUCE

No milk, egg, corn, wheat, rye, or citrus

Makes 4 cups

1 15-ounce can beets
1 15-ounce can carrots
½ cup canned pumpkin
1 onion, quartered
3 cloves garlic

4 tablespoons apple cider vinegar
2 teaspoons salt
1 teaspoon oregano
¼ cup unsweetened Applesauce* (optional)

Put beets and carrots in blender with their juice and purée. Add pumpkin, onion, and garlic and continue to blend until smooth.

Pour into a medium saucepan and add other ingredients. Applesauce should be added if a milder taste is desired. Bring to a boil and simmer for 20 to 30 minutes. Adjust seasonings to personal taste.

This is a very good substitute for the regular tomato spaghetti sauce.

Pickles and Relishes

CORN RELISH

No milk, egg, wheat, rye, or citrus

Makes 8 to 10 pints

12 full-size ears of corn	2 cups apple cider vinegar
6 pounds (2 medium heads) cabbage	2 cups water
	2 cups pure maple syrup
3 large green peppers	2 tablespoons dry mustard
1 cup chopped celery	5 tablespoons salt
3 whole pimentoes	½ teaspoon tumeric
4 onions	

Cut corn off the cobs and place the kernels in large kettle. Chop cabbage, peppers, celery, pimentoes, and onions and add to corn. Stir in all other ingredients and cook over medium heat until tender, about ½ hour, then boil rapidly for 5 minutes. Pack in sterilized canning jars, leaving about 1-inch headspace. Seal and process in hot water for 15 minutes.

DILL PICKLES

No milk, egg, corn, wheat, rye, or citrus

Makes 4 pints

2 quarts water	2 cups apple cider vinegar
½ cup plus 2 tablespoons pickling salt	2 cups water
	6 cloves garlic
8 cups long strips unwaxed cucumbers or zucchini	8 tablespoons dill seed
	4 teaspoons mustard seed

In a large bowl combine water and ½ cup pickling salt. Place cucumber or zucchini strips in the brine and allow to soak overnight. In the morning drain and rinse strips in clear cold water. In a saucepan combine vinegar, water, remaining 2 tablespoons pickling salt, and garlic cloves. Bring to a boil. Remove from heat and allow to steep for about 15 minutes. Meanwhile, pack the strips tightly in sterilized canning jars. In each pint jar, put 2 tablespoons dill seed and 1 teaspoon mustard seed. Remove the garlic from the vinegar mixture and pour while hot over the strips, making sure the strips are completely covered and leaving ½-inch headspace. Seal jars tightly and process in a boiling water bath for 10 minutes.

SWEET PICKLES

No milk, egg, corn, wheat, rye, or citrus

Makes 4 pints

8 cups sliced unwaxed cucumbers or zucchini	1 cup water
4 cups water	1 2-inch stick cinnamon
¼ cup pickling lime	1 whole nutmeg, cracked into large pieces
2 cups pure maple syrup	1 teaspoon celery seed
3 cups apple cider vinegar	1 teaspoon salt

Soak sliced cucumber or zucchini in water mixed with the pickling lime overnight. In the morning, drain, rinse several times in clear water, and let stand in clear cold water for 3 hours. Combine the remaining ingredients and bring to a boil. Pour the hot syrup over the drained slices and allow to stand overnight. When ready to pack, bring syrup to boil again. Remove cinnamon stick and nutmeg, and while hot, pack pickles and syrup into hot sterilized jars, leaving ½-inch headspace. Cap, seal, and process in boiling water bath for 10 minutes.

WATERMELON PICKLES

No milk, egg, corn, wheat, rye, or citrus

Makes 4 pints

8 cups cut-up watermelon rind	2 cups apple cider vinegar
Water to cover	2 cups water
4 cups water	4 2-inch sticks cinnamon
¼ cup pickling salt	2 whole nutmegs, cracked into pieces
2 cups pure maple syrup	¼ teaspoon mustard seed

Before measuring, peel the watermelon rind, cut off all pink portions, and cut into 1-inch chunks. Soak overnight in water mixed with the salt. In the morning drain and rinse several times with cold water. Place in a saucepan, cover with water, and boil until rind is tender. Drain. Combine maple syrup, vinegar, and 4 cups water in pan. Tie the spices in a piece of cheesecloth and add to vinegar solution. Bring to a boil and continue to cook for 10 minutes. Remove from heat and allow to steep for an additional 15 minutes. Take the spices from the syrup, add drained watermelon rind, and cook until transparent. Pack rind into sterilized jars and pour syrup to cover rind, leaving ½-inch headspace. Cap, seal, and process in boiling water bath for 10 minutes.

Bread Crumbs and Croutons

DRY BREAD CRUMBS

No milk, egg, corn, wheat, rye, citrus, or salicylates

Several slices stale allowed bread

Oven 300°

Place stale bread on a cookie sheet and heat until dried. Put through blender, meat grinder, or place between two sheets of waxed paper and crush with a rolling pin. Place the crumbs in a covered container.

SOFT BREAD CRUMBS

No milk, egg, corn, wheat, rye, citrus, or salicylates

Several slices 2- to 4-day-old allowed bread

Bread may be broken up very lightly with your fingers or gently pulled apart using a fork. To retain the light texture, don't crush the bread when preparing the crumbs. When measuring soft bread crumbs, pile them lightly into a measuring cup without packing them down.

CHEESY CROUTONS

No egg, corn, wheat, rye, citrus, or salicylates

Several slices day-old allowed bread
Uncolored butter or allowed margarine
Grated Parmesan cheese

Oven 375°

Spread slices of bread with butter or margarine and sprinkle them well with Parmesan cheese. Cut bread into cubes and brown them in oven, about 15 minutes.

CROUTONS ITALIANO

No milk, egg, wheat, corn, rye, citrus, or salicylates

Makes 4 cups

4 cups cubed allowed bread
2 teaspoons Italian herb seasoning
½ teaspoon garlic salt
½ cup uncolored butter or allowed margarine, melted

Oven 350°

Place cubes in a 12x8x2-inch baking dish (or equivalent) and bake in oven until cubes begin to dry, about 10 minutes. Sprinkle herb seasoning and garlic salt evenly over the cubes. Drizzle with melted shortening and toss to coat all cubes. Return to oven for

30 to 45 minutes, stirring every 10 minutes until croutons are very crisp and dry. Cool and store in a tightly covered container.

Stocks

BEEF STOCK

No milk, egg, corn, wheat, rye, citrus, or salicylates

Makes 1 quart

6 pounds beef soup bones or 2 pounds cheap cut of beef
2½ quarts cold water
1 cup sliced onions
½ cup chopped celery with leaves

1 bay leaf
Several sprigs fresh parsley or dried flakes
2 teaspoons salt
Pepper, as desired

In a large pot or Dutch oven, cover beef bones or beef with cold water. Bring to a boil, add rest of ingredients, and simmer covered for 2 hours. Strain. Remove meat from bones and store in refrigerator for further use. Refrigerate broth. When ready to use, skim off fat and reheat.

CHICKEN STOCK

No milk, egg, corn, wheat, rye, citrus, or salicylates

Makes 2 quarts

4 pounds (about) chicken bones or whole carcass, broken up
4 quarts cold water

1 medium onion, diced, or ¼ cup instant minced onion
1 carrot, diced
Several stalks celery, diced
Salt and pepper to taste

Cover chicken bones with cold water in a Dutch oven. Add onion, carrot, and celery and bring slowly to a boil. Simmer for 2 to 3 hours. Strain, season, and cool. Refrigerate. Skim off layer of fat on top when ready to use stock.

Dessert Sauces and Syrups

APPLE OR PEAR MAPLE SYRUP

No milk, egg, corn, wheat, rye, citrus, or salicylates

Makes about 1 cup

1 cup unsweetened Applesauce or Pearsauce*
¼ cup pure maple syrup
¼ teaspoon cinnamon or allspice (optional)

Combine all ingredients in a heavy saucepan. Heat until hot. Keep warm until serving time. Spoon over waffles or pancakes.

This syrup contains less sugar per serving than pure maple syrup. About 1 tablespoon maple syrup per ¼ cup serving.

CAROB SYRUP

No milk, egg, corn, wheat, rye, citrus, or salicylates

Makes 1½ cups

⅜ cup pure maple syrup or honey
½ cup carob powder
¼ teaspoon salt

1 cup milk or Soy Milk*
2 teaspoons pure vanilla extract

Combine maple syrup or honey, carob powder, salt, and milk in a heavy saucepan. Stir until smooth. Bring to a boil over medium heat, stirring constantly. Reduce heat and continue cooking and stirring for 1 minute.

Remove pan from heat and add vanilla. Cool to room temperature, then refrigerate. Use in milk shakes, for making carob milk, sodas, or as a sauce for ice cream.

CAROB FUDGE SAUCE

No milk, egg, corn, wheat, rye, citrus, or salicylates

Makes 1¼ cups

¾ cup carob powder
¼ teaspoon salt
⅔ cup milk or Soy Milk*
½ cup honey

2 tablespoons uncolored
butter or allowed
margarine
1 teaspoon pure vanilla
extract

Combine carob powder and salt in a medium saucepan. Slowly stir in milk and honey and mix until smooth. Add shortening. Bring to a boil over medium heat, stirring constantly. Cook over low heat, stirring frequently, for 5 to 7 minutes until very thick. Remove from heat and stir in vanilla. Let cool and store in covered container. Refrigerate. Serve cold or reheat in a double boiler.

LEMON OR ORANGE SAUCE

No milk, egg, corn, wheat, rye, or salicylates

Makes 1 cup

4 teaspoons cornstarch or
potato starch flour
1 cup cold water
¼ cup honey
1 tablespoon pure allowed
vegetable oil or un-
colored butter or allowed
margarine
⅛ teaspoon salt

2 tablespoons pure lemon
juice or 3 tablespoons
pure unsweetened orange
juice
½ teaspoon grated uncolored
unwaxed lemon rind or 1
teaspoon grated un-
colored unwaxed
orange rind (optional)

In a saucepan, mix cornstarch or potato starch and water. Bring to a boil over medium heat. Stir constantly. When sauce starts to boil continue stirring and boil for 1 minute. Remove from heat. Add honey, shortening, salt, and lemon or orange juice. Lemon or orange rind may be added. Serve warm over gingerbread, on ice cream or yogurt, or use as a cake filling.

PINEAPPLE SYRUP

No milk, egg, corn, wheat, rye, citrus, or salicylates

Makes 1¾ to 2 cups

1 20-ounce can unsweetened crushed pineapple
¼ to ½ cup honey

Place undrained pineapple in blender on highest speed until smooth. Pour into a heavy saucepan. Stir in honey. Bring to a boil, stirring frequently. Cool. Refrigerate in a covered container. Use as needed for pineapple milk shakes, sodas, popsicles, or as a topping for ice cream.

WHIPPED TOPPING

No egg, corn, wheat, rye, citrus, or salicylates

Makes 3 cups

½ teaspoon unflavored
  gelatin
¼ cup cold water
½ cup evaporated milk

1 teaspoon pure vanilla
  extract
1 tablespoon honey

Soften gelatin in cold water. In small saucepan heat milk over medium heat. Add softened gelatin and stir until completely dissolved. Pour milk into a shallow bowl and chill for 1 hour. Place mixing bowl in refrigerator to chill. Whip milk in chilled bowl until it holds its shape. Add vanilla and honey and continue beating until well mixed. Refrigerate covered until ready to use.

NON-DAIRY WHIPPED TOPPING

No milk, egg, corn, wheat, rye, citrus, or salicylates

Makes 4 cups

2 envelopes unflavored
  gelatin
½ cup cold water
1 cup honey
¾ cup boiling water

½ teaspoon salt
1 teaspoon pure vanilla
  extract
¼ cup ice water

Soften gelatin in cold water. In a 2-quart heavy saucepan add honey to boiling water. Continue boiling until syrup reaches the thread stage (230° to 234° or thread forms when syrup is dropped from the edge of a spoon). Remove from heat.

Add softened gelatin to hot syrup and stir until dissolved. Cool 10 to 15 minutes. Add salt and vanilla. Beat with mixer until mixture becomes thick and cool. Add ice water and continue beating until fluffy.

Store sauce in a covered container in the refrigerator. If sauce is too thick, it may be thinned by heating in the top of double boiler over hot water and beating until fluffy and creamy.

This sauce is high in natural sugars (1 tablespoon honey per ¼ cup sauce) and offers little nutritionally. However, this sauce is free of the common allergy-causing foods and may be used sparingly in place of whipped cream as a topping.

Jams and Jellies

CRANBERRY SAUCE

No milk, egg, corn, wheat, rye, or citrus

Makes 2 cups

1 pound fresh or frozen (thawed) cranberries, washed
2 cups unsweetened apple juice
4 very ripe pears, peeled and sliced
2 tablespoons honey (optional)

In a large saucepan combine berries and apple juice. When juice comes to the boil, cover the saucepan. Cook cranberries until very soft. Put the berries through a food mill or press firmly through a strainer. Add sliced pears. Bring mixture to a full boil. Reduce heat and simmer until sauce is thick. Honey may be added if needed. Cover and refrigerate.

BLUEBERRY JAM

No milk, egg, corn, wheat, rye, citrus, or salicylates

Makes 1¼ cups

2 cups fresh or frozen (thawed) blueberries
¼ cup water
1 tablespoon potato starch flour (optional)
1 tablespoon cold water (optional)

Mash blueberries in the bottom of a heavy saucepan. Add water. Bring slowly to boil. Cover and reduce heat. Simmer blueberries until tender. Continue cooking until jam thickens. If extra thickening is needed, mix potato starch flour in water and add to blueberries. Stir well and remove from heat. Pour boiling hot into sterilized canning jars. Seal. Or cool and refrigerate in a covered container.

BLUEBERRY-PINEAPPLE JAM

No milk, egg, corn, wheat, rye, citrus, or salicylates

Makes 2 cups

2 cups fresh or frozen (thawed) blueberries
1 cup finely chopped fresh pineapple or drained unsweetened crushed canned pineapple
¼ cup unsweetened pineapple juice or water

Combine fruit and juice or water in a heavy saucepan. Slowly bring to a boil. Cover and reduce heat, simmering until blueberries are soft. Whir in a blender until large lumps disappear.

Return mixture to stove, cooking rapidly until thick. As mixture thickens, stir frequently. Pour mixture boiling hot into sterilized canning jars. Seal. Or cool and refrigerate in a covered container and use as needed.

GRAPE JELLY

No milk, egg, corn, wheat, rye, or citrus

Makes ½ cup

4 cups purple grapes, washed
1 unwaxed apple, quartered and cored
½ cup water
2 cups bottled unsweetened grape juice

Place grapes, apple, and water in a heavy saucepan. Bring to a boil. Reduce heat and simmer fruit until soft. Press soft fruit through a sieve, reserving juice and sieved pulp. Return juice and pulp to saucepan. Add grape juice. Insert candy thermometer. Cook over medium heat until syrup reaches the sheeting stage (220° to 222° F.) or when the jam dropped from a spoon divides into two distinct drops that run together and sheet from edge of spoon. The cooking time will vary. Pour boiling hot into sterilized canning jars. Seal. Or cool and refrigerate in a covered container. Use only small amounts. This jelly is high in concentrated natural sugars.

MARMALADE

No milk, egg, corn, wheat, or rye

Makes 5 cups

3 large uncolored unwaxed oranges
1 uncolored unwaxed lemon
6 cups cold water
1½ cups chopped dates
1 to 3 tablespoons honey (optional)

Wash oranges and lemon well. Quarter and remove seeds. Soak oranges and lemon in cold water in the refrigerator for 24 hours. Cut fruit into very small pieces. In a large saucepan or kettle, using the water the fruit was soaked in, return chopped fruit to water. Add dates. Bring to a boil. Reduce heat and simmer until syrup sheets from a spoon (220° to 222° F.). If marmalade is too tart, add honey tablespoon by tablespoon, tasting after each addition. Pour boiling hot into sterilized canning jars, leaving ½-inch headspace. Seal. Or cool and refrigerate in a covered container.

This marmalade is high in natural fruit sugars, so use sparingly.

PAPAYA AND PINEAPPLE JAM

No milk, egg, corn, wheat, rye, citrus, or salicylates

Makes 2 cups

1 cup drained unsweetened crushed canned pineapple, reserving the liquid
½ cup unsweetened pineapple juice
2 cups peeled chopped papayas
2 teaspoons pure lemon juice (optional)

Pour pineapple and juice into blender. Add chopped papayas. Blend for several seconds until fruit has the desired consistency.

Pour fruits into a heavy saucepan. Add lemon juice. Bring to a boil, stirring frequently. Simmer jam until it thickens, about 20 to 30 minutes. Pour boiling hot into sterilized canning jars. Seal. Or cool and refrigerate in a covered container.

PINEAPPLE JAM

No milk, egg, corn, wheat, rye, or salicylates

Makes about 1 cup

2 cups finely chopped fresh pineapple or drained unsweetened crushed canned pineapple
½ cup water or unsweetened pineapple juice
2 tablespoons honey
2 teaspoons pure lemon juice

Combine all ingredients in a heavy saucepan. Slowly bring to boil, stirring occasionally. Over low heat, cook until thick, about 30 minutes. As jam thickens, stir frequently to prevent sticking. Pour boiling hot into sterilized canning jars. Seal. Or cool and refrigerate in a covered container.

PLUM JAM

No milk, egg, corn, wheat, rye, or citrus

Makes 2½ cups

2 pounds (about 18) fresh
     plums
1 cup water
½ cup honey

1½ tablespoons potato starch
     flour
¼ cup cold water

Cut each plum into several pieces. In a covered large heavy saucepan bring to a boil and simmer plums in water until very soft. Cool. Put through a sieve or food mill. Return sieved plums to saucepan. Add honey. Bring to a boil over medium heat and continue cooking until jam sheets from a spoon (220° to 222° F.). Skim off any foam. Mix together potato starch flour and water. Slowly add to jam, stirring constantly. Pour boiling hot into sterilized canning jars leaving ½-inch headspace. Seal. Or cool and refrigerate in a covered container.

RHUBARB JAM

No milk, egg, corn, wheat, rye, citrus, or salicylates

Makes 2 cups

1 pound fresh or frozen (thawed) rhubarb, cut up
½ cup honey
½ cup water
1 teaspoon pure lemon juice (optional)

In a heavy saucepan over high heat, combine rhubarb, honey, and water. Bring to a boil. Reduce heat and simmer until rhubarb is soft. Cool. Place in blender on high speed for a few seconds until desired consistency is reached.

Return mixture to saucepan and add lemon juice. Cook over medium heat until jam thickens. Cool. Pour boiling hot into sterilized canning jars. Seal. Or cool and refrigerate in a covered container.

STRAWBERRY JAM

No milk, egg, corn, wheat, rye, or citrus

Makes about 1¼ cups

¼ cup honey
2 cups washed quartered strawberries
1 unwaxed apple, peeled, cored, and sliced
¼ cup water

Pour honey over prepared strawberries. Crush berries and let stand 15 minutes. In a large saucepan, combine sweetened strawberries, apple, and water. Bring to a boil over medium heat, stirring occasionally. Continue boiling until sheeting stage (220° to 222° F.) is reached or when the jam dropped from a spoon divides into two distinct drops that run together and sheet from edge of spoon. Pour boiling hot into sterilized canning jars. Seal. Or cool and refrigerate in a covered container.

ZUCCHINI AND PINEAPPLE JAM

No milk, egg, corn, wheat, rye, citrus, or salicylates

Makes 3 cups

4 cups (about 2 pounds)
   thinly sliced zucchini,
   peeled if waxed
2 cups unsweetened crushed
   canned pineapple,
   drained, reserving juice
½ cup unsweetened pineapple juice
¼ cup honey
1 tablespoon pure lemon juice (optional)

Place all ingredients in a large, heavy saucepan. Cover and bring to a boil, then simmer 15 to 30 minutes, stirring occasionally, until zucchini is tender. Chop in blender if finer texture is desired. Return to saucepan and simmer until mixture thickens. Pour boiling hot into sterilized canning jars. Seal. Or cool and refrigerate in a covered container.

Food Colorings

BLUE COLORING

No milk, egg, corn, wheat, rye, citrus, or salicylates

1 cup blueberries and 1 cup water *or* unsweetened grape
juice

Boil blueberries and water slowly for about 5 minutes. Strain
well, reserving the liquid. Or use grape juice. A few drops will
color icing a bluish-purple color and, of course, the taste is delicious.

To dye eggs, add 1 tablespoon apple cider vinegar to 1 cup of
blueberry or grape juice. Eggs turn a pretty bluish-lavender color.

BROWN COLORING

No milk, egg, corn, wheat, rye, citrus, or salicylates

1 cup coffee

One cup of coffee with 2 tablespoons apple cider vinegar added
will dye eggs brown.

Use carob powder to color icing brown.

GREEN COLORING

No milk, egg, corn, wheat, rye, citrus, or salicylates

Alfalfa tea

Alfalfa tea may be purchased at health foods stores if you can't
find it elsewhere. It will not work as an egg dye, but small
amounts can be added to icing to make it green. However, the
icing does taste like grass, so you may wish to limit its use to small
amounts for leaves or other trimming.

PEACH COLORING

No milk, egg, corn, wheat, rye, citrus, or salicylates

1 part Yellow Coloring*
1 part Red Coloring*

This combination turns icing a pretty peach color. Likewise, when eggs are submerged in the solution with 1 tablespoon apple cider vinegar added, they also turn a pretty peach color.

PINK COLORING

No milk, egg, corn, wheat, rye, citrus, or salicylates

Cranberry Sauce*

Mix cranberry jelly into icing a teaspoon at a time. Adds a delicious flavor.

RED COLORING

No milk, egg, corn, wheat, rye, citrus, or salicylates

Canned beets

Strain, reserving liquid for coloring. For red icing, substitute the beet juice for some of the liquid in icing recipe. The icing picks up little of the beet flavor.

To dye eggs pink, add 2 tablespoons apple cider vinegar to 1 cup beet juice.

YELLOW COLORING

No milk, egg, corn, wheat, rye, citrus, or salicylates

1 teaspoon saffron or ¼ teaspoon tumeric
1 cup water

Saffron and tumeric can be found in the spice section of many supermarkets. Saffron is expensive but a little goes a long way. Add saffron or tumeric to water and boil slowly for about 5 minutes. Let stand until cool. Strain well.

Add a few drops of the coloring to icing for a pretty yellow color. The sweetness of the icing counteracts the bitterness of the spice.

For egg dye, add 1 tablespoon apple cider vinegar to 1 cup of saffron or tumeric dye and submerge egg. Will dye the egg bright yellow.

YELLOW/ORANGE COLORING

No milk, egg, corn, wheat, rye, citrus, or salicylates

1 carrot and ¼ cup water or canned carrot juice

Wash carrot well and cut into pieces skin and all. Place in blender with water on high speed until smooth. Add small amounts of the paste to icing to color it orange.

Carrot juice may be used to color icing yellow or orange. Decrease liquid in icing recipe slightly and substitute carrot juice. Carrot paste or juice will not dye eggs, however.

Miscellaneous

APRICOT EGG REPLACER

No milk, egg, corn, wheat, rye, or citrus

Makes 1¼ cups

6 ounces sun-dried apricots
1½ cups water

Cook apricots in water until soft. Cool. Purée in the blender. Keep refrigerated in a covered container. Use 2 tablespoons apricot egg replacer for each egg. Works best in cookies and quick fruit breads.

One half extra teaspoon baking powder per egg in a given recipe can be added to make batters rise.

When eggs are used for binding purposes as in cookies, meat loaf, muffins, etc., this may be used as a substitute if your child is sensitive to eggs. This will not act as a leavening agent, though.

SOY EGG YOLK SUBSTITUTE

No milk, egg, corn, wheat, rye, citrus, or salicylates

1 cup soy powder or soy flour
2 cups water
2 tablespoons pure allowed vegetable oil
¼ teaspoon salt

Thoroughly blend powder and water in a blender at high speed. Pour into the top of a double boiler and cook over boiling water, covered, for about 1 hour. Beat in oil and salt with an electric mixer. Refrigerate. Will thicken when cooled.

Use about ¼ cup of the substitute for each egg. One half extra teaspoon baking powder per egg can be added to make batter rise.

CAROB POWDER

No milk, egg, corn, wheat, rye, citrus, or salicylates

Carob flour

Oven 300°

If you buy carob in flour form, you can make it into powder by toasting it in the oven. Spread the flour in a thin layer on a cookie sheet and toast for about 15 minutes or until the color of cocoa (light brown).

A general rule in using carob powder as a substitute for chocolate is 2 to 3 tablespoons of carob powder equals one square or ounce of unsweetened chocolate.

CORN-FREE BAKING POWDER

No milk, egg, corn, wheat, rye, or citrus

Makes ¾ cup

¼ cup baking soda
¼ cup cream of tartar
¼ cup potato starch

Sift each ingredient before measuring. Mix together thoroughly. Sift again. Keep baking powder dry in a tightly covered jar. To check if baking powder is still active, add several drops of water to a little baking powder. If it bubbles vigorously, it is still good. Use as you would any commercial double-acting baking powder.

NUT, BANANA, OR OAT MILK

No milk, egg, corn, wheat, rye, citrus, or salicylates

Makes 1 cup

⅓ cup nuts or seeds (cashews, walnuts, sliced almonds, sunflower seeds, sesame seeds) *or* 2 teaspoons rolled oats *or* ½ small banana
1 cup water

Combine nuts, seeds, oats, or banana and water in blender on highest speed until smooth. Use instead of cow's milk for baking and on cereals. Banana milk is good on cereal but must be used immediately.

SOY MILK

No milk, egg, corn, wheat, rye, citrus, or salicylates

Makes 7 cups

½ pound (1¼ cups) dry soybeans
8 cups water

Soak dry beans in 4 cups water for at least 12 hours. Drain well and discard water. Place half the beans in a blender. Add 2 cups water. On high speed finely grind the beans. Repeat with other half of the beans and another 2 cups water. Heat mixture in a heavy saucepan over medium heat, stirring frequently to prevent scorching until temperature reaches 131° F. or is too hot to touch comfortably. Cool. Strain mixture through a cloth, reserving all the liquid. Heat this liquid in the top of a double boiler for 45 minutes, stirring frequently. Add enough water to make in all 7 cups soy milk. Keep refrigerated. Use measure for measure to replace milk in recipes.

CHAPTER SEVEN

BASIC BREADS

You will probably have to make your own bread. We've listed in Appendix F several brands of commercial breads that are better and more nutritious than most, but these contain small amounts of sugar, corn syrup, or molasses. They may contain milk or shortenings you'll need to avoid.

If you make your own bread products, you will know precisely what ingredients are used, a definite advantage when you're searching for clues as to what is bothering your child. The recipes we've included are all easily prepared. If wheat is a problem for your child, some of the other grains may be tolerated in moderation.

Don't use raw wheat germ in these bread recipes because it will make the dough sticky. Instead, use toasted wheat germ.

WHITE BREAD

No milk, egg, corn, rye, citrus, or salicylates

Makes 2 loaves

2 packages dry yeast or 2 cakes compressed yeast
2 cups warm milk or water or potato water
1 tablespoon honey (optional)
1 egg, slightly beaten (optional)

1 tablespoon salt
¼ cup pure allowed vegetable oil (optional)
½ cup toasted wheat germ
4½ to 5½ cups unbleached flour

Oven 400°

Dissolve yeast in warm liquid. Add honey, egg, salt, and oil. Stir in wheat germ. Add half the flour and beat with an electric mixer on medium speed for 2 minutes. Slowly work in enough flour until dough is no longer sticky. Place on floured surface and knead until dough is smooth and elastic, about 8 to 10 minutes.

Place dough in a greased bowl, turning to grease the top too. Cover. Let rise in a warm place until double in bulk, about 1 or 2 hours. Punch dough down. Let dough rise again until double in bulk, about 1 hour. Place on lightly floured surface. Divide dough into two parts. Cover with cloth and let rest about 15 minutes. Make into two loaves and place in two greased 8½x4½-inch loaf pans. Cover and let rise until double in bulk, about ½ hour. Bake for 30 to 35 minutes. Remove from pans. If bottom of loaf sounds hollow when tapped, bread is done. Cool on wire racks.

HIGH PROTEIN BREAD

No corn, rye, citrus, or salicylates

Makes 2 loaves

Dry milk, soy flour, and eggs add extra nutrition to this tasty bread.

2 packages dry yeast or 2 cakes compressed yeast
⅔ cup warm water
1 tablespoon honey (optional)
1 cup instant or non-instant dry milk powder
1 tablespoon salt
1¾ cups warm water

5½ to 6½ cups whole wheat flour
1 cup soy flour or soy powder
2 eggs
¼ cup pure allowed vegetable oil
Uncolored butter or allowed margarine

Oven 375°

Dissolve yeast in ⅔ cup warm water. Add honey and stir. Set aside for 10 minutes. In the meantime, add dry milk and salt to 1¾ cups warm water. Stir until dissolved. In a large bowl, add yeast mixture to milk mixture. Add 2 cups whole wheat flour and stir well, using wooden spoon. Stir in soy flour. Beat with an electric mixer for 5 minutes. Add eggs and oil and mix thoroughly.

Add enough of remaining whole wheat flour to make a kneadable dough. Turn dough out on lightly floured surface. Cover and let rest 20 minutes. Knead for 8 minutes or until dough is smooth and elastic. Place dough in an oiled 4-quart bowl. Turn completely over so that top is oiled. Place in a warm location until double in bulk, about 1 hour. Punch down. Divide into two portions. Cover and let rest 10 minutes. With a rolling pin, roll each portion into a 9x14-inch rectangle. Roll dough tightly into a cylinder. Pinch seam to seal. Place in well-greased 9x5-inch loaf pans. Let rise in warm place until double in bulk, about 1 hour. Bake for 40 to 45 minutes. When done, remove from pans immediately and cool on wire racks. Brush top of hot loaves with shortening for tender crust.

RYE BREAD

No milk, egg, corn, citrus, or salicylates

Makes 2 loaves

2 packages dry yeast or 2 cakes compressed yeast
1¾ cups warm water
⅓ cup honey
1 tablespoon salt
2 tablespoons pure allowed vegetable oil
1 tablespoon caraway seeds
1 tablespoon grated unwaxed uncolored orange peel (optional)
3 cups rye flour
1½ to 2 cups unbleached flour
Uncolored butter or allowed margarine

Oven 400°

Dissolve yeast in warm water. Add honey, salt, and oil. Add caraway seeds, orange peel, and 2 cups rye flour. Beat with mixer until very smooth. With a heavy spoon, stir in the rest of the rye flour and enough white flour to make dough leave sides of the bowl. Turn dough out onto a lightly floured board and knead gently until smooth and elastic, adding flour when necessary. Place dough in a greased bowl and turn greased side to the top. Cover and allow to rise in a warm place until double in bulk, about 1 hour. Punch down and shape into two loaves. Place in greased 9x5-inch loaf pans, cover, and allow to rise again until double in bulk, about ½ hour. Bake 30 to 35 minutes. Remove from pans. If bottoms of loaves sound hollow when tapped, bread is done. Place on wire racks, brush tops lightly with shortening, and allow to cool.

ALL-RYE BREAD

No milk, egg, corn, wheat, citrus, or salicylates

Makes 2 loaves

2 packages dry yeast or 2 cakes compressd yeast
2½ cups warm water or milk
2 teaspoons salt
2 tablespoons pure allowed vegetable oil

1 tablespoon honey (optional)
1 tablespoon caraway seeds (optional)
4½ to 5 cups rye flour
Uncolored butter or allowed margarine

Oven 350°

Dissolve yeast in warm water or milk. Stir in salt, oil, honey, and caraway seeds. Add 2 cups flour and stir well. Cover and let rise for ½ hour. Add 2 cups flour a little at a time. Dough will be stiff. Cover and let rise 1½ hours. Sprinkle ½ cup flour over a flat surface. Knead flour into dough a little at a time until dough is no longer sticky. Add more rye flour, if necessary. Knead about 5 to 8 minutes. Divide dough in two and shape into loaves. Place on greased baking sheet. Brush loaves with shortening. Cover and let rise, about 2 hours. Bake for about 1 hour or until loaf sounds hollow when tapped on the bottom.

ALL-OAT BATTER BREAD

No milk, egg, corn, wheat, rye, citrus, or salicylates

Makes 1 loaf

2 packages dry yeast or 2 cakes compressed yeast
1½ cups warm water or milk
2 teaspoons salt

¼ cup pure allowed vegetable oil
1 tablespoon honey
1 cup rolled oats
3 cups oat flour

Oven 375°

Dissolve yeast in warm water or milk. Stir in salt, oil, and honey. Add rolled oats. With an electric mixer beat in oat flour and continue to beat for 5 minutes. Pour into a greased 9x5-inch loaf pan. Let rise in a warm place for about 45 minutes. Bake about 40 to 45 minutes until top is browned. Cool for 5 minutes. Carefully remove from pan and cool completely on wire rack. Handle bread with care as it crumbles easily.

Only use this recipe for a child on the Common Foods Elimination Diet or for one who can't tolerate wheat or rye. If your child doesn't like the flavor of this bread, try the Banana,* Date and Nut,* Pumpkin,* or Zucchini* bread which can be made without wheat. This bread tastes best toasted in the oven and spread with allowed jam and/or peanut butter.

NO-KNEAD WHITE BATTER BREAD

No milk, egg, corn, rye, citrus, or salicylates

Makes 2 loaves

3 packages dry yeast or 3 cakes compressed yeast
3 cups warm water or warm milk
2 tablespoons honey (optional)

¼ cup melted uncolored butter or allowed margarine or pure allowed vegetable oil
1 tablespoon salt
½ cup toasted wheat germ
5 cups unbleached flour

Oven 400°

In a large mixing bowl dissolve yeast in warm liquid. Stir in honey, shortening, and salt. Add wheat germ. Add half the flour. Beat for several minutes with an electric mixer. Work in remaining flour. Pour into two well-greased 8½x4½-inch loaf pans. Cover. Let rise in a warm place until double in bulk (about 30 to 45 minutes). Bake for 50 to 60 minutes. Remove from pans. If bottoms of loaves sound hollow when tapped, bread is done. Cool on wire racks. May be well wrapped and frozen.

NO-KNEAD WHOLE WHEAT BATTER BREAD

No milk, egg, corn, rye, citrus, or salicylates

Makes 2 loaves

½ cup uncolored butter or allowed margarine, melted

2 cups scalded milk or warm water

2 tablespoons honey

1 tablespoon salt

3 packages dry yeast or 3 cakes compressed yeast

1 cup warm water

3 cups whole wheat flour

2½ to 2¾ cups unbleached white flour

Uncolored butter or allowed margarine

Oven 400°

Combine shortening, milk or water, honey, and salt and cool until lukewarm. Dissolve yeast in warm water. Set aside for 10 minutes. Add to liquid mixture. Stir in whole wheat flour and part of the white flour. Beat with an electric mixer for 2 minutes. Add remaining white flour and stir well, using a heavy spoon. Pour into two well-greased 9x5-inch loaf pans. Cover and let rise in a warm place for about 45 minutes or until double in bulk. Bake for 1 hour. Remove from pans. If bottom of loaf sounds hollow when tapped, bread is done. While still warm, lightly spread shortening on tops of loaves for a softer crust. Let loaves cool thoroughly on a wire rack.

NO-KNEAD WHITE REFRIGERATOR ROLLS

No milk, egg, corn, rye, citrus, or salicylates

Makes 2 dozen rolls

2 packages dry yeast or 2 cakes compressed yeast

2 cups warm milk or water

1 tablespoon honey

2 teaspoons salt

⅓ cup pure allowed vegetable oil

1 egg (optional)

½ cup toasted wheat germ

3½ to 4½ cups unbleached flour

Oven 400°

Dissolve yeast in warm milk or water. Add honey, salt, and oil. Beat in egg. Stir in wheat germ. Add half the flour and beat with an electric mixer for 2 minutes. Gradually add remaining flour and continue beating until dough is smooth. Cover with a damp cloth, placing waxed paper or foil over the cloth to keep the moisture in. Refrigerate. Dough will keep for several days and can be used any time. If any dough remains after about 4 days, make it up into rolls that can be served immediately or frozen for future use.

To bake rolls, remove desired amount of dough from refrigerator several hours prior to baking. With floured hands, pat the dough out on a floured surface and cut out rolls with a round cookie cutter. Fold one half of each circle over onto itself and place on a greased baking sheet or pan. Place rolls so that they are just touching each other. Cover with a cloth and let rise in a warm place for about 1½ hours. Bake about 15 minutes, depending on the size of the rolls. Remove from pan and serve warm.

NO-KNEAD WHOLE WHEAT REFRIGERATOR ROLLS

No milk, egg, corn, rye, citrus, or salicylates

Makes 2 dozen rolls

2 packages dry yeast or 2
   cakes compressed yeast
2 cups warm water
2 tablespoons honey
   (optional)

2 teaspoons salt
¼ cup pure allowed vege-
   table oil
2 cups whole wheat flour
2¼ cups unbleached flour

Oven 400°

Dissolve yeast in warm water. Stir in honey. Let sit 10 minutes. Add salt and oil. Stir in whole wheat flour. Beat with an electric mixer for 2 minutes. Stir in unbleached flour. Mix well. Cover dough with a damp cloth. May refrigerate for up to several days. Punch dough down as needed.

When ready to bake rolls, remove dough from refrigerator. Punch dough down. With floured hands, pinch off pieces of dough of desired size. Form into balls and place close together in a well-greased pan. Cover with a cloth and let rise in a warm place until almost double in bulk, 30 to 45 minutes. Bake for 15 minutes or until rolls are lightly browned on the bottom. Remove all rolls from pan and serve. Leftovers may be frozen and reheated.

ENGLISH MUFFINS

No milk, egg, corn, rye, citrus, or salicylates

Makes about 22 3-inch rounds

2 packages dry active yeast or
   2 cakes compressed yeast
½ cup warm water
1 tablespoon honey
   (optional)
1½ cups warm water or milk,
   scalded and cooled
3 tablespoons pure allowed
   vegetable oil

2 teaspoons salt
¼ cup toasted wheat germ
1 cup whole wheat flour
3½ to 4 cups unbleached
   flour
Corn meal or whole wheat
   flour

Dissolve yeast in warm water. Add honey. Set aside. Combine milk or water, oil, and salt. Add wheat germ, whole wheat, and half the flour and mix well. Stir in yeast mixture. Gradually beat in enough flour to form a moderately stiff dough. Knead 6 to 8 minutes until smooth and elastic. Place in a greased bowl, turning to grease top too. Cover with a damp cloth. Let rise in a warm place until dough doubles in bulk, about 1 to 1½ hours. Place on a lightly floured surface and knead about 1 minute.

Roll out dough until ¼ inch thick. Cut circles of desired size with drinking glass, cookie cutters, sharp tin cans, or a doughnut cutter without the hole. Sprinkle a little corn meal or whole wheat flour on both sides of each muffin. Let stand in a warm place about 15 minutes or until they begin to rise.

Lightly grease a heavy skillet or griddle. Preheat stove top or griddle to medium heat. Place muffins on hot surface. Turn when browned. Total cooking time is about 8 to 10 minutes. Serve hot or let cool. Cut in half and toast. Or freeze muffins in plastic bags and remove as needed.

INDIAN FRY BREAD

No milk, egg, corn, wheat, rye, citrus, or salicylates

Makes 28 rolls

1 package dried yeast or 1 cake compressed yeast
2 cups warm water
2 to 4 tablespoons honey
2 cups whole wheat flour and 2 cups unbleached flour

or 5 to 5⅓ cups oat flour
1 teaspoon salt
5 teaspoons baking powder
Pure allowed vegetable oil

Sprinkle yeast over water. Stir in honey. Mix together all dry ingredients. Add yeast and honey mixture to dry ingredients. Mix well. Pat dough out on a floured surface until it is about ¾ inch thick. Use additional flour to avoid stickiness. Tear or cut off pieces about the size of a small biscuit. Deep fry in allowed oil at 365° F. Turn to brown both sides. Be certain that bread is done in the middle and not doughy. Serve hot with allowed butter or margarine and/or desired jam or fruit butters.

Wrap leftovers tightly in foil and refrigerate. Reheat in foil in oven.

PITA POCKET BREAD

No milk, egg, corn, rye, citrus, or salicylates

Makes about 20 4-inch loaves

2 packages dry yeast or 2 cakes compressed yeast
2½ cups warm water
1 teaspoon honey
1½ tablespoons salt

1 tablespoon pure allowed vegetable oil
½ cup toasted wheat germ
5½ to 6 cups unbleached flour

Oven 500°

Dissolve yeast in water. Add honey, salt, oil, and wheat germ. Using an electric mixer, add half the flour and beat well. Gradually add flour until dough is sticky. Work in enough remaining flour so dough is no longer sticky and knead dough for 5 to 10 minutes until smooth and elastic. Divide dough into about twenty pieces (fewer if you desire larger loaves). Let rise for about 2 hours.

Place rounds on ungreased cookie sheet. If your oven will hold two sheets on one oven rack, you may bake them together. Otherwise, bake only one sheet at a time. Place cookie sheet on lowest rack of the oven. Bake for 5 minutes undisturbed. Then move sheet to higher shelf and bake loaves until puffy and lightly browned, about 3 to 5 minutes.

Immediately wrap hot loaves well in foil or plastic bags to prevent crispness and ensure a chewy, spongy texture. As the loaves cool, they will lose their puffy appearance. When cool, slit one side and fill the pocket with Egg Salad Sandwich Spread,* Tomatoless Chili,* Sloppy Joes,* etc. Loaves may be frozen for future use.

Kids really enjoy these tasty chewy individual "loaves" with a hollow pocket inside, just right for their favorite filling.

SANDWICH BUNS

No milk, egg, corn, rye, citrus, or salicylates

Makes 18 buns

4½ to 5 cups unbleached
    flour
1 package dry yeast or 1 cake
    compressed yeast
½ cup toasted wheat germ
    (optional)
2 cups warm water

1 tablespoon honey
2 tablespoons pure allowed
    vegetable oil
2 teaspoons salt
Uncolored butter or allowed
    margarine

Oven 350°

In a large mixing bowl combine 2 cups flour, yeast, and wheat germ. In another bowl, combine warm water, honey, oil, and salt. Add to dry ingredients and beat with mixer at low speed until blended. Mix at high speed for 3 minutes. Stir in by hand enough of the remaining flour to make a fairly stiff dough. Turn out onto a floured board and knead for about 10 minutes or until smooth and elastic. Place in a greased bowl and turn over dough so top is greased. Cover and let rise in a warm place until double in bulk, about 1½ hours. Punch down and let dough rest for 10 minutes. Roll out so dough is ½ inch thick and cut into 3-inch rounds with a floured cutter. Place on a greased cookie sheet, cover, and let rise until double in bulk, about 1 hour. Bake for 20 to 25 minutes or until lightly browned. While still warm from the oven, brush tops lightly with shortening.

BANANA BREAD

No milk, egg, corn, wheat, rye, citrus, or salicylates

Makes 1 loaf

1½ cups rice flour *or* 1 cup unbleached flour and 1 cup whole wheat flour
2½ teaspoons baking powder
¼ teaspoon allspice

6 tablespoons pure allowed vegetable oil
⅓ cup honey
2 tablespoons water
2 ripe bananas, mashed
¾ cup finely chopped pecans

Oven 350°

In a small bowl combine flour, baking powder, and allspice. Set aside. In a large bowl beat together on low speed oil, honey, water, and bananas. Gradually add flour mixture and nuts. Pour into a greased 9x5-inch loaf pan and bake for 45 minutes, or until toothpick inserted in the middle comes out clean. Cool in pan for 15 minutes. Turn out on wire rack and cool completely. Wrap and store in refrigerator.

DATE AND NUT BREAD

No milk, egg, corn, wheat, rye, citrus, or salicylates

Makes 1 loaf

1 cup chopped dates
¾ cup boiling water
1⅛ cups rice flour or 1½ cups unbleached flour
2 teaspoons baking powder
½ teaspoon salt

3 tablespoons pure allowed vegetable oil
4 tablespoons water
¼ cup pure maple syrup
1 teaspoon pure vanilla extract
¾ cup chopped walnuts

Oven 350°

In a small bowl soak dates in boiling water. Place in refrigerator to cool. In another small bowl combine flour, baking powder, and salt. Set aside. In a large bowl beat together oil, water, maple syrup, and vanilla. Gradually add flour mixture, alternating with soaked dates and water until mixture is well blended. Stir in chopped walnuts. Pour into a greased 9x5-inch loaf pan. Bake for 1 hour or until toothpick inserted in the middle comes out clean. Cool in pan for 15 minutes. Turn out onto wire rack. Cool completely. Wrap in foil and refrigerate.

PUMPKIN BREAD

No milk, egg, corn, wheat, rye, citrus, or salicylates

Makes 1 loaf

1⅛ cups rice flour *or* 2 cups unbleached flour

½ cup honey

½ teaspoon cinnamon

½ teaspoon salt

¼ teaspoon nutmeg

1 teaspoon baking soda

½ teaspoon baking powder

¾ cup canned or cooked pumpkin

¼ cup pure allowed vegetable oil

½ cup water

½ cup chopped nuts

¼ cup wheat germ (optional)

Oven 350°

Combine all ingredients in a large mixing bowl. Mix until just blended. Pour batter into greased 9x5x3-inch loaf pan. Bake 50 to 60 minutes or until a toothpick inserted in the center comes out clean. Cool in pan for 10 minutes. Turn out onto wire rack. Cool completely.

ZUCCHINI BREAD

No milk, egg, corn, wheat, rye, citrus, or salicylates

Makes 1 loaf

1⅛ cups rice flour *or* 1¼ cups unbleached flour and ¼ cup wheat germ

½ teaspoon baking soda

½ teaspoon salt

¼ teaspoon nutmeg

½ teaspoon cinnamon
3 tablespoons water
1 egg (optional)
⅓ cup pure allowed vege-
    table oil

1 teaspoon pure vanilla
    extract
½ cup honey
1 cup chopped zucchini,
    peeled if waxed
¼ cup chopped nuts

Oven 350°

In a large bowl mix together flour, soda, salt, nutmeg, and cinnamon. Add water, egg, oil, vanilla, and honey. Beat until thoroughly blended. Stir in zucchini and nuts. Pour into a 9x5x3-inch
greased loaf pan. Bake for 50 to 55 minutes. Let cool in the pan.
Remove from pan and cool completely.

CAKE DOUGHNUTS

No milk, corn, rye, citrus, or salicylates

Makes 2 dozen doughnuts

3 eggs
½ cup honey
2 tablespoons uncolored
    butter or allowed mar-
    garine, softened
1 cup mashed potatoes

3 cups unbleached flour
1 tablespoon baking powder
1 teaspoon salt
½ teaspoon cinnamon
¼ teaspoon nutmeg

In a large mixing bowl beat eggs until very light and fluffy. Add
honey and shortening and continue to beat until very light. Blend in
mashed potatoes. In a separate bowl combine the dry ingredients.
Slowly add to the egg mixture, beating on low speed. When the
flour mixture has been evenly mixed in, turn out the dough onto a
floured board. Knead gently, using only enough additional flour to
keep it from sticking to the board. Roll out the dough to ⅓-inch
thickness and cut with a floured doughnut cutter. Deep fry both
doughnuts and holes at 370° until golden brown on both sides.
One teaspoon honey per doughnut.

ZUCCHINI DOUGHNUTS

No milk, corn, rye, citrus, or salicylates

Makes 2 dozen doughnuts

Follow Cake Doughnuts* recipe, substituting 1 cup grated zucchini for mashed potatoes. Add ½ to 1 cup additional flour to make a stiff dough.

YEAST DOUGHNUTS

No milk, egg, corn, rye, citrus, or salicylates

Makes 18 to 24 doughnuts

1 package dry yeast or 1 cake compressed yeast
¼ cup warm water
3 tablespoons uncolored butter or allowed margarine, melted
1 cup warm water or milk, scalded
⅓ cup honey
1 teaspoon salt
1 egg, beaten (optional)
3½ to 4 cups sifted unbleached flour

Sprinkle yeast over warm water and allow to dissolve. Add shortening to scalded milk or warm water. When liquid is lukewarm, stir in yeast, honey, salt, and egg. Mix thoroughly. Stir in 2 cups flour and beat with mixer until very smooth. With heavy spoon stir in enough flour so that dough leaves sides of the bowl. Turn dough out on a lightly floured board and knead until dough is smooth and elastic, adding flour if necessary. Place dough in greased bowl, turning greased side to the top. Cover and put in a warm place until double in bulk, about 1 hour. Punch down dough and turn out on board. Roll dough out to ⅓-inch thickness. Cut with floured doughnut cutter and place on cookie sheet. Knead scraps together slightly and reroll to cut more doughnuts. Cover doughnuts and allow to rise until almost double in bulk, about 1 hour. Fry in 3 inches of oil at 370° until golden brown on both sides. Glaze doughnuts while still warm by drizzling honey over the tops, if desired.

CHAPTER EIGHT

BREAKFAST:
GETTING A GOOD START
TO THE DAY

Your child needs a good nutritious breakfast to start his day. It doesn't have to require a lot of preparation time nor does it have to be a large meal. Be sure to include some protein source. You'll know best what kind of breakfast will appeal to your child.

Most kids really miss the forbidden additive-filled sugary cereals, orange drinks, or instant breakfast drinks. Some of the recipes in this chapter may help. Or you may be able to locate some cereals he can eat (see Appendix F). Try serving oatmeal with a little pure maple syrup or honey. Top with fresh sliced fruit.

If your child likes eggs and is not sensitive to them, he can have these prepared as he desires. But no bacon or ham in any form. You can substitute by using the homemade sausage recipe or goetta. Store-bought sweet rolls are taboo but you can easily make your own in quantity and freeze them for future use. Pancakes may be prepared from whole grains—wheat, rye, rice, and without milk and eggs. Serve with pure maple syrup or honey and uncolored butter or allowed margarine. Fresh unsweetened fruits and their juices should be encouraged. Bananas are also nutritious, satisfying and liked by many kids.

If your child doesn't like breakfast foods, try serving some non-breakfast-type items—hamburgers, fried chicken, pizza, homemade fruit gelatin, French fries or hash browns, peanut butter and homemade jelly on allowed bread or crackers, or grilled cheese sandwiches.

BREAKFAST FRUIT PIZZA

No egg, corn, rye, citrus, or salicylates

Makes 8 individual pizzas

These breakfast pizzas make a tasty, nutritious start to the day. They may be made ahead of time and reheated. They are also great snacks or desserts.

1 recipe Pizza Crust*
Blueberry Filling:
    4 cups fresh or frozen (thawed) blueberries
    ¼ cup water
    ¼ cup unbleached flour
16 ounces cream cheese, softened (optional)
Mozzarella cheese, grated or sliced

Oven 450°

Prepare pizza crust. While dough is rising, prepare filling. Put blueberries in a saucepan. Add water. Heat until blueberries are tender. Add flour and cook until mixture thickens. Remove from heat.

Divide dough into eight portions. Roll out each piece and place on oiled cookie sheet or pizza pan. Turn up the edges and spread each with cream cheese, if desired. Add blueberry filling. Bake for 15 minutes. Top with mozzarella cheese and return to oven for another 5 to 10 minutes or until crust is browned. Serve hot.

Pizzas may also be prepared ahead of time and frozen without adding the mozzarella cheese. In the morning, remove from freezer, add cheese, and cook at 350° until cheese is melted.

BREAKFAST-ON-A-BUN

No egg, corn, rye, citrus, or salicylates

Serves 4

2 tablespoons uncolored
    butter or allowed
    margarine
2 English Muffins,* split
½ pound (4 patties) Home-
    made Sausage Patties,*
    fried or broiled

4 slices unsweetened canned
    pineapple
4 slices uncolored Swiss
    cheese

Toast English muffins and spread with shortening. Top each muffin half with a sausage patty, pineapple, and cheese slice on top. Broil until cheese melts and serve immediately.

GRANOLA CEREAL OR BARS

No milk, egg, corn, wheat, rye, or citrus

Makes 10 cups

4 cups rolled oats
1 cup toasted sesame seeds
1 cup toasted wheat germ
    (optional)
1 cup shredded unsweetened
    coconut

1 cup chopped nuts
2 cups raisins or currants
½ cup pure maple syrup
½ cup honey
¼ cup pure allowed vege-
    table oil

Oven 250°

Combine all dry ingredients in a large bowl. Mix the maple syrup, honey, and oil together and pour over dry ingredients while stirring. Continue to stir until evenly distributed. Spread granola out on two or three lightly greased cookie sheets and bake in the oven for 30 minutes, stirring about every 10 minutes. Allow the cereal to cool on the baking sheets and then store in airtight containers. The granola will not be crunchy when you take it from the oven but will be after it cools.

To make the mixture into bars, press into the bottom of baking pans until about ⅜ inch deep. Bake in the oven for 30 minutes. Do not stir. As soon as you remove the granola from the oven cut into bars of desired size with a sharp knife. Allow to cool in the pans. Remove and store bars in airtight containers. Almost 5 teaspoons sweetener per cup cereal.

QUICKIE BREAKFAST

No egg, corn, wheat, rye, citrus, or salicylates

Serves 1

1 cup milk
1 banana, sliced
2 tablespoons honey
　(optional)
½ teaspoon brewers' yeast
　(optional)

1 raw egg (optional)
1 tablespoon wheat germ
　(optional)
1 tablespoon carob powder

Put all ingredients except carob into a blender and mix. Add carob while continuing to mix and blend until smooth.

BREAKFAST SOUP

No milk, egg, corn, wheat, rye, citrus, or salicylates

Makes 2¾ cups

2 cups Chicken Stock*
1 cup salted diced cooked
　potatoes
1 cup finely diced cooked
　chicken

1 teaspoon instant minced
　onion
Salt to taste
Dried parsley flakes
　(optional)
Paprika (optional)

In a heavy saucepan combine stock, potatoes, chicken, onion, and salt. Bring to a boil stirring constantly. Remove from stove and purée in blender or food mill.

Refrigerate overnight. Reheat, adding water for desired consistency. Salt to taste and serve with parsley flakes or paprika sprinkled on top of each serving.

GOETTA

No milk, egg, corn, wheat, rye, citrus, or salicylates

Serves 12 to 18

1 pound freshly ground pork	3 bay leaves
4 cups water	1 medium onion, finely
1½ teaspoons salt	chopped
¼ teaspoon pepper	2 cups pinhead oatmeal

Crumble pork into a saucepan and cover with water. Add salt, pepper, bay leaves, and onion and bring to boil. Mash the pork so it is very fine. Add oatmeal and continue to cook over low heat, about 35 minutes. Stir frequently and add more water if necessary. Mixture should be very thick. Pour into a 9x5x3-inch loaf pan. Refrigerate overnight. Cut into ½-inch slices, as needed, and fry until lightly browned and heated through. Serve as a breakfast meat.

HOMEMADE SAUSAGE PATTIES

No milk, egg, corn, wheat, rye, citrus, or salicylates

Makes 12 patties

2 pounds coarsely ground pork shoulder or lean ground beef	½ teaspoon basil
	1½ teaspoons salt
	½ teaspoon black pepper
4 teaspoons sage	⅔ cup water
½ teaspoon thyme	1 tablespoon pure allowed
½ teaspoon marjoram	vegetable oil

Combine all ingredients in a large mixing bowl. Mix thoroughly. Shape into twelve patties and fry or place on a cookie sheet and freeze until firm. Package for freezing and use patties as needed.

To cook, place frozen patty in a skillet and fry slowly in oil until fully cooked and slightly browned.

BREAKFAST CASSEROLE

No corn, wheat, rye, citrus, or salicylates

Serves 6

4 slices allowed bread,
   cubed
½ pound (4 patties) Home-
   made Sausage Patties*
1 cup grated sharp un-
   colored cheese

6 eggs
1 cup milk
½ teaspoon dry mustard
½ teaspoon salt

Oven 350°

Place the cubed bread in the bottom of a 1½-quart greased casserole dish. Brown the sausage in a skillet and break into small pieces. Drain and sprinkle over the bread cubes. Sprinkle cheese evenly over top. Beat the eggs, milk, mustard, and salt together and pour over the casserole. May be covered and refrigerated overnight. In the morning, bake uncovered for 40 to 45 minutes.

WHEAT BISCUITS

No milk, egg, corn, rye, citrus, or salicylates

Makes 15 2-inch biscuits

1 cup whole wheat flour
1 cup unbleached flour
2½ teaspoons baking powder
½ teaspoon salt

¼ cup pure allowed vege-
   table oil
¾ cup milk or Soy Milk*

Oven 450°

Mix ingredients thoroughly. Turn out on floured surface and roll out to ½-inch thickness. Cut with floured cutter and place close together on greased baking sheet or 1 inch apart for crusty biscuits. Bake for 10 to 12 minutes.

CORN MUFFINS OR CORN BREAD

No milk, egg, rye, citrus, or salicylates

Makes 1 dozen muffins
or 1 9-inch round
corn bread

1 cup corn meal (stone
  ground preferred)
1 cup sifted unbleached flour
  or whole wheat flour
4 teaspoons baking powder
½ teaspoon salt
2 tablespoons honey
  (optional)

1 egg (optional)
1 cup milk or Soy Milk*
¼ cup pure allowed vege-
  table oil or uncolored
  butter or allowed
  margarine, melted

Oven 375°

Mix together all dry ingredients. Add honey, egg, milk, and shortening. Beat by hand or with electric mixer until smooth.

Fill greased muffin cups two-thirds full. Bake 20 to 25 minutes. Or pour batter into greased 9-inch round cake pan and bake for 20 to 25 minutes at 400°.

RICE MUFFINS

No milk, corn, wheat, rye, citrus, or salicylates

Makes 9 muffins

1½ cups rice flour
2 teaspoons baking powder
½ teaspoon baking soda
½ teaspoon salt
⅔ cup milk or water
2 tablespoons honey

1 tablespoon pure allowed
  vegetable oil
1 egg
¾ cup fresh or frozen
  (thawed) blueberries
  (optional)

Oven 350°

Combine all ingredients except blueberries in a mixing bowl. Stir until thoroughly blended. Gently fold in blueberries. Fill greased muffin tins one-half full. Bake until lightly browned. Remove from pan while still hot. Serve warm. Less than 1 teaspoon honey per muffin.

WHEATLESS MUFFINS

No milk, corn, wheat, or citrus

Makes 16 muffins

2 cups rolled oats
1 cup rye flour
2 teaspoons baking powder
2 teaspoons baking soda
½ teaspoon salt
¾ cup unsweetened apple juice
¼ cup honey
¼ cup pure allowed vegetable oil

2 eggs
¾ cup chopped fruit (currants, diced apples, pears, raisins, drained unsweetened crushed canned pineapple, dates, dried apricots, etc.) (optional)

Oven 350°

Combine dry ingredients. Add all other ingredients and stir until thoroughly mixed. Fill greased muffin cups half full and bake 15 minutes until lightly browned. About ¾ teaspoon honey per muffin.

OAT OR RICE PANCAKES

No milk, egg, corn, wheat, rye, citrus, or salicylates

Makes 6 medium pancakes

1 cup oat flour or rice flour
1 teaspoon baking powder
½ teaspoon baking soda
1 teaspoon salt
1 egg or equivalent egg replacer

2 tablespoons pure allowed vegetable oil
½ cup milk, Soy Milk,* unsweetened apple juice, or water

Combine all ingredients and mix until smooth. Add more liquid if necessary until you get a fairly thin batter. Cook on a lightly greased griddle until browned on both sides. When using the oat flour, make sure the inside of the pancake is done before removing from griddle. Serve hot with honey or pure maple syrup.

POTATO PANCAKES

No milk, egg, corn, wheat, rye, citrus, or salicylates

Makes 8 pancakes

4 medium potatoes, coarsely grated
4 tablespoons unbleached flour or rice flour
2 teaspoons salt
1 egg or 4 tablespoons Mayonnaise* or Eggless Mayonnaise*

Combine all ingredients until thoroughly blended. Fry on a greased griddle until lightly browned on both sides. Serve for breakfast or as a potato dish at dinner.

WHOLE WHEAT OR RYE PANCAKES

No milk, egg, corn, wheat, rye, citrus, or salicylates

Makes 10 pancakes

1¼ cups whole wheat flour
  or rye flour
3 teaspoons baking powder
½ teaspoon salt
1 egg, beaten, or 2 tablespoons water and ½
  teaspoon baking powder

1 cup plus 2 tablespoons
  milk or unsweetened
  pineapple juice
2 tablespoons pure allowed
  vegetable oil

Stir together dry ingredients. Stir together liquid ingredients and add to dry ingredients. Stir until just mixed. Bake on greased griddle or in a lightly oiled skillet. Batter may be thinned as needed with extra milk or juice. Serve hot with Honey or Maple Butter,* or Apple or Pear Maple Syrup,* or allowed homemade jam.

RICE FLOUR CREPES

No milk, corn, wheat, rye, or citrus

Makes 10 crepes

1 cup rice flour
½ teaspoon baking powder
½ teaspoon salt
2 eggs, slightly beaten

1 cup unsweetened apple
   juice
2 tablespoons water

Combine together the rice flour, baking powder, and salt. Add all other ingredients and mix thoroughly until smooth. Mixture should be very thin, adding more water if necessary.

Heat a 5- or 6-inch crepe pan or heavy skillet over medium high heat. Brush lightly with pure allowed vegetable oil. Pour in 3 tablespoons of batter and swirl pan until bottom is completely covered. Cook until lightly browned on the bottom, turn and cook until browned on the other side. Stack crepes with paper towels in between until ready to fill.

Filling can be Applesauce,* chopped fresh fruit, or sweetened whipped cream.

WAFFLES

No corn, rye, citrus, or salicylates

Makes 4 waffles

1 cup whole wheat flour
1 cup unbleached flour
3 tablespoons pure allowed
   vegetable oil

1 egg
1¾ cups milk

Mix ingredients together thoroughly. Bake on preheated waffle iron until golden brown.

RYE OR OAT HONEY CAKE

No milk, egg, corn, wheat, or rye

Makes 1 loaf

2 cups rye flour or oat flour
½ teaspoon baking soda
2 teaspoons baking powder
½ teaspoon salt
1 tablespoon cinnamon or 1
    extra teaspoon allspice
½ teaspoon allspice
¼ teaspoon nutmeg
½ cup honey or pure maple
    syrup

¾ cup water plus 2 table-
    spoons
1 tablespoon pure unsweet-
    ened frozen (thawed)
    orange juice concentrate
1 tablespoon grated un-
    colored unwaxed orange
    rind
½ cup finely chopped nuts
    (optional)

Oven 350°

Combine dry ingredients except nuts. Mix together honey or maple syrup and water in a saucepan and heat until mixture just starts to boil. Pour over dry ingredients. Beat with an electric mixer for 5 minutes. Beat in orange juice, orange rind, and nuts. Batter will be thick. Spread evenly in a greased 4½x8½-inch loaf pan. Place a pan of water on lowest oven rack. Place loaf pan on rack above. Bake for 1 hour. Remove from pan and cool on wire rack. Wrap well in foil.

Makes great toast. Taste improves with aging but bread may also be eaten right away. Keeps well.

CARAMEL SWEET ROLLS

No milk, egg, corn, rye, citrus, or salicylates

Makes 20 to 24 rolls

1 cup milk or water
¼ cup uncolored butter or
    allowed margarine,
    melted
3 tablespoons honey
1 teaspoon salt
1 package dry yeast or 1
    cake compressed yeast

¼ cup warm water
4 cups unbleached flour
¼ cup uncolored butter or
    allowed margarine
⅓ cup honey
½ cup finely chopped nuts or
    wheat germ (optional)

Oven 375°

Heat together milk or water, shortening, honey, and salt until shortening is melted. Cool to lukewarm. In the meantime, dissolve yeast in warm water and then add to first mixture. Add about half the flour and beat for several minutes with an electric mixer. Work in remaining flour with spoon. Place in greased bowl, turning dough to coat the top. Let rise in a warm place until double in bulk, about 1½ hours. Punch down. With floured hands shape into balls about 1½ inches in diameter.

In the bottom of greased muffin pans place about ½ teaspoon shortening and 1 teaspoon honey in each cup. A few finely chopped nuts or wheat germ may also be added. Place balls of dough on top, filling cups half full. Let rise until almost double in bulk, about 30 to 45 minutes. Bake for about 12 minutes or until lightly browned on top. When removed from oven turn pans upside down on a cookie sheet. Do not remove pan from rolls for several minutes so topping will run down over rolls.

May be frozen wrapped tightly in foil. Defrost. In the morning reheat in foil and serve hot.

BASIC SWEET YEAST DOUGH

No milk, egg, corn, rye, citrus, or salicylates

Makes enough dough for 2 large or 3 small cakes

½ cup warm water
2 packages dry yeast or 2 cakes compressed yeast
1¾ cups scalded milk or potato water, cooled to lukewarm
½ cup honey
2 teaspoons salt

½ cup uncolored butter or allowed margarine, softened
2 eggs or equivalent egg replacer
2 cups whole wheat flour
5½ to 6 cups sifted unbleached flour

Pour water into a large mixing bowl. Sprinkle yeast on top and mix until dissolved. Add milk or potato water, honey, salt, shortening, and eggs or replacer. Stir in whole wheat flour and mix until smooth. Add enough of the remaining flour so that the dough leaves the sides of the bowl. Knead on a floured board until the dough is very smooth. Put into a greased bowl. Turn the greased side up and cover. Let rise in a warm place until double in bulk, about 1½ hours. Punch down. Divide dough and make into desired shapes. Allow to rise again before baking, as directed in recipes calling for Basic Sweet Yeast Dough.*

HONEY BUBBLE COFFEE CAKE

No milk, egg, corn, rye, citrus, or salicylates

Serves 8 to 10

½ recipe Basic Sweet Yeast Dough*
½ cup uncolored butter or allowed margarine
¼ cup honey
1½ cups finely chopped nuts *or* ¾ cup toasted wheat germ

Oven 350°

Prepare yeast dough. Melt 3 tablespoons of shortening in bottom of an ungreased 10-inch tube pan. Add 2 tablespoons of honey. Melt the rest of shortening in a small pan. Cut the dough into walnut-sized pieces with a scissors. Roll each ball in the melted shortening, then in the chopped nuts or wheat germ. Place the ball in tube pan. Continue with the remainder of the dough making two full layers in the pan. Spoon the rest of the honey over top. Cover and let rise until double in bulk, about 45 minutes. Bake for 30 to 35 minutes. As soon as the cake is removed from the oven invert onto a plate and remove pan. Break cake into pieces with a fork when ready to serve.

HONEY NUT COFFEE CAKE

No milk, egg, corn, rye, citrus, or salicylates

Makes 1 8- or 9-inch round cake

6 tablespoons uncolored butter or allowed margarine
⅓ cup honey
½ cup pecan halves
½ recipe Basic Sweet Yeast Dough*

Oven 350°

Melt 3 tablespoons shortening in an 8- or 9-inch cake pan. Add the honey and pecan halves. Stir until combined and the nuts are evenly distributed. Cut the dough into walnut-sized pieces with scissors. Melt the other 3 tablespoons shortening in a small pan. Roll each piece of dough in the shortening and place on top of the honey-nut mixture. Place the pieces of dough so they are almost touching. Cover and let rise until almost double in bulk, about 45 minutes. Bake for 30 minutes. Turn the cake over onto a plate when removed from the oven and let stand for a minute to let the topping run down over the rolls. Serve warm.

TEA RING

No milk, egg, corn, rye, citrus, or salicylates

Makes 1 12-inch cake

½ recipe Basic Sweet Yeast Dough*
¼ cup honey
¾ teaspoon cinnamon
½ cup chopped nuts
½ cup chopped dates or raisins
½ cup wheat germ

Oven 350°

Roll dough into a 10x20-inch rectangle. Spread evenly with 3 tablespoons honey. Sprinkle cinnamon over dough, adding the nuts, fruit, or wheat germ on top. Roll the dough tightly, starting from the wide side, and pinching the edges to seal. Stretch the dough slightly and place in a ring on a lightly greased baking sheet with seam down. Pinch ends together. Cut at 1-inch intervals around the outside of the ring almost through to center. Turn each slice slightly on its side. Cover and let rise until almost double in bulk, about 45 minutes. Bake for 25 to 30 minutes. Drizzle 1 tablespoon honey over the top when removed from oven but still warm.

CHAPTER NINE

PACKING THE LUNCH BOX

If your child has been buying his lunch at school, he will probably have to carry a lunch box or "brown bag it" most days. Younger children seem to enjoy carrying a lunch box filled with a variety of good foods and may be delighted to do so all through grade school. Most older children are happier with a sandwich, a piece of fruit, dessert, or whatever.

Here are some tips for packing your child's lunch to make his meal as delicious and pleasant as possible. Pick the ones appropriate for your child and his diet.

Lunch Box Tips

Include whatever plastic utensils are needed for his lunch. Holiday or special napkins may cheer his day.

Include some small surprise on occasion, like a yo-yo, small toy, marbles, etc.

Slip in a small note wishing him a good day and sending your love. Or include an appropriate drawing he'll recognize.

Buy an inexpensive joke book and each day slip in several jokes he can share with his friends.

If you are including a special sweet treat, send enough pieces so he can share with his friends.

Food Tips

If your child is "brown bagging it," and can drink milk, have him buy his white milk at school. A small disposable container of carob syrup may be included so he can make his own "chocolate" milk.

Vary his lunch from day to day. A varied diet helps prevent future allergies and ensure good nutrition.

Try to pack only those foods he really likes.

Prepare as much of the lunch box as possible the night before to save yourself time in the morning. Sandwich spreads may be made and stored. Sliced meat sandwiches may be made up in quantity and frozen. They'll keep well up to one month. Label each. Place one in the lunch box in the morning and it will be defrosted by noon. Freezing egg salad or similar sandwiches doesn't work out well.

Pack lettuce leaves separately from the sandwich so they can be added just before eating. Otherwise they'll wilt and be unappetizing.

Hot dishes like chili, stew, macaroni and cheese may be packed in a wide-mouth thermos. Include allowed whole grain crackers as desired and necessary utensils.

Cold foods like applesauce, puddings, cottage cheese, and gelatin desserts may also be packed in a wide-mouth thermos.

Pack your child's favorite homemade soups in a thermos. Include allowed crackers and spoon.

For variety, pack a half sandwich with one filling and a half sandwich with another filling. Or make one half sandwich with one kind of bread and use another bread for the other half.

Spread sandwich filling between buns for variety.

Several thin slices of meat in a sandwich taste much better than one thick slice and make the sandwich easier to eat.

Spread bread with allowed butter or margarine before spreading with salads made with mayonnaise to prevent soggy sandwiches.

Instead of always packing sandwiches, or if wheat and rye are to be avoided, pack a piece of meat (like fried chicken). Include a special bread (made of oat or rice flour) like pumpkin, zucchini, or banana. These breads freeze well. Freeze individually wrapped slices and use as needed. If your child can eat cheese, pack cheese and allowed crackers on occasion.

Bananas are easy to carry and peel. Well-washed unwaxed fresh pears and apples, peaches, grapes, and plums can be packed and eaten with no preparation. Other allowed fruits on the diet may be prepared in small containers.

Include some treats occasionally like natural potato chips fried in pure allowed vegetable oil or corn chips. Check the labels on your local brands. Raw peanuts and other nuts may be included. A small bag of homemade popcorn would also be a treat.

Carrot sticks, cucumber slices, zucchini slices, cherry tomatoes, celery sticks, etc., add color, variety, and nutrition. A small package of allowed peanut butter may be included. The carrot sticks or the celery may be packed already spread with peanut butter or cream cheese.

Small cans of unsweetened fruit juice are easy to pack. Remember if milk is allowed, serve no more than 16 ounces a day.

Include some homemade pickles, if desired.

A hard-cooked egg, if allowed, will add protein and iron to the lunch. Wrap sea salt in small foil package.

For the younger child, cut the sandwiches with cookie cutters or into distinctive shapes for variety.

Spread thin slices of date-nut or zucchini bread with cream cheese.

Soups

BEAN SOUP

No milk, egg, corn, wheat, rye, citrus, or salicylates

Serves 4

2 cups Chicken Stock*
2 cups water
½ cup dried navy beans
1 bay leaf

1 cup diced carrots
1 cup diced celery
1 small onion, thinly sliced

In a large pot combine stock and water. Bring to a boil. Add beans and bay leaf. Simmer ingredients in covered pot for 2 hours. Remove bay leaf and add carrots, celery, and onion. Simmer for 30 minutes.

Put mixture through a sieve or blender. Return mixture to the pot and add enough water to thin the soup to required consistency. Reheat to boiling and serve.

CHICKEN SOUP

No milk, egg, corn, wheat, rye, citrus, or salicylates

Serves 6

1 3-pound chicken, cut up
6 cups water
2 teaspoons salt
Pepper to taste
1 bay leaf

2 stalks celery, cut up
6 carrots, cut up
1 large onion, minced
1 cup uncooked noodles or
    rice (optional)

Place chicken in a large saucepan. Cover with water and add salt, pepper, and bay leaf. Cover, bring to a boil, and simmer for 1 hour or until chicken is tender. When chicken is done remove from stock. Refrigerate overnight and skim fat from the top of the broth. Reheat broth, add the vegetables, and cook for 35 minutes or until vegetables are almost tender. Skin and bone chicken and cut meat into small pieces. Add chicken and noodles or rice to broth and cook for an additional 15 minutes.

CREAM SOUP

No egg, corn, wheat, rye, citrus, or salicylates

Makes 1½ quarts

¼ cup pure allowed vegetable oil
3 tablespoons unbleached flour or rice flour
2 cups milk

2 cups Chicken Stock*
Dash of salt and paprika
2 cups leftover vegetables and/or meat chunks

In a heavy saucepan mix oil and flour over low heat. Gradually add milk, stirring constantly. When mixture begins to boil add chicken stock and continue to stir until well mixed and hot. Add seasonings.

Any cooked vegetables may be used. Drain liquid from vegetables and purée in blender or food mill. Add to soup and cook until hot.

FISH CHOWDER

No milk, egg, corn, wheat, rye, citrus, or salicylates

Makes 2 quarts

1 cup finely diced carrots
1 cup diced uncooked potatoes
1 cup chopped onion
½ cup finely diced celery
1 bay leaf
1½ cups water
1 12-ounce package frozen (thawed) fish fillets

¼ cup pure allowed vegetable oil
¼ cup unbleached flour or rice flour
2 teaspoons salt
3½ cups Chicken Stock* or milk
Dried parsley flakes

In a large saucepan place carrots, potatoes, onion, celery, and bay leaf. Add water and bring to a boil. Turn to simmer and cook

15 minutes. Add fish and cook 15 minutes longer. With a fork break fish into small chunks. Discard bay leaf. Cover pan and set aside.

Heat oil in another saucepan, add flour, salt, and mix. Stir in stock or milk gradually. Cook over medium heat, stirring constantly until mixture bubbles. Combine with fish mixture. Serve hot with sprinkling of parsley flakes.

This is a delicious soup and may be served as a main course for supper.

ONION AND POTATO SOUP

No milk, egg, corn, wheat, rye, citrus, or salicylates

Serves 8

¼ cup plus 2 tablespoons pure allowed vegetable oil

2 to 3 medium onions, thinly sliced

¾ teaspoon salt

2 tablespoons unbleached flour or rice flour

3 cups Chicken Stock*

2 cups salted diced cooked potatoes

Paprika (optional)

Heat ¼ cup oil in skillet. Add onions and ¼ teaspoon salt. Cook onions until tender, stirring frequently.

In a heavy saucepan mix 2 tablespoons oil and flour. Add 3 cups stock and ½ teaspoon salt. Stir and heat well. Add onions to white sauce and potatoes. Purée mixture in blender. Heat thoroughly. Serve with a dash of paprika on each portion.

PEA SOUP

No milk, egg, corn, wheat, rye, citrus, or salicylates

Makes 1 pint

2 cups fresh peas or 1 10-ounce package frozen peas

⅛ teaspoon crushed dried sweet basil

1 teaspoon onion powder

1 cup Chicken Stock*

Cook fresh peas until tender or prepare frozen peas according to package directions. Using either a blender or food mill purée the peas with the water in which they were cooked.

Add basil and onion powder and blend well. Combine chicken stock with pea purée. Reheat to boiling point.

TOMATO SOUP

No milk, egg, corn, wheat, rye, or citrus

Makes 1 pint

1 6-ounce can tomato paste
2 cups Chicken Stock*
¼ teaspoon instant minced onion
¼ teaspoon celery salt
¼ teaspoon salt
1 tablespoon honey

In a large saucepan combine all ingredients. Bring to a boil and then simmer for 5 minutes.

TURKEY SOUP

No milk, egg, corn, wheat, rye, citrus, or salicylates

1 turkey carcass, broken up
Water
Celery, diced
Carrots, diced
Onion, diced
Salt and pepper to taste
Uncooked rice or noodles or barley (optional)

Place turkey carcass in a Dutch oven or similar large covered pot. Pour water over the bones so that about one half to two thirds of pot is filled. Bring to a boil. Skim. Cover and reduce heat. Simmer for 2 hours. Remove carcass and pick off any bits of remaining meat from the bones. Add meat to stock. Discard carcass. Refrigerate soup overnight. Skim off fat.

Place soup in a heavy pot and add celery, carrots, and onion as desired. Salt and pepper to taste. Bring to a boil. If desired, add rice, noodles, or barley and cook until they are done.

VEGETABLE BEEF SOUP

No milk, egg, corn, wheat, rye, citrus, or salicylates

Makes 1½ quarts

1 beef soup bone
8 cups water
1 tablespoon salt
2 bay leaves
¼ teaspoon chili powder
⅓ cup chopped onion
1 cup diced celery

1 cup diced carrots
1 cup diced potatoes
1 cup diced cabbage or
    chopped tomatoes
Uncooked rice or barley or
    noodles, as desired

Cook bone with water, salt, and seasonings for 3 hours. Add vegetables. Cover and simmer 1 hour longer. Remove bone and bay leaves. Remove any meat from bone and add to soup. Refrigerate overnight. Skim off fat. Reheat and add rice, barley, or noodles and cook until done.

Sandwich Spreads

CHICKEN OR TURKEY SANDWICH SPREAD

No milk, egg, corn, wheat, rye, or citrus

Makes 1½ cups

1 cup finely chopped cooked
    chicken or turkey
1 hard-cooked egg, chopped
    (optional)
⅓ cup chopped celery

2 tablespoons capers or
    chopped Sweet Pickles*
¼ teaspoon salt
3 tablespoons Mayonnaise*
    or Eggless Mayonnaise*

Combine all ingredients above and mix well. Spread as desired on buttered bread. Refrigerate any remaining spread in a covered container.

CHEESE SANDWICH SPREAD

No egg, corn, wheat, rye, citrus, or salicylates

Makes about 2 cups

2 tablespoons uncolored butter or allowed margarine
2 tablespoons unbleached flour or oat flour
1 cup milk

½ pound uncolored cheese, grated
1 egg, slightly beaten (optional)
Salt and pepper to taste

Melt shortening in a medium saucepan. Remove from heat and blend in flour. Return to heat and slowly add milk, stirring until smooth and slightly thickened. Add the grated cheese and continue to stir until completely melted. Stir in egg, salt, and pepper. Remove from heat and cool. When cold, spread on slices of allowed bread or crackers. Store leftovers in refrigerator.

This can be prepared and then reheated in the top of a double boiler to serve hot as a cheese sauce to top vegetables or open-faced sandwiches.

CREAM CHEESE AND PINEAPPLE SPREAD

No egg, corn, wheat, rye, citrus, or salicylates

Makes about ½ cup

1 3-ounce package cream cheese, softened
2 tablespoons drained unsweetened crushed canned pineapple
1 tablespoon non-instant dry milk powder

Mix cheese and pineapple together. Stir in milk powder. Use as sandwich filling on Date and Nut Bread* or buttered White Bread.* Refrigerate leftover spread. Cream cheese is rather low in protein, so the added milk powder makes this spread more nutritious.

EGG SALAD SANDWICH SPREAD

No milk, corn, wheat, rye, or citrus

Makes ½ cup

2 hard-cooked eggs, chopped
1 tablespoon chopped celery
1 tablespoon capers or
    chopped Sweet Pickles*

2 tablespoons Mayonnaise*
¼ teaspoon dry mustard
⅛ teaspoon salt

Mix all ingredients well. Use immediately or refrigerate in a covered container. Spread as desired on buttered bread or allowed crackers.

PEANUT BUTTER SPREAD

No milk, egg, corn, wheat, rye, citrus, or salicylates

Makes 1½ cups

1 cup chunky or creamy additive-free peanut butter
½ cup coarsely grated carrots
2 tablespoons raisins
2 tablespoons toasted wheat germ (optional)

Combine all ingredients. Serve on allowed bread, crackers, or celery ribs.

PORK OR VEAL SALAD SPREAD

No milk, egg, corn, wheat, rye, or citrus

Makes about 3 cups

2 cups finely chopped cooked
    pork or veal
1 cup diced celery
½ cup chopped stuffed olives
¼ teaspoon garlic salt

1 cup Mayonnaise* or
    Eggless Mayonnaise*
½ teaspoon salt
Pepper to taste

Mix all ingredients together and store in refrigerator. When ready to serve, spread on buttered bread.

SALMON SALAD SPREAD

No milk, egg, corn, wheat, rye, or citrus

Makes 3 cups

2 cups drained canned salmon (packed in water)
¼ cup diced onion
1 cup diced celery

1 cup Mayonnaise* or Eggless Mayonnaise*
½ teaspoon salt
Pepper to taste

Mix all ingredients together and store in refrigerator. Spread on buttered bread when ready to serve.

SARDINE SANDWICH SPREAD

No egg, corn, wheat, rye, or citrus

Makes 1 cup

1 3¾-ounce can sardines in pure allowed oil, drained
1 tablespoon Mayonnaise* or Eggless Mayonnaise*
3 tablespoons chopped Sweet Pickles*
½ cup additive-free cottage cheese

Mash sardines and mix with other ingredients. Spread on buttered bread for sandwiches. Store unused portion in refrigerator.

TUNA SALAD SANDWICH SPREAD

No milk, egg, corn, wheat, rye, or citrus

Makes 1 cup

1 7-ounce can tuna (packed in water or pure allowed oil), drained and flaked
3 tablespoons capers or chopped Sweet Pickles*
2 tablespoons finely chopped celery
Mayonnaise* or Eggless Mayonnaise*

Mix tuna, capers or pickles, and celery together. Add enough mayonnaise for a moist filling. Spread on buttered bread when ready to serve. Refrigerate any leftover spread in a covered container.

Other

DEVILED EGGS

No milk, corn, wheat, rye, or citrus

Makes 4 half eggs

2 hard-cooked eggs
2 tablespoons Mayonnaise*
¼ teaspoon dry mustard

1 tablespoon capers or
    chopped Sweet Pickles*
Dash of salt
Paprika (optional)

Cut eggs in half. Press yolks through sieve. Add mayonnaise, mustard, capers or pickles, and salt. Mix well. Refill white halves with mixture. Sprinkle with paprika. Refrigerate.

To pack eggs in the lunch box, refrigerate until last moment before packing them with the rest of the lunch.

CHAPTER TEN

MEAT, FISH, AND POULTRY

Meat, fish, and poultry entrées for dinner shouldn't cause many new problems. Some recipes in this chapter will substitute for prepared items like commercial chicken-coating mixes and stuffing. You'll probably have many family favorites too that can be prepared as usual or adapted to the limits of your diet. Avoid ham, bacon, self-basting turkeys, prepared breaded frozen fish, and purple stamping on meat cuts.

Beef

BEEF POT PIE

No milk, egg, corn, rye, citrus, or salicylates

Serves 4

2 cups cubed leftover pot
    roast, roast beef, or stew
2 cups leftover gravy, slightly
    thickened

2 cups leftover peas and/or
    carrots (optional)
Salt and pepper to taste
1 recipe Wheat Piecrust*

Oven 475°

Place beef cubes, gravy, vegetables, and seasonings in a round casserole dish. Cover with single pastry crust, pressing dough firmly around the edge of the dish. Prick dough at regular intervals to allow steam to escape. Bake for 15 minutes or until crust is brown around the edge.

BEEF STEW

No milk, egg, corn, wheat, rye, citrus, or salicylates

Serves 6

2 pounds stewing beef, cut up
2 tablespoons pure allowed
    vegetable oil
Water
Salt to taste
½ cup diced carrots

½ cup diced celery
1 onion, sliced
½ cup 1-inch diced potatoes
½ cup cold water
¼ cup unbleached flour,
    cornstarch, or rice flour

Oven 300°

In the bottom of a Dutch oven, brown meat quickly in oil. Barely cover meat with water and salt to taste. Cover and cook in oven for 3 hours. An hour before serving, add carrots, celery, onion, and potatoes. Make a paste of water and starch and add as needed to thicken gravy before serving.

For the lunch box, pour hot stew into a wide-mouth thermos. Include crackers and a plastic spoon or fork in the box.

POT ROAST

No milk, egg, corn, wheat, rye, citrus, or salicylates

Serves 8

1 4-pound blade cut or any
    other cut suitable for pot
    roast
¼ cup unbleached flour or
    rice flour, seasoned with
    salt and pepper
2 tablespoons pure allowed
    vegetable oil
1 cup water

8 carrots, cut into chunks
8 peeled potatoes, cut into
    chunks
1 small onion, sliced
Salt
½ cup water
¼ cup unbleached flour or
    rice flour

Oven 300°

Dredge roast in seasoned flour. Brown quickly on all sides in oil. Remove from skillet and place in a Dutch oven or deep casserole. Add water and cover tightly. Cook in oven for 4 hours. One hour before serving time add carrots and potatoes. Place slices of onion on meat and salt. When ready to serve, remove meat to platter. Surround with vegetables. Thicken gravy by making a paste of water and flour. Add slowly to gravy, as needed, stirring until it thickens.

SLOW-COOKED ROAST

No milk, egg, corn, wheat, rye, citrus, or salicylates

Slow cooking turns an inexpensive cut of meat into a juicy, tender roast. Allow lots of cooking time. If roast is large, it may be started the night before. You will soon get a feel for the cooking time needed.

1 beef roast, any cut
2 tablespoons uncolored butter, allowed margarine, or pure allowed vegetable oil

Oven 300°

Early in the day spread meat with butter or coat with oil on all surfaces. Do not season. Place on a rack in a roasting pan. Bake for 1 hour to kill surface bacteria. Reduce heat to about 150° or 160°. Insert a meat thermometer and cook until thermometer registers desired internal temperature indicating degree of doneness. For a beef roast to be medium done, temperature should be about 150°. A 5-pound roast, medium done, will require at least 6 hours' total cooking time.

TONGUE

No milk, egg, corn, wheat, rye, or citrus

Serves 8 to 10

1 3-pound beef tongue
Boiling water to cover
2 teaspoons salt
3 bay leaves
½ teaspoon nutmeg
½ teaspoon cinnamon
3 whole black peppercorns

1 tablespoon apple cider
   vinegar
1 onion, sliced
1 carrot, sliced
1 stalk celery, sliced
6 to 8 sprigs fresh parsley,
   chopped

Wash tongue. Cover with boiling water. Add all other ingredients. Simmer uncovered about 3 hours. Cool in cooking liquid. Skin and trim away excess tissue. Slice and serve with Horseradish Sauce.*

For sandwiches, slice thin. Bread may be spread with butter or allowed margarine and/or Mayonnaise* and Horseradish Sauce* as desired. Wrap well for lunch box.

Veal

VEAL CUTLETS

No milk, egg, corn, wheat, rye, citrus, or salicylates

Serves 4

1 12-ounce veal cutlet
Water
Allowed Dry Bread Crumbs*
3 tablespoons pure allowed vegetable oil

Oven 325°

Cut cutlet in two. Moisten each piece with water. Dip in crumbs until well coated. Brown cutlets quickly on both sides in oil in a heavy skillet. Cover and bake in skillet for about 50 minutes. Cut into 4 servings.

GOURMET VEAL CUTLETS

No egg, corn, rye, citrus, or salicylates

Serves 4

Veal Cutlets*
Pesto Sauce*
White cheese

Prepare meat as in veal cutlets recipe. After cutlets have been cooked, spread pesto sauce over cutlets. Top with slices of cheese so that each piece is covered. Broil until cheese is melted and bubbling.

VEAL CHOPS

No milk, egg, corn, wheat, rye, citrus, or salicylates

Serves 4

¼ cup pure allowed vege-
  table oil
2 medium onions, sliced in
  thin rings
4 veal chops
Salt and pepper to taste
1 cup Chicken Stock*

1 bay leaf
1 teaspoon dried parsley
  flakes
¼ cup unbleached flour, rice
  flour, or cornstarch
½ cup cold water

Heat oil in heavy skillet or pot. Add sliced onions. Cover and simmer very slowly until transparent, about 15 minutes. Remove onions to side dish. Turn heat up and quickly brown chops on each side. Salt and pepper. Add more oil while browning chops if necessary.

Remove chops and set aside. Pour oil out of skillet. Heat chicken stock in skillet and simmer for 1 minute. Return chops to pan with any juice that collected in dish. Add cooked onions on top of chops and bay leaf and parsley. Cover pan and simmer very slowly for about 30 minutes or until tender. Place chops and onions on a warm platter. Discard bay leaf. Thicken juices in pan with flour or cornstarch mixed with cold water. Stir until thickened. Pour over chops and onions.

Lamb

BROILED LAMB CHOPS

No milk, egg, corn, wheat, rye, citrus, or salicylates

Serves 4

4 lamb rib chops
Salt and pepper to taste
Garlic powder

Sprinkle both sides of lamb rib chops with salt, pepper, and garlic powder. Slash fat edge at 1-inch intervals. Place on rack in broiler pan so chops are 3 inches from preheated broiler. Broil 5 to 7 minutes on each side.

LAMB STEW

No milk, egg, corn, wheat, rye, citrus, or salicylates

Serves 6

2 pounds lamb, cubed
¼ cup unbleached flour or
    rice flour, seasoned with
    salt and pepper
4 to 6 tablespoons pure
    allowed vegetable oil
½ cup sliced onions

Boiling water to cover
1 cup sliced carrots
1 cup diced celery
½ cup water
¼ cup unbleached flour or
    rice flour

Coat lamb cubes with seasoned flour. In a heavy saucepan brown them quickly in oil. Drain cubes on paper towels. Brown onions in remaining oil over medium heat. Return lamb to the pot and cover with boiling water. Cover the pot and simmer for about 2 hours. Add carrots and celery. Bring to a boil, then simmer for ½ hour. Thicken stock with a mixture of water and flour stirred in slowly. Salt and pepper to taste. Good served over hot rice.

Pork

BUTTERFLY PORK CHOPS

No milk, egg, corn, wheat, rye, citrus, or salicylates

Serves 4

4 butterfly pork chops or 4 loin pork chops or shoulder pork
    chops
¼ cup unbleached flour or rice flour, seasoned with salt and
    pepper
3 tablespoons pure allowed vegetable oil

Oven 275°

Dip chops in flour. In a heavy skillet over medium heat brown
chops in oil for about 10 minutes. Cover and cook in oven for 50
minutes more. Turn every 10 minutes.

PORK CHOPS, SWEET AND SOUR

No milk, egg, corn, wheat, rye, or citrus

Serves 6

6 pork chops
1 teaspoon ginger
1 teaspoon salt
½ teaspoon pepper
½ teaspoon paprika
¼ cup unbleached flour or
    rice flour

3 tablespoons pure allowed
    vegetable oil
1 cup unsweetened pineapple
    juice
1 tablespoon apple cider
    vinegar
1 tablespoon honey

Oven 275°

Coat both sides of chops with mixture of ginger, salt, pepper,
paprika, and flour. In a skillet brown chops in oil over low heat,
turning once. Mix together other ingredients and pour over chops.
Cover skillet. Place in oven and cook chops 1 hour or until tender. A covered baking dish may be used instead of the skillet for
the oven baking.

STUFFED PORK CHOPS

No milk, egg, corn, wheat, rye, citrus, or salicylates

Serves 4

4 pork chops, cut 1 inch thick
1 cup Bread Stuffing* or Rice Stuffing*
¼ cup pure allowed vegetable oil

¾ cup milk or unsweetened apple juice
Salt and pepper to taste

Oven 350°

Cut pockets in the pork chops and stuff, using toothpicks to hold edges together. In a heavy skillet, brown chops on both sides in oil. Place chops in an ovenproof dish, pour milk or apple juice over all. Season with salt and pepper. Cover and bake for 1 hour or until tender.

SPARERIBS WITH MARINADE

No milk, egg, corn, wheat, or rye

Serves 4

2 cups unsweetened apple juice
1 medium onion, thinly sliced
1 tablespoon pure lemon juice
1 teaspoon salt

⅛ teaspoon pepper
¼ teaspoon ginger
½ teaspoon additive-free soy sauce
4 pounds lean spareribs

Oven 350°

Combine all ingredients except spareribs in a saucepan and simmer slowly for 5 minutes. Place ribs in a shallow dish and pour hot apple mixture over them. Marinate in refrigerator for at least 3 hours, turning occasionally. When ready to cook, drain off juice, pour ½ cup marinade over spareribs, and cover loosely with foil. Bake for 1½ hours. Every ½ hour pour some of the remaining sauce over the ribs. Uncover for the last 20 to 30 minutes to brown.

Fish

EASY BAKED FISH

No milk, egg, corn, wheat, rye, or citrus

Serves 4

24 ounces any inexpensive
frozen (thawed) fish
fillets (cod is delicious
this way)
Mayonnaise* or Eggless
Mayonnaise*

Allowed Soft Bread Crumbs,*
seasoned with salt and
pepper
Salt
Paprika
Dried parsley flakes

Oven 500°

Spread fish fillets with mayonnaise. Roll in seasoned soft bread crumbs. Place in a well-greased pan. Sprinkle each fillet with salt, paprika, and parsley. Bake for 10 minutes. Test with fork to be sure fish flakes easily and is done. Serve with lemon wedges or Tartar Sauce.*

PLAIN BAKED FISH

No milk, egg, corn, wheat, rye, citrus, or salicylates

Oven 350°

Line a shallow pan with aluminum foil. Place fillets in pan, brush with a little oil, and sprinkle well with paprika. Bake for about 15 minutes for thin fillets, 20 minutes for thicker ones. Test with a fork to be sure fish flakes easily and is done.

TUNA AND CHEESE PIE

No corn, wheat, rye, or salicylates

Serves 4 to 6

1 recipe allowed piecrust
1 6½-ounce can tuna (packed in water), drained and flaked
6 ounces grated uncolored cheese
2 tablespoons instant minced onion

2 eggs, beaten
1 cup evaporated milk
1 tablespoon pure lemon juice
1 teaspoon dried chives
1 clove garlic, minced
1 teaspoon salt
⅛ teaspoon pepper

Oven 450°

Prepare piecrust. Bake for 5 minutes. Sprinkle tuna, cheese, and onion over crust. Combine eggs, milk, lemon juice, and seasonings. Pour over tuna. Bake 15 minutes. Reduce oven to 350° and continue baking another 12 to 15 minutes or until top is lightly browned.

Poultry

BARBECUED CHICKEN

No milk, egg, corn, wheat, rye, or citrus

Serves 6

2 3-pound chickens, cut up
1 egg (optional)
1 cup pure allowed vegetable oil
2 cups apple cider vinegar

⅓ cup salt
1 tablespoon poultry seasoning
½ teaspoon pepper

Oven 350°

Arrange chicken in a shallow baking dish. Beat the egg and gradually add the oil. Add remaining ingredients and stir thoroughly. Pour marinade over chicken and let stand for at least 1 hour. Drain chicken and either cook on a grill or bake for 1 hour. Baste the pieces of chicken several times while cooking.

BROILED CHICKEN PARTS

No milk, egg, corn, wheat, rye, citrus, or salicylates

Serves 4 to 6

4 chicken thighs and 4
   chicken breasts *or* 8
   chicken wings and 8
   chicken legs
⅓ to ½ cup pure allowed
   vegetable oil

2 tablespoons dried parsley
   flakes
2 tablespoons frozen or dried
   chopped chives

Line a pan with foil. Place chicken pieces on foil. Combine oil, parsley flakes, and chopped chives. Pour over chicken. Let stand at room temperature for about 1 hour. Drain.

Broil chicken breasts and thighs on top rack of oven for 25 to 30 minutes, chicken legs and wings for 20 minutes, turning the pieces once.

CHICKEN PIE

No milk, egg, corn, rye, citrus, or salicylates

Serves 4

2 tablespoons pure allowed
   vegetable oil
¼ cup unbleached flour or
   rice flour
1 teaspoon salt
Dash of pepper

2 cups Chicken Stock*
2 cups cubed cooked chicken
1 cup diced cooked carrots
1 cup cooked peas
1 recipe Wheat Piecrust*

Oven 475°

In a large saucepan combine oil and flour over medium heat. Add seasonings and chicken stock. Stir constantly until sauce boils. Turn to simmer and add chicken, carrots, and peas. Pour mixture into a round casserole dish. Place prepared pastry dough on top, pressing edges to sides of casserole dish. At intervals prick crust with a fork to allow steam to escape. Bake 12 to 15 minutes or until crust begins to brown around the edges.

CHICKEN SHAKE

No milk, egg, corn, wheat, rye, citrus, or salicylates

Enough coating for
4 cut-up chickens

4 cups allowed Dry Bread
  Crumbs*
½ cup pure allowed vege-
  table oil
1 tablespoon paprika
1 tablespoon celery salt

1 tablespoon salt
1 teaspoon pepper
1 3-pound frying chicken, cut
  up
1 cup water or milk

Oven 375°

Blend crumbs and oil thoroughly in a mixing bowl. Add seasonings and mix well. Store in a covered container in the refrigerator.
Use about 1 cup of the mixture for one cut-up frying chicken.

Place mixture in a paper bag. Dip chicken pieces in water or
milk. Shake off excess. Shake two to three pieces at a time in the
mixture until well coated. Place coated chicken on a cookie sheet.
Bake about 50 to 60 minutes. Cover lightly with foil toward end
of cooking time if necessary. Serve hot.

Wrap one or more cold chicken pieces for the lunch box. Include a package of salt, if desired.

CHICKEN TURNOVERS

No milk, egg, corn, rye, citrus, or salicylates

Makes 6 turnovers

Double recipe Wheat
  Piecrust*
1 cup finely chopped cooked
  chicken
½ cup chicken gravy

¼ cup chopped mushrooms
⅛ teaspoon poultry sea-
  soning
Salt and pepper to taste

Oven 350°

Prepare piecrust and divide in two. Roll each half out between
sheets of waxed paper and cut the pastry into 5-inch squares.

Combine chicken with rest of the filling ingredients and mix well. Divide chicken mixture evenly onto the pastry squares. Fold pastry over the top of the filling and seal by pressing edges together with a fork. Place on a greased cookie sheet. Bake for 20 to 25 minutes or until golden brown. Serve hot or freeze for future use.

For the lunch box, pack the frozen turnover in the morning and by noon it will be thawed for lunch.

CREAMED CHICKEN

No milk, egg, corn, wheat, rye, citrus, or salicylates

Serves 4

2 tablespoons pure allowed vegetable oil
2 tablespoons unbleached flour or rice flour
1 cup Chicken Stock*

½ teaspoon salt
⅛ teaspoon paprika
1 teaspoon frozen or dried chives
2 cups diced cooked chicken

In a saucepan mix oil and flour. Add stock and bring to a boil, stirring constantly. Add salt, paprika, and chives. Stir in chicken and simmer for a few minutes until chicken is heated. Stir so the sauce does not stick to the pan.

Serve mixture over rice, noodles, or atop buttered toast.

FAR EAST CHICKEN

No milk, egg, corn, wheat, rye, citrus, or salicylates

Serves 4

4 half chicken breasts
4 tablespoons uncolored butter or allowed margarine
½ cup chopped celery
½ cup chopped green pepper (optional)
¼ cup chopped onion
1 8-ounce can bamboo

shoots, drained, reserving liquid
1 8-ounce can sliced water chestnuts, drained, reserving liquid
1¼ cups Chicken Stock*
Salt to taste
2 tablespoons unbleached flour or rice flour

Skin and bone chicken breasts and cut meat into ½-inch strips. Melt shortening in a skillet and quickly cook chicken strips a few at a time. Remove from skillet when done. In remaining shortening partially cook the celery, green pepper, and onion. Add bamboo shoots, water chestnuts, chicken stock, salt, and chicken pieces. Cover and simmer slowly for 20 to 25 minutes. Mix the flour with ½ cup liquid reserved from the water chestnuts and bamboo shoots. Pour into skillet until sauce is slightly thickened. Serve over brown rice.

FRIED CHICKEN

No milk, egg, corn, wheat, rye, citrus, or salicylates

Serves 4 to 6

1 cup unbleached flour or whole wheat flour or oat flour or rice flour
2 teaspoons salt
1 teaspoon poultry seasoning

1 2½- to 3-pound frying chicken, cut up
1 cup milk or water
½ cup pure allowed vegetable oil
¼ cup water

In a plastic bag combine the flour, salt, and poultry seasoning. Dip chicken in milk or water and shake a few pieces at a time in bag with flour until well coated. Heat oil in skillet and brown chicken on all sides. Reduce heat, add water, cover, and continue to cook chicken about 40 to 45 minutes or until tender. Remove cover and cook an additional 10 minutes until crispy.

Chicken can also be cooked after browning by placing pieces on cookie sheet and baking in the oven for 45 minutes at 350°. This gives a very crisp crust.

PINEAPPLE CHICKEN

No milk, egg, corn, wheat, rye, citrus, or salicylates

Serves 6

1 2½- to 3-pound frying chicken

¾ cup unbleached flour or rice flour

2 teaspoons salt

1½ teaspoons ginger

1 cup water

½ cup pure allowed vegetable oil

1 cup unsweetened crushed canned pineapple with juice

½ cup water

Cut chicken into serving pieces. Combine flour, salt, and ginger in a bag. Dip chicken pieces in water and coat with flour mixture. Brown in a skillet with the oil a few pieces at a time. Return all the pieces to the skillet and pour the pineapple mixed with ½ cup water over all. Cover and simmer gently for 45 minutes. Uncover and cook an additional 15 minutes or until tender.

STEWED CHICKEN

No milk, egg, corn, wheat, rye, citrus, or salicylates

Serves 6

6 chicken breasts

4 stalks celery, including leaves, chopped

4 carrots, sliced

¼ cup instant minced onion

Boiling water to cover

Place chicken in a Dutch oven. Add chopped celery, sliced carrots, and onion. Cover with boiling water. Cover the pot and bring to a boil, then turn to simmer. Cook until tender, 1½ hours. Test with a fork for tenderness. Chicken may be served with a little of the chicken stock poured over the pieces.

The stock which is left may be strained to remove vegetables. Store in a covered container in refrigerator. The next day remove hardened fat from the top. Stock may be used in other recipes or served as chicken broth.

ROAST CHICKEN, CAPON, OR TURKEY

No milk, egg, corn, wheat, rye, citrus, or salicylates

1 chicken, capon, or turkey, at room temperature
1 tablespoon salt
Bread Stuffing* or Rice Stuffing*
Uncolored butter or allowed margarine

Oven 400°

Wash bird thoroughly inside and out. Dry well. Rub salt inside the bird. Fill cavity with stuffing. Tie legs together and wings together. Place on large sheet of heavy-duty foil. Rub legs and breast with shortening. Fold foil to cover bird completely. If necessary use more foil over breasts.

Roast in a large pan for 20 minutes. Reduce heat to 350°. For a chicken or capon, allow 25 minutes per pound. A turkey under 10 pounds also requires 25 minutes per pound. A larger turkey needs only 20 minutes per pound. About 30 to 45 minutes before the bird is done, open and fold back foil. Baste frequently with pan drippings as bird browns.

ROCK CORNISH HENS

No milk, egg, corn, wheat, rye, or salicylates

Serves 4

2 tablespoons pure lemon juice
½ cup pure allowed vegetable oil
4 Cornish hens, at room temperature
Salt and pepper to taste

Oven 350°

Mix lemon juice and oil thoroughly. Place hens in roasting pan. Coat with oil mixture. Bake. After 30 minutes salt and pepper hens. Baste. Bake 20 minutes longer. Turn oven temperature to 400° and bake 10 more minutes or until done and lightly browned. Baste with more oil if necessary during cooking.

Stuffings

BREAD STUFFING

No milk, egg, corn, wheat, rye, citrus, or salicylates

Makes enough stuffing for 10-pound turkey

1½ teaspoons poultry seasoning
¼ teaspoon nutmeg
2 teaspoons salt
8 cups small pieces dried allowed bread

2 tablespoons grated onion
2 eggs, slightly beaten (optional)
½ cup pure allowed vegetable oil

Combine dry ingredients with bread pieces. Add onion, eggs, and oil. Mix well.

RICE STUFFING

No milk, egg, corn, wheat, rye, citrus, or salicylates

Makes enough stuffing for 2 3½-pound chickens

2 tablespoons uncolored butter or allowed margarine
½ cup minced onion
2 4-ounce cans mushroom pieces, drained

2 to 3 cups cooked brown rice
½ teaspoon poultry seasoning

Melt shortening in a heavy skillet and sauté onion until partially cooked. Add mushroom pieces and cook for several more minutes. Add rice and poultry seasoning. Mix thoroughly. Stuff chickens and cook as directed. Any leftover stuffing can be heated in a covered ovenproof dish.

Ground Meats

CHICKEN PATTIES

No milk, egg, corn, wheat, rye, citrus, or salicylates

Serves 4

¼ cup uncolored butter or allowed margarine
¼ cup unbleached flour or rice flour
1 cup Chicken Stock*
3 cups ground cooked chicken
1 tablespoon minced parsley
1 teaspoon salt
¼ teaspoon pepper
1 tablespoon grated onion
1 cup allowed Dry Bread Crumbs*
½ cup pure allowed vegetable oil
1 cup chicken gravy

Melt shortening in a medium saucepan. Stir in flour. When mixture is smooth, slowly add chicken stock and continue to stir until sauce is thickened. Remove from heat and add ground chicken, parsley, salt, pepper, and onion. Spread mixture around the bottom and sides of pan and refrigerate for several hours until thoroughly chilled. When ready to cook, shape chicken into eight patties. Dip the patties into the dried bread crumbs, pressing crumbs onto the patties until fully covered. Fry in oil in a heavy skillet over medium heat until lightly browned. Serve hot and topped with chicken gravy.

HAMBURGER PIE

No milk, egg, corn, wheat, rye, citrus, or salicylates

Serves 4

1 heaping cup (½ pound) sliced cleaned mushrooms
2 tablespoons pure allowed vegetable oil
¼ cup chopped onion
¼ cup chopped green pepper (optional)
1 pound ground beef
½ teaspoon salt
Dash of pepper
⅛ teaspoon chili powder
1 recipe allowed piecrust,* baked
Uncolored cheese (optional)
Paprika

Oven 350°

Brown mushrooms in oil. Set aside. In the same skillet, adding more oil if needed, brown chopped onion and green pepper. Add ground beef, salt, pepper, and chili powder. Simmer for 20 minutes. Using a slotted spoon to drain off oil, place mixture in pie shell. Spread mushrooms on top and over that place slices of cheese until top is covered. Sprinkle with paprika. Bake for 15 minutes.

ITALIAN HAMBURGERS

No milk, egg, corn, wheat, rye, citrus, or salicylates

Ground lean beef
Pesto Sauce*
Uncolored cheese (optional)

Form ground beef into patties. Broil on one side. Turn patties over and spread pesto sauce over each one. Return to the broiler. If cheese is used, when nearly done place slices of cheese on top of each. When cheese has melted, remove from oven and serve.

ITALIAN SAUSAGE

No milk, egg, corn, wheat, rye, citrus, or salicylates

Maks 1½ pounds

1½ pounds coarsely ground
  pork or lean ground beef
1 teaspoon garlic salt
1 teaspoon fennel seed
½ teaspoon salt
½ teaspoon Italian seasoning

½ teaspoon chili powder
⅛ teaspoon pepper
2 tablespoons water
2 tablespoons pure allowed
  vegetable oil

Combine all ingredients except oil, so spices are evenly distributed. Shape into patties. Fry in oil until fully cooked.

This is delicious on pizzas. Instead of shaping into patties, crumble sausage into skillet and brown. Sprinkle over pizza sauce and top with mozzarella cheese.

MEAT LOAF I

No corn, wheat, rye, citrus, or salicylates

Serves 6

1½ pounds ground beef
¾ cup allowed Dry Bread
    Crumbs*
1 cup milk
1 egg, beaten
1 tablespoon onion powder
¼ teaspoon pepper
1 teaspoon salt

¼ teaspoon dry mustard
¼ teaspoon celery salt
¼ teaspoon garlic salt
¼ teaspoon sage
⅛ teaspoon Tabasco sauce
1 tablespoon additive-free
    soy sauce

Oven 350°

Combine all ingredients and mix thoroughly. Shape into a loaf. Place in shallow pan and bake 1 to 1½ hours.

Slice cold meat loaf into thin slices for sandwiches. Bread may be spread with butter, and/or Mayonnaise,* Mild Mustard,* or allowed Catsup.* Wrap well for lunch box.

MEAT LOAF II

No milk, egg, corn, wheat, rye, or citrus

Serves 4

1 pound ground beef
1½ teaspoons instant minced
    onion
3 ounces tomato paste
5 tablespoons water

¼ cup quick oatmeal
¼ teaspoon celery salt
¼ teaspoon garlic salt
¼ teaspoon dry mustard

Oven 350°

Mix all the ingredients thoroughly. Place in a greased 9x5x3-inch loaf pan. Bake for 1 hour.

TOMATO SAUCE OR PESTO SPAGHETTI

No milk, egg, corn, rye, citrus, or salicylates

Serves 4

8 ounces spaghetti (whole grain, if possible)
2 cups Tomato Spaghetti Sauce* or Tomatoless Spaghetti
    Sauce* or 1 recipe Pesto Sauce*
½ pound ground beef or Italian Sausage*
Grated Parmesan cheese (optional)

Cook spaghetti according to package directions. Prepare tomato
spaghetti sauce, tomatoless spaghetti sauce, or pesto sauce. Brown
ground beef or sausage in heavy skillet. Drain off any excess
grease. Add sauce and heat through. Pour over cooked spaghetti
and serve topped with grated Parmesan cheese if desired.

LASAGNE

No egg, corn, rye, citrus, or salicylates

Serves 8

6 cups Tomato Spaghetti Sauce* or Tomatoless Spaghetti Sauce*

1 pound ricotta cheese or additive-free cottage cheese

8 ounces lasagne noodles (whole grain, if possible), cooked and drained

8 ounces mozzarella cheese, shredded

1 cup grated Parmesan cheese

Oven 350°

Spread 2 cups spaghetti sauce in the bottom of a 9x13-inch
baking pan. Alternate layers of noodles, cheese, and sauce ending
with mozzarella and Parmesan cheese on top. Bake for 50 minutes
until bubbly. Remove from oven and let stand 10 minutes before
serving.

TOMATOLESS LASAGNE

No egg, corn, rye, citrus, or salicylates

Serves 4 to 6

8 ounces uncooked lasagne
    noodles
¾ pound lean ground beef
¾ cup Pesto Sauce*
1 teaspoon Italian seasoning
¼ cup minced onion

1½ cups additive-free
    cottage cheese
8 ounces mozzarella cheese,
    shredded
¼ cup grated Parmesan
    cheese

Oven 350°

Prepare lasagne noodles according to package directions. In the meantime, brown beef and add pesto sauce, Italian seasoning, and onion. Bring to a boil and simmer for 10 minutes.

In a greased 8x8-inch baking dish, place one layer of noodles. Add half the meat mixture and half the cottage cheese. Add another layer of noodles. Place half the mozzarella cheese, remaining meat, and remaining cottage cheese in layers. Add the last noodles and cover with mozzarella cheese. Sprinkle with Parmesan cheese. Bake for 20 to 25 minutes or until the cheese is just melted.

SKILLET DINNER

No milk, egg, corn, wheat, rye, or citrus

Serves 4 or 5

1 pound ground beef
⅓ cup pure allowed vege-
    table oil
1 tablespoon instant minced
    onion
3 tablespoons chopped green
    pepper

1 cup cooked brown rice
6 ounces tomato paste
6 ounces water
Salt and pepper
Grated Parmesan cheese
    (optional)

In a large skillet brown beef in oil. Add onion, green pepper, and brown rice. Combine tomato paste with water and add to the

mixture. Cover and simmer 20 minutes. Salt and pepper to taste.
Serve with Parmesan cheese sprinkled on top.

SWEET AND SOUR MEATBALLS

No milk, egg, corn, wheat, rye, or citrus

Serves 4 to 6

1½ pounds lean ground beef
1 cup allowed Dry Bread
    Crumbs*
1½ teaspoons salt
¼ teaspoon pepper
1 tablespoon grated onion
1 egg (optional)
3 tablespoons pure allowed
    vegetable oil

1½ cups unsweetened pine-
    apple juice
⅔ cup apple cider vinegar
¾ cup honey
2 tablespoons unbleached
    flour or rice flour
¼ cup water

Combine beef, bread crumbs, salt, pepper, onion, and egg in a
bowl and mix until thoroughly blended. Form into 1½-inch balls.
Heat oil in a skillet over medium heat and slowly brown the meatballs, frying only a few at a time. When all the meatballs have
been browned, drain away the excess grease. Pour pineapple juice,
vinegar, and honey into the skillet and heat until bubbly. Return
the meatballs to this mixture and simmer in the covered skillet
until thoroughly cooked, about 20 to 25 minutes. Remove meatballs from the sauce to a serving dish. Combine flour with the
water to form a paste. Add slowly to sauce until slightly thickened. Pour over meatballs and serve over rice or buttered noodles.

TOMATOLESS CHILI

No milk, egg, corn, wheat, rye, citrus, or salicylates

Serves 4 to 6

½ pound dried kidney beans
1 large onion, chopped
1 green pepper, chopped
1 pound ground beef
1½ tablespoons chili powder
1½ teaspoons salt

¼ teaspoon pepper
1 bay leaf
⅛ teaspoon paprika
½ cup water
¼ cup unbleached flour or
    rice flour

Prepare dried kidney beans according to directions on package. In a deep skillet brown onion, green pepper, and beef. Add cooked beans, including the liquid in which they were cooked. Add chili powder, salt, pepper, bay leaf, and paprika. Simmer covered 1½ hours. Just before serving, make a paste of water and flour and add to chili if it is too thin. Good with grated Parmesan cheese sprinkled on top.

For the lunch box, pour hot chili into a wide-mouth thermos. Include crackers and a plastic spoon in the box.

May also be frozen for future use.

SLOPPY JOES

No milk, egg, corn, wheat, rye, or citrus

Makes 6 to 8 sandwiches

1 pound lean ground beef	¾ cup water
½ cup minced onion	½ teaspoon dry mustard
¼ cup minced green pepper (optional)	1 teaspoon salt
	¼ teaspoon black pepper
1 6-ounce can tomato paste	1 to 2 teaspoons chili powder
2 tablespoons apple cider vinegar	

Brown the ground beef in a heavy skillet. Add onion and green pepper and continue to cook until vegetables are partially cooked. Add all other ingredients and mix thoroughly. Simmer 20 to 25 minutes. Serve on rice or Sandwich Buns* or in Pita Pocket Bread.*

For lunch box, pack heated sloppy joe mixture in a thermos and buns separately. When ready to serve, spoon meat mixture onto buns.

TACOS

No milk, egg, wheat, rye, or citrus

Makes 8 to 10 tacos

1 recipe Sloppy Joes*
1 to 2 teaspoons Tabasco
  sauce
8 to 10 additive-free taco
  shells

Chopped tomatoes
Chopped lettuce
Chopped onions
Uncolored cheese, grated
  (optional)

Fix sloppy joes according to the recipe, adding the Tabasco sauce. Spoon 2 or 3 tablespoons of meat mixture into a taco shell. Top with any or all of other ingredients according to taste.

STUFFED ZUCCHINI

No milk, egg, corn, wheat, rye, citrus, or salicylates

Serves 4

4 medium unwaxed zucchini
Boiling water
1 pound lean ground beef
¼ cup allowed Dry Bread
  Crumbs*
1 teaspoon salt
½ teaspoon garlic salt
1 egg (optional)

1 tablespoon dried parsley
  flakes
1½ cups Tomato Spaghetti
  Sauce* or Tomatoless
  Spaghetti Sauce*
Grated Parmesan cheese
  (optional)

Oven 350°

Scrub the zucchini thoroughly and cut in half lengthwise. Drop into a pot of boiling water for 8 to 10 minutes until partially cooked. Drain. Scoop the centers out of the zucchini halves, forming a ¼-inch shell. Chop the zucchini that you scooped out into small pieces and mix thoroughly with the rest of ingredients except sauce and cheese. Place the zucchini halves in a 13x9-inch baking dish. Spoon the meat mixture into the hollowed-out zucchini, dividing it evenly. Pour the spaghetti sauce over all. Bake for 45 minutes. Remove from oven and sprinkle with Parmesan cheese, if desired, and serve.

CHAPTER ELEVEN

CASSEROLES

If your family enjoys casserole dishes, you'll no doubt be able to use or adapt some of your family's favorites. This chapter may give you some other ideas too. The only disadvantage of serving casseroles is they may add many different ingredients to a meal. If a reaction occurs, it's harder to trace the problem.

Poultry

CHICKEN CASSEROLE

No milk, egg, corn, wheat, rye, or citrus

Serves 4

2 cups cubed cooked chicken
2 cups finely chopped celery
¾ teaspoon instant minced onion
1 cup Mayonnaise* or Eggless Mayonnaise*

Allowed Soft Bread Crumbs*
Uncolored butter or allowed margarine
⅓ cup grated Parmesan cheese (optional)

Oven 350°
Mix all ingredients except bread crumbs and cheese. Place in a

greased 2-quart casserole. Sprinkle crumbs on top. Dot with shortening. Top with cheese if allowed. Bake for 30 minutes or until
heated through and lightly browned.

CHICKEN AND BROCCOLI CASSEROLE

No milk, egg, corn, wheat, rye, or citrus

Serves 4

1 10-ounce package frozen
   broccoli
1 cup cubed cooked chicken
2 tablespoons pure allowed
   vegetable oil
2 tablespoons unbleached
   flour or rice flour
1 cup Chicken Stock*

Salt and pepper to taste
½ cup Mayonnaise* or
   Eggless Mayonnaise*
½ teaspoon instant minced
   onion
Allowed Soft Bread Crumbs*
Uncolored butter or allowed
   margarine

Oven 350°

Cook broccoli according to package instructions. In a greased
2-quart casserole, place broccoli and cooked chicken. In a saucepan mix oil and flour and add chicken stock. Stir constantly over
medium heat until sauce boils. Remove from heat. Lightly salt and
pepper the sauce, add mayonnaise and onion. Stir until well
mixed. Pour over casserole. Top with soft bread crumbs. Dot with
shortening. Bake for 30 minutes.

CHICKEN AND POTATO CASSEROLE

No milk, egg, corn, wheat, rye, citrus, or salicylates

Serves 6

4 cups sliced peeled potatoes
2 cups cubed cooked chicken
1 10-ounce package frozen
   peas
¼ cup uncolored butter or
   allowed margarine
¼ cup unbleached flour or
   potato flour

2 cups Chicken Stock*
1 tablespoon instant minced
   onion
¼ teaspoon dry mustard
2 teaspoons salt
⅛ teaspoon pepper
Dash of Tabasco sauce

Oven 375°

Place a layer of 2 cups sliced potatoes in the bottom of an 11x7x2-inch greased casserole and cover with cubed chicken. Pour frozen peas over chicken and top with remaining potatoes.

Melt shortening in a saucepan and blend in flour. Slowly add chicken stock and cook until thickened. Add onion, mustard, salt, pepper, and Tabasco. Pour evenly on top of potatoes. Bake for about 1 hour or until potatoes are done. If the potatoes start to brown too much, cover for the last few minutes with aluminum foil.

CHICKEN AND RICE CASSEROLE

No milk, egg, corn, wheat, rye, or salicylates

Serves 6

2 cups cooked brown rice
½ cup cooked chopped
  mushrooms (optional)
2 cups diced cooked chicken
1 cup finely diced celery
2 tablespoons pure allowed
  vegetable oil
2 tablespoons unbleached
  flour or rice flour

1½ cups Chicken Stock*
1 tablespoon pure lemon
  juice
1 teaspoon instant minced
  onion
Salt and pepper to taste
Grated Parmesan cheese
  (optional)
Paprika

Oven 350°

Mix rice and mushrooms together. In a greased casserole place half the mixture. Combine chicken and celery and place on top. Cover with the rest of rice and mushrooms.

In a saucepan heat oil. Blend in flour. Add chicken stock over medium heat, stirring constantly, until sauce boils. Add lemon juice and onion and mix well. Remove from heat. Pour over casserole. Salt and pepper lightly. Sprinkle with enough Parmesan cheese to cover. Sprinkle with paprika. Bake for 25 minutes or until lightly browned.

CHICKEN-MACARONI CASSEROLE

No milk, egg, corn, rye, citrus, or salicylates

Serves 6

3 tablespoons pure allowed
   vegetable oil
3 tablespoons unbleached
   flour
2 cups Chicken Stock*
Salt and pepper to taste
1 cup uncooked macaroni,
   cooked and drained

2 cups diced cooked chicken
1 teaspoon frozen or dried
   chopped chives
   (optional)
Grated Parmesan cheese
   (optional)

Oven 375°

In a large saucepan combine oil and flour. Add chicken stock
and cook over medium heat, stirring constantly until mixture
boils. Remove from heat and season with salt and pepper. Stir in
cooked macaroni, chicken, and chives. Pour ingredients into a
large greased casserole. Top generously with Parmesan cheese.
Bake for 30 minutes.

TURKEY CASSEROLE

No milk, egg, corn, wheat, rye, or citrus

Serves 8

2 10-ounce packages frozen
   broccoli, cooked
Salt and pepper to taste
2 cups cubed cooked turkey
¼ cup pure allowed vege-
   table oil
¼ cup unbleached flour or
   rice flour
2 cups milk or Chicken
   Stock*
1 teaspoon salt

1 teaspoon instant minced
   onion
1 cup Mayonnaise* or
   Eggless Mayonnaise*
1 teaspoon pure lemon juice
   (optional)
½ cup allowed Dry Bread
   Crumbs*
Uncolored butter or allowed
   margarine
½ cup grated uncolored
   cheese (optional)

Oven 325°

Place cooked, well-drained broccoli in greased 2-quart casserole. Season with salt and pepper. Cover with turkey.

In a saucepan mix oil, flour, and milk or stock over medium heat. Stir constantly until mixture boils. Add salt, onion, mayonnaise, and lemon juice. Pour over turkey. Top with crumbs and dot with shortening. If allowed, sprinkle grated cheese on top. Bake uncovered for 25 minutes or until lightly browned.

Beef

BEEF AND VEGETABLE CASSEROLE

No milk, egg, corn, wheat, rye, citrus, or salicylates

Serves 4

¼ cup chopped onion	Pepper to taste
¼ cup chopped green pepper (optional)	2 cups any leftover vegetables (beans, diced potatoes, peas, etc.)
¾ to 1 pound ground beef	
¼ cup pure allowed vegetable oil	Stuffed olives, sliced (optional)
¼ cup chopped celery	Uncolored cheese (optional)
½ teaspoon salt	Paprika

Oven 350°

In a heavy skillet sauté onion, green pepper, and ground beef in oil. Add celery and seasonings and simmer for 15 minutes, stirring occasionally. Add vegetables, more oil if needed, and cook 5 more minutes. With a slotted spoon place mixture in a greased 1½-quart casserole. Place sliced olives on top. If allowed, cover with slices of cheese. Sprinkle with paprika. Bake 15 minutes.

SHEPHERD'S PIE

No egg, corn, wheat, rye, citrus, or salicylates

Serves 6

3 to 4 cups cubed cooked beef
1 small onion, chopped, or 1 tablespoon instant minced onion

1½ cups leftover gravy
1 cup cooked vegetables
Salt and pepper to taste
4 cups leftover mashed potatoes

Oven 350°

Combine beef, onion, gravy, and vegetables in a saucepan and heat to boiling. Season with salt and pepper. Spread 2 cups mashed potatoes in a greased 1½-quart casserole. Pour beef mixture over potatoes and spoon the remaining 2 cups potatoes on top. Bake in oven for 30 minutes until potatoes are lightly browned.

Fish

FISH CASSEROLE

No milk, egg, corn, wheat, rye, citrus, or salicylates

Serves 3 or 4

2 tablespoons pure allowed vegetable oil
2 tablespoons unbleached flour or rice flour
1 cup milk or 1 cup Chicken Stock*
½ teaspoon salt

1½ teaspoons instant minced onion
1 16-ounce package frozen (thawed) fish fillets, drained
¾ cup allowed Soft Bread Crumbs*
1 teaspoon parsley flakes

Oven 350°

In a saucepan, mix oil and flour. Stir in stock and cook over medium heat, stirring constantly until sauce boils. Add salt and instant onion. Stir well and remove from heat.

In a greased casserole place defrosted fish, cut into bite-size pieces. Pour the cream sauce over it. Top with crumbs. Sprinkle parsley over crumbs. Bake in the upper part of oven for 30 minutes or until lightly browned.

SALMON CASSEROLE

No milk, egg, corn, wheat, rye, or citrus

Serves 4

1 16-ounce can salmon (packed in water)
1 tablespoon instant minced onion
¼ cup pure allowed vegetable oil
⅓ cup salmon liquid

⅓ cup allowed Dry Bread Crumbs*
¼ cup Mayonnaise* or Eggless Mayonnaise*
1 tablespoon chopped parsley
1 teaspoon dry mustard

Oven 350°

Drain salmon and save liquid. Flake salmon. Add other ingredients and mix well. Place in greased 10x6x2-inch loaf pan. Bake 30 minutes. If desired, garnish with lemon wedges.

SALMON AND ZUCCHINI CASSEROLE

No egg, corn, wheat, rye, or citrus

Serves 4

⅔ cup sour cream
½ cup Mayonnaise* or Eggless Mayonnaise*
1 teaspoon curry powder (optional)
1 1-pound can salmon (packed in water), drained and flaked

1 medium zucchini, peeled and thinly sliced
1 cup finely chopped celery
¼ cup diced onion
Allowed Dry Bread Crumbs*
Uncolored butter or allowed margarine

Oven 350°

Combine sour cream, mayonnaise, and curry powder. Set aside. In a greased 1½-quart casserole combine salmon, zucchini, celery, and onion. Cover with sauce. Sprinkle top with bread crumbs. Dot with shortening. Bake for 25 to 30 minutes.

SEAFOOD CASSEROLE DELUXE

No egg, corn, wheat, rye, citrus, or salicylates

Serves 6

1 pound frozen (thawed) fish fillets
Water to cover
1 cup Medium White Sauce*
1 tablespoon instant minced onion
1 cup shredded uncolored cheese

½ cup sour cream
½ cup diced mushrooms
1 cup frozen (partially thawed) peas
1 tablespoon parsley flakes
1 cup allowed Dry Bread Crumbs*

Oven 400°

Put fish fillets in a skillet and cover with water. Simmer until fish is done and flakes easily. Drain and break into bite-size pieces.

Prepare medium white sauce. Remove from heat and add onion and grated cheese. Stir until cheese melts and mixture is smooth.

Stir in sour cream, mushrooms, peas, and parsley. Add the fish and pour into a greased 1½-quart casserole. Sprinkle dry bread crumbs on top. Bake for 15 to 20 minutes until bubbly.

SHRIMP ORIENTAL

No milk, corn, wheat, rye, citrus, or salicylates

Serves 4

⅓ cup chopped onion
⅓ cup chopped green pepper (optional)
3 tablespoons pure allowed vegetable oil
1 cup drained canned bean sprouts
⅓ cup drained canned mushroom pieces

1 8-ounce can water chestnuts, drained and sliced
1 4½-ounce can shrimp, drained
3 eggs
½ cup milk or water
1 teaspoon salt

Oven 350°

Sauté onion and green pepper in oil until partially cooked. Add bean sprouts, mushrooms, water chestnuts, and shrimp and heat through. Pour this mixture into a 1½-quart casserole dish. Combine eggs, milk or water, and salt in a small bowl and beat until well mixed. Pour the eggs over the shrimp mixture in the casserole. Put the casserole dish in a pan filled with 1 inch of water and bake for 45 to 50 minutes or until a knife inserted in the mixture comes out clean.

SHRIMP AND CORN CASSEROLE

No milk, wheat, rye, citrus, or salicylates

Serves 6

1 12-ounce package frozen shelled deveined raw shrimp

1 cup Chicken Stock* or milk

1 10-ounce package frozen (thawed) corn or 2 cups fresh corn

3 eggs

1 cup broken allowed bread pieces

⅓ cup chopped onion

2 tablespoons chopped green pepper (optional)

½ teaspoon salt

½ teaspoon garlic salt

⅛ teaspoon pepper

Oven 350°

Cook shrimp according to directions on label. Drain thoroughly and cut into small pieces. Put stock or milk and corn in blender and blend until corn is slightly chopped. In a large bowl beat eggs. Stir in corn mixture, bread pieces, onion, green pepper, salt, garlic salt, and pepper. Mix thoroughly. Add the shrimp and stir well. Turn into a 1½-quart greased casserole. Bake for 1½ hours or until knife inserted in the middle comes out clean.

SPAGHETTI WITH CLAM SAUCE

No milk, egg, corn, rye, citrus, or salicylates

Serves 4

¾ pound spaghetti
½ cup chopped onion
1 clove garlic, minced
¼ cup pure allowed vege-
   table oil

2 8-ounce cans minced clams,
   reserving juice
½ cup dried parsley
1 teaspoon dried sweet basil

Cook spaghetti according to package instructions. In a medium-sized skillet sauté onion and garlic in oil until tender. Add the minced clams and their juice. Stir in parsley and basil. Heat through. Serve over spaghetti.

TUNA AND ZUCCHINI CASSEROLE

No milk, egg, corn, wheat, rye, or salicylates

Serves 6

2 7-ounce cans tuna (packed
   in water), drained and
   flaked
1½ cups Chicken Stock*
½ cup Mayonnaise* or
   Eggless Mayonnaise*
1 cup shredded sharp
   uncolored cheese
4 teaspoons pure lemon juice
2 cups finely chopped peeled
   (if waxed) zucchini

2 tablespoons instant minced
   onion
½ teaspoon salt
Dash of pepper
2 slices allowed bread,
   broken into very small
   pieces
Grated Parmesan cheese
   (optional)
Uncolored butter or allowed
   margarine
Paprika

Oven 350°

In a large mixing bowl combine tuna, stock, mayonnaise, shredded cheese, lemon juice, zucchini, onion, salt, and pepper. Pour mixture into a greased 2-quart casserole. Sprinkle small pieces of bread and Parmesan cheese on top. Dot with shortening. Sprinkle with enough paprika to cover. Bake for 40 minutes or until top begins to brown.

TUNA SPAGHETTI OR RICE

No milk, egg, corn, wheat, rye, or salicylates

Serves 4

¾ pound uncooked spaghetti or ¾ cup uncooked brown rice

1 small onion, chopped

1 ounce dried parsley flakes

½ cup pure allowed vegetable oil

1 9¼-ounce can tuna fish (packed in water), undrained and flaked

1 tablespoon pure lemon juice

Salt and pepper to taste

Grated Parmesan cheese (optional)

Prepare spaghetti or rice according to directions on package. In a heavy skillet sauté onion and parsley in oil until onion is yellow. Add tuna. Stir in lemon juice, salt, and pepper, and warm over low heat. Pour over hot spaghetti or rice and toss to mix. If allowed, serve with Parmesan cheese.

CHAPTER TWELVE

SALADS AND SALAD DRESSINGS

You'll probably have to make your own salad dressings, but they're easily prepared. Select pure allowed vegetable oils like soy, corn (if allowed), safflower, or sunflower. Or look for some brands of salad dressings made with honey at your health foods store. You'll have to make your own gelatin salads as all the prepared mixes are artificially colored, flavored, and contain sugar.

Gelatin

CRANBERRY GELATIN

No milk, egg, corn, wheat, rye, citrus, or salicylates

Serves 4

1 envelope unflavored gelatin
1¼ cups Cranberry Juice* or
    Cranapple Juice*
¾ cup boiling water
¼ cup honey (optional)

1 tablespoon pure lemon
    juice (optional)
1½ cups chopped fruits or
    vegetables (optional)

Sprinkle gelatin over ¼ cup cranberry juice to soften. Add

boiling water and honey. Stir until dissolved. Add remaining cranberry juice and lemon juice. Chill. When almost set, stir in desired fruits or vegetables. Pour into serving dishes or 1-quart mold and chill until set. About 1 tablespoon honey per serving.

GRAPE OR ORANGE GELATIN

No milk, egg, corn, wheat, rye, or citrus

Serves 4

1 envelope unflavored gelatin
¼ cup cold water
1¾ cups unsweetened grape juice or pure unsweetened orange juice
1½ cups chopped fruits or vegetables (optional)

Soften gelatin in cold water. Heat grape or orange juice over low heat and stir in gelatin until well dissolved. Chill. When almost set stir in desired fruits or vegetables. Return to refrigerator until firm.

LEMON OR LIME GELATIN

No milk, egg, corn, wheat, rye, or salicylates

Serves 4

1 envelope unflavored gelatin
½ cup cold water
¼ to ½ cup honey
1¼ cups hot water
6 ounces pure lemon or lime juice (about 6 lemons or limes, squeezed for juice)
1½ cups chopped fruit or vegetables (optional)

Soften gelatin in cold water. In a saucepan add softened gelatin and honey to hot water and heat until both are well dissolved. Add lemon or lime juice. Chill. When partially set, stir in desired fruits or vegetables. Return to refrigerator until firm. About 1 to 2 tablespoons honey per serving.

PAPAYA GELATIN

No milk, egg, corn, wheat, rye, citrus, or salicylates

Serves 4

1 envelope unflavored gelatin
¼ cup cold water or unsweetened pineapple juice
1¾ cups Papaya Juice*
1½ cups chopped fruit or vegetables (optional)

Soften gelatin in cold liquid. Cook over low heat and stir until gelatin is dissolved. Add to papaya juice and mix well. Chill.

When gelatin has thickened fold in 1½ cups chopped fruit or vegetables. Pour into serving dishes or 1-quart mold and return to refrigerator until firm.

Makes a delicious, colorful salad or dessert.

PINEAPPLE GELATIN

No milk, egg, corn, wheat, rye, citrus, or salicylates

Serves 4

1 envelope unflavored gelatin
½ cup cold water
1½ cups unsweetened pine-
    apple juice
½ cup water
1½ cups chopped fruits or
    vegetables

In a saucepan dissolve gelatin in ½ cup cold water. Stir over medium heat until liquid is clear. Remove from heat. Add pineapple juice and ½ cup water. Chill. When almost set, stir in fruits or vegetables. Pour into serving dishes or 1-quart mold and chill until set.

PINEAPPLE AND GRAPEFRUIT GELATIN

No milk, egg, corn, wheat, rye, or salicylates

Serves 6

1 envelope unflavored gelatin
¼ cup cold water
1 to 2 tablespoons honey
½ cup hot unsweetened
    pineapple juice
½ cup hot unsweetened
    grapefruit juice
¼ cup pure lemon juice or
    pure unsweetened orange
    juice

¼ teaspoon salt
1 cup drained unsweetened
    grapefruit sections,
    reserving juice
1 cup drained unsweetened
    pineapple tidbits or
    chunks, reserving juice

Soften gelatin in cold water. Dissolve softened gelatin and honey in hot fruit juices. Add lemon juice or orange juice and salt. Refrigerate. When mixture begins to thicken, fold in grapefruit and pineapple. Chill in a covered container. May be packed in a wide-mouth thermos for the lunch box. About ½ to 1 teaspoon honey per serving.

MOLDED TUNA SALAD

No milk, egg, corn, wheat, rye, or salicylates

Serves 6

2 7-ounce cans tuna (packed
    in water), drained and
    flaked
1 tablespoon chopped onion
1 tablespoon chopped green
    pepper (optional)
½ cup chopped celery

2 tablespoons pure lemon
    juice
¾ cup Mayonnaise* or
    Eggless Mayonnaise*
1½ teaspoons unflavored
    gelatin
2 tablespoons cold water
Paprika

In a large bowl combine tuna, onion, green pepper, chopped celery, lemon juice, and mayonnaise. Soften gelatin in cold water;

dissolve over hot water. Stir liquid gelatin into tuna mixture. Turn into a 2-quart ring mold. Cover and refrigerate.

Line a platter with lettuce, unmolding tuna in the middle. Sprinkle top with paprika. Fill the center with cottage cheese topped with chopped chives. Or fill the center with cold cooked peas seasoned with chives. Garnish the platter with carrot sticks and wedges of hard-cooked eggs. Serve with hot biscuits or rolls. Makes a great main course for a summer supper.

TUNA SALAD

No milk, egg, corn, wheat, rye, or salicylates

Serves 6

Follow instructions for Molded Tuna Salad* (above) but omit the gelatin and water. Cover and chill. Serve on lettuce.

MOLDED VEGETABLE SALADS

No milk, egg, corn, wheat, rye, citrus, or salicylates

Serves 6

1 envelope unflavored gelatin
½ cup cold water
1 tablespoon honey
½ teaspoon salt
1 tablespoon apple cider
   vinegar (optional)
1 cup Chicken Stock* or
   water
1½ cups raw vegetables
   (Two different vegetables
   are attractive. For example, shredded cabbage
and finely diced green
pepper or shredded
carrots and thawed
frozen peas which have
not been cooked.) or
1½ cups cooked vege-
tables (For example,
sliced or diced carrots
and peas or lima beans
and corn.)

Sprinkle gelatin over cold water in a small saucepan. Place over low heat and stir constantly until gelatin has completely dissolved. Remove from heat. Add honey, salt, vinegar, stock or water. Pour into bowl or a 2-quart mold and refrigerate until mixture becomes partially thickened. Fold in either 1½ cups raw or cooked vegetables. Refrigerate covered until firm. Individual molds can be used. About ½ teaspoon honey per serving.

RED, WHITE, AND BLUE HOLIDAY SALAD

No egg, corn, wheat, rye, or salicylates

Serves 15

BLUE LAYER:
1 envelope unflavored gelatin
1 cup cold blueberry juice (reserved from 1 15-ounce can unsweetened blueberries) or unsweetened grape juice

1 cup unsweetened pineapple juice (reserved from 1 can crushed unsweetened pineapple)
½ cup drained unsweetened crushed canned pineapple

WHITE LAYER:
1 envelope unflavored gelatin
½ cup cold water
1 tablespoon honey
3 tablespoons pure lemon juice

1 cup half and half cream
1 cup additive-free cottage cheese

RED LAYER:
1 envelope unflavored gelatin
2 cups cold Cranberry Juice*

½ cup drained unsweetened crushed canned pineapple

Allow 24 hours for preparing salad. First, prepare blue layer by softening gelatin in cold blueberry or grape and pineapple juices. Heat juices over low heat until gelatin dissolves. Chill. When almost firm, fold in crushed pineapple. Pour into bottom of large mold (3-quart size, at least) or into individual molds. Chill until firm.

In the meantime, start preparing white layer. In a saucepan soften gelatin in cold water. Dissolve gelatin over medium heat. Add honey. Remove from heat. When cool, add lemon juice and cream. Chill until gelatin mixture is slightly thickened. Fold in cottage cheese. Pour on top of blue layer. Chill until firm.

Meantime, prepare the red layer by softening gelatin in cold cranberry juice. Stir over low heat until gelatin dissolves. Chill. When almost firm, fold in pineapple. Pour on top of white layer. Chill until firm.

Fruit

FRUIT CUPS

No milk, egg, corn, wheat, rye, citrus, or salicylates
Combine fruit together in any one of the following combinations:

1. Watermelon, cantaloupe, and honeydew melon balls
2. Papayas, unsweetened pineapple, and unsweetened coconut
3. Sliced bananas, unsweetened pineapple chunks, and grapefruit segments
4. Pears and blueberries
5. Grapefruit sections, orange sections, unsweetened pineapple chunks
6. Bananas, oranges, and apples
7. Freshly washed cherries or grapes served in a large bowl so each person can help himself

Sprinkle banana slices, apples, and pears with lemon juice to prevent discoloration. Combine with other fruits and chill before serving.

Fruit cups can be served as an appetizer, salad, or a refreshing summertime dessert.

APPLESAUCE OR PEARSAUCE

No milk, egg, corn, wheat, rye, citrus, or salicylates

Makes 2 cups

3 large apples or pears, quartered and cored
1 cup water or unsweetened apple juice
Cinnamon (optional)

In a heavy covered saucepan cook apples or pears in water or juice until quite soft. Press through sieve or food mill. Add cinnamon if desired. May be packed in a wide-mouth thermos for the lunch box.

CANDLE SALAD

No milk, egg, corn, wheat, rye, or citrus

Serves 4

4 unsweetened canned pine-
    apple rings
Lettuce leaves
2 medium-sized bananas

Mayonnaise* or Eggless
    Mayonnaise*
4 red sweet cherries

Place 1 pineapple ring on a lettuce leaf on individual salad plates. Cut bananas in half and place vertically (candlestick) in each pineapple hole. Place a spoonful of mayonnaise on top of each banana and top each with a cherry (flame).

PINEAPPLE AND CABBAGE SALAD

No milk, egg, corn, wheat, rye, citrus, or salicylates

Serves 4

2 cups shredded cabbage
4 ounces well-drained unsweetened crushed canned pineap-
    ple
Creamy Slaw Dressing*

Mix cabbage and crushed pineapple. Add creamy slaw dressing sparingly. Toss with a fork. If necessary, more dressing may be added according to taste.

PINEAPPLE-CHICKEN SALAD

No milk, egg, corn, wheat, rye, or citrus

Serves 4

2 cups cubed cooked chicken
½ cup diced celery
½ cup drained diced un-
    sweetened canned pine-
    apple chunks

Mayonnaise* or Eggless
    Mayonnaise*
Salt and pepper to taste
Paprika

In a large bowl combine chicken, celery, and pineapple. Add enough mayonnaise to moisten ingredients. Salt and pepper to taste. Serve with paprika sprinkled on top.

WALDORF SALAD

No milk, egg, corn, wheat, rye, or citrus

Serves 4

2 cups chopped unwaxed apples (core but do not peel)
1 cup chopped celery
¾ cup chopped nuts
½ cup Mayonnaise* or Eggless Mayonnaise*

Combine all ingredients and serve on a lettuce leaf for a salad.

FRUIT DIP

No egg, corn, wheat, rye, or salicylates

Makes 1 cup

1 cup sour cream or yogurt
1 tablespoon pure lemon juice
2 tablespoons honey
1 teaspoon grated uncolored
    unwaxed lemon or
    orange rind

Dash of salt
Fresh fruit (pineapple chunks,
    apples, banana slices,
    strawberries, grapes,
    cherries, etc.)

Blend together first five ingredients. Chill and serve as a dip with chilled fresh fruit.

Vegetable

CABBAGE SALAD

No milk, egg, corn, wheat, rye, or citrus

Serves 4

4 cups (½ head) very thinly sliced or coarsely chopped cabbage

1 Spanish onion, very thinly sliced

½ green pepper, coarsely chopped

1 teaspoon honey

½ cup Simple Salad Dressing*

In a large bowl lightly mix cabbage, onion, and green pepper. Add honey to salad dressing and mix well. Slowly pour salad dressing to cover entire top surface. Cover and let stand at room temperature for 1 hour. Refrigerate for 5 to 6 hours. Toss salad thoroughly before serving.

COLD STUFFED TOMATOES

No milk, egg, corn, wheat, rye, or citrus

Serves 4

4 large tomatoes, skinned

Scoop out the insides. Turn tomatoes upside down to drain on a paper towel for 10 minutes. Refrigerate until ready to use.
Fill tomatoes with one of the following:

Chicken or Turkey Sandwich Spread*
Tuna Salad Sandwich Spread*
Diced cooked carrots combined with Mayonnaise* or Eggless Mayonnaise*
Cooked peas combined with Mayonnaise* or Eggless Mayonnaise*
Diced celery combined with Mayonnaise* or Eggless Mayonnaise*

Serve on lettuce.

LAYERED SALAD

No milk, egg, corn, wheat, rye, or citrus

Lettuce, broken in pieces
Frozen (thawed) peas, uncooked
Carrots, shredded
Unsweetened canned pineapple chunks, well drained
Bermuda onion rings, very thinly sliced
Mayonnaise* or Eggless Mayonnaise*
Cheesy Croutons* (optional)
Grated Parmesan cheese (optional)

In a large bowl layer lettuce, peas, carrots, pineapple chunks, and onion rings. Place spoonfuls of mayonnaise on this mixture. Repeat the layers again, adding mayonnaise, until desired amount is made. Cover bowl and refrigerate 2 or 3 hours. Before serving, top with croutons and grated Parmesan cheese. Do not toss.

SUMMER DINNER SALAD

No milk, egg, corn, wheat, rye, citrus, or salicylates

Lettuce, torn into bite-size pieces
Chicken, cooked and cubed
Uncolored cheese, sliced in thin strips (optional)
Hard-cooked eggs, sliced (optional)
Ripe olives, pitted (optional)
Avocado, cut in wedges (optional)
Radishes, sliced (optional)
Carrots, sliced (optional)
Green pepper, chopped (optional)
Onion, sliced (optional)
Tomatoes, peeled and cut in wedges (optional)
Cheesy Croutons* (optional)
Creamy Salad Dressing,* or desired salad dressing

In a large bowl place pieces of lettuce, cubed chicken, strips of cheese and sliced hard-cooked eggs. Add ripe olives, avocado wedges, radishes, carrots, green pepper, sliced onion, and tomato wedges to your taste. Toss gently. Add croutons. Pour salad dressing on top. Toss again until all the salad ingredients are coated with dressing.

RAW VEGETABLES WITH DIPS

No milk, egg, corn, wheat, rye, or citrus

Raw vegetables are a nutritious change from the usual salads. On a large plate or platter arrange groups of carrot sticks, celery cut in 2- or 3-inch lengths, zucchini or cucumber washed well and peeled if waxed, cut in short sticks, unwaxed green pepper slices, cherry tomatoes, radishes, and cauliflower cut into small pieces. Serve with a dip. Children enjoy finger foods.

VEGETABLE DIP I

No egg, corn, wheat, rye, or citrus

Makes 1 cup

½ cup Mayonnaise* or
   Eggless Mayonnaise*
½ cup sour cream
1½ teaspoons dill seed

1½ teaspoons dried parsley
   flakes
1½ teaspoons instant minced
   onion
½ teaspoon celery salt

Combine all ingredients and mix well. Refrigerate in a covered container. Serve as a dip for vegetables, potato chips, a spread for crackers, or as a delicious creamy salad dressing.

VEGETABLE DIP II

No corn, wheat, rye, or citrus

Makes 1 cup

½ cup Thousand Island Dressing*
4 ounces cream cheese, softened
1 hard-cooked egg, chopped
1 tablespoon chopped fresh or dried parsley

Cream together dressing and cream cheese. Mix in egg and parsley. Use as a dip for fresh vegetables.

ZIPPY CURRY DIP

No milk, egg, corn, wheat, rye, or citrus

Makes 1 cup

1 cup Mayonnaise* or
   Eggless Mayonnaise*
1 teaspoon curry powder
¼ teaspoon dry mustard

½ teaspoon garlic salt
½ teaspoon onion salt
2 drops Tabasco sauce

Combine all ingredients and chill. Serve as a dip with raw vegetables.

Others

COLD POTATO SALAD

No milk, egg, corn, wheat, rye, or citrus

Serves 5 or 6

1 cup Mayonnaise* or
   Eggless Mayonnaise*
1 teaspoon dry mustard
2 teaspoons pure lemon juice
   (optional)
¼ teaspoon celery seed
½ teaspoon onion salt

5 cups cold cubed cooked
   potatoes
3 hard-cooked eggs, chopped
   (optional)
½ cup chopped celery
Salt and pepper to taste

Combine first five ingredients and mix thoroughly. Place potatoes, eggs, and celery in a large bowl and pour mayonnaise mixture on top. Toss lightly until dressing is evenly distributed. Adjust seasonings by adding salt and pepper to taste.

MACARONI SALAD

No milk, egg, corn, rye, or citrus

Serves 6

1 cup uncooked macaroni
1 tablespoon pure allowed
   vegetable oil
2 cups diced celery
2 tablespoons chopped fresh
   or frozen chives

1 teaspoon salt
Pepper to taste
¼ cup Mayonnaise* or
   Eggless Mayonnaise*
Paprika

Cook macaroni according to package directions. Drain. After 5 minutes add oil and toss with a fork to mix. Refrigerate for several hours. Add celery, chives, salt, pepper, and mayonnaise. Mix thoroughly with macaroni. Serve on lettuce with a sprinkling of paprika on each serving.

Dressings

CREAMY SALAD DRESSING

No egg, corn, wheat, or rye

Makes 1¾ cups

1 tablespoon pure lemon juice
½ cup pure whipping cream
2 tablespoons apple cider
   vinegar

1 tablespoon dried parsley
   flakes
1 tablespoon onion salt
1 cup Mayonnaise* or
   Eggless Mayonnaise*

Add lemon juice to cream. Mix thoroughly with other ingredients. Refrigerate.

CREAMY SLAW DRESSING

No milk, egg, corn, wheat, rye, or citrus

Makes 1 cup

1 cup Mayonnaise* or Eggless Mayonnaise*
2 tablespoons pure lemon juice or 1 tablespoon unsweetened
  pineapple juice
4 teaspoons honey (2 teaspoons if using pineapple juice)

Mix together thoroughly. Refrigerate in a covered jar.

CREAMY ONION OR CREAMY GARLIC DRESSING

No egg, corn, wheat, rye, or citrus

Makes 2 cups

1 recipe French Dressing*
1 teaspoon onion or garlic salt
½ cup half and half cream

Prepare French dressing but reduce salt to 1 teaspoon. Add
onion or garlic salt. Pour into blender. On high speed slowly add
cream until dressing is thick and creamy. Refrigerate in a covered
container. Stir well before serving.

FRENCH DRESSING

No milk, egg, corn, wheat, rye, or citrus

Makes 1⅓ cups

3 tablespoons honey   ½ cup apple cider vinegar
2 teaspoons salt   1 cup pure allowed vegetable
½ teaspoon pepper   oil
1 teaspoon paprika

Combine all ingredients in a covered jar. Shake thoroughly. Refrigerate. Shake well before using.

CREAMY FRENCH DRESSING

No egg, corn, wheat, rye, or citrus

Makes 2 cups

1 recipe French Dressing*
½ cup half and half cream

Pour French dressing in blender. On high speed slowly add cream until dressing is thick and creamy. Refrigerate in a covered container. Stir well before serving.

FRUIT SALAD DRESSING

No milk, egg, corn, wheat, rye, or citrus

Makes 1¾ cups

1 heaping teaspoon paprika
½ teaspoon dry mustard
¼ teaspoon onion salt
½ teaspoon celery seed
1 cup pure allowed vegetable oil
½ cup apple cider vinegar
⅓ cup honey

Mix dry ingredients thoroughly. Stir in oil, vinegar, and honey. Beat until well blended. Store in covered jar in refrigerator. Best left for 24 hours before using. This is also good with a tossed salad.

SIMPLE SALAD DRESSING

No milk, egg, corn, wheat, rye, or citrus

Makes ⅔ cup

¼ cup apple cider vinegar
⅓ cup pure allowed vegetable oil
2 teaspoons honey
1 teaspoon salt
½ teaspoon dry mustard

Combine ingredients in a jar with a lid. Shake well. Refrigerate. Shake again before using.

SWEET FRENCH DRESSING

No milk, egg, corn, wheat, rye, or citrus

Makes 1½ cups

¼ cup honey
1 heaping teaspoon paprika
¼ teaspoon dry mustard

1 cup pure allowed vegetable
   oil
½ cup apple cider vinegar
1 piece raw onion (optional)

Mix all ingredients together. Place in covered container and re-frigerate. Remove onion after several days.

THOUSAND ISLAND DRESSING

No milk, corn, wheat, rye, or citrus

Makes 1½ cups

1 cup Mayonnaise*
¼ cup Catsup I* or Catsup
   II* or Tomato Catsup*
2 hard-cooked eggs, chopped

2 tablespoons capers or
   chopped Sweet Pickles*
2 tablespoons chopped celery
1 teaspoon instant minced
   onion

Combine all ingredients. Keep refrigerated in a covered container.

CHAPTER THIRTEEN

VEGETABLES AND STARCHES

Corn and legumes are the most common vegetables causing allergic problems. You should avoid any skins that appear to be waxed —zucchini, green peppers, eggplant, and so on. Sometimes sweet potatoes may be dyed on the outside. Don't use prepared potato, rice, or pasta mixes. Frozen vegetables may be prepared in colored butter. Canned vegetables may contain dyes and sugar. Fresh vegetables are preferred both for nutrition and taste. Frozen vegetables are usually superior to canned. If vegetables are not your family's favorite, try serving raw vegetables with a dip.

Green

ASPARAGUS AND EGG CASSEROLE

No corn, wheat, rye, or citrus

Serves 6

¼ cup pure allowed vegetable oil
¼ cup unbleached flour or rice flour
1 cup milk

½ cup sour cream
¼ cup Mayonnaise*
1 16-ounce can asparagus pieces, drained and ¼ cup liquid reserved

1 teaspoon salt
5 hard-cooked eggs, thinly
   sliced

Allowed Dry Bread Crumbs*
Uncolored butter or allowed
   margarine

Oven 350°

In a large saucepan combine oil and flour, stir in milk, and continue to stir over medium heat until sauce begins to boil. Remove from heat and add sour cream, mayonnaise, liquid from asparagus, and salt. Mix well over low heat. Add asparagus. In a greased 2-quart casserole, place three sliced hard-cooked eggs. Pour half the creamed asparagus over them. Add remaining eggs and creamed asparagus. Top with crumbs. Dot with uncolored butter or allowed margarine. Bake for ½ hour or until crumbs begin to brown.

BROCCOLI CASSEROLE

No milk, egg, corn, wheat, rye, citrus, or salicylates

Serves 4

2 tablespoons pure allowed
   vegetable oil
2 tablespoons unbleached
   flour or rice flour
1 cup milk or Chicken Stock*
¼ teaspoon salt
¼ teaspoon instant minced
   onion

1 10-ounce package frozen
   broccoli pieces, cooked
   and drained
Allowed Dry Bread Crumbs*
Uncolored butter or allowed
   margarine

Oven 350°

In a saucepan over medium heat blend oil and flour. Add milk or chicken stock and bring to a boil, stirring constantly. Add salt and dried onion. Combine with cooked broccoli. Place in a well-greased 1½-quart casserole and top with crumbs. Dot with uncolored butter or allowed margarine. Bake for 30 minutes.

CREAMED PEAS OR CARROTS

No milk, egg, corn, wheat, rye, citrus, or salicylates

Serves 4 to 6

1 tablespoon pure allowed
   vegetable oil
1 tablespoon unbleached
   flour or rice flour
1 cup milk or Chicken Stock*
¼ teaspoon salt

Dash of pepper
½ teaspoon instant minced
   onion
2 cups drained cooked peas
   or carrots

In a saucepan over medium heat mix oil and flour. Stir in milk or chicken stock and continue stirring until mixture comes to a boil. Add salt, pepper, and onion and cook a minute longer. Stir until well blended. Reduce heat to simmer and add peas or carrots. Cover and allow peas or carrots to heat. Serve in individual sauce dishes.

GREEN BEANS WITH PESTO AND CHEESE

No egg, corn, wheat, rye, citrus, or salicylates

Serves 4

2 cups cut fresh green beans, cooked or 1 12-ounce can cut
   green beans
1 tablespoon Pesto Sauce*
½ cup grated uncolored cheese

In a saucepan heat the green beans. Add a little water to keep them from sticking. When they reach the boiling point drain off all liquid. (Instead of discarding the liquid, which is full of vitamins, add it to your homemade soup.) Stir in pesto sauce and mix well. Add grated cheese. Cover saucepan, remove from heat, and set aside until cheese has melted. Stir ingredients well and serve at once.

LIMA BEANS WITH MUSHROOMS

No milk, egg, corn, wheat, rye, citrus, or salicylates

Serves 4

1 10-ounce package frozen
   lima beans
1 pound mushrooms
½ medium onion, chopped

2 to 3 tablespoons pure
   allowed vegetable oil
Salt and pepper to taste

Cook lima beans as directed on the package. Wipe mushrooms with a damp cloth and slice. Sauté onion in oil, add mushrooms, and cook until tender. Drain lima beans (saving vitamin-filled liquid for homemade soups). Add onion and mushrooms. Stir together and salt and pepper to taste.

SPINACH AND RICE

No milk, egg, corn, wheat, rye, citrus, or salicylates

Serves 4 to 6

1 10-ounce package frozen chopped spinach
1 cup cooked brown rice
1 teaspoon instant minced onion
Salt and pepper to taste

Cook spinach according to package instructions. Remove from heat but do not drain. Add rice, minced onion, and salt and pepper to taste. Return to stove and simmer for 5 minutes. Drain and serve.

SPINACH SUPREME

No egg, corn, wheat, rye, citrus, or salicylates

Serves 6

2 10-ounce packages frozen
   chopped spinach
1 cup sour cream or yogurt

1½ teaspoons curry powder
⅛ teaspoon thyme
Salt and pepper to taste

Oven 350°

Cook spinach according to package instructions. Drain (reserve vitamin-filled liquid for homemade soups). Combine with other ingredients and pour into a greased 2-quart baking dish. Bake for 30 minutes.

ZUCCHINI CASSEROLE

No egg, corn, wheat, rye, citrus, or salicylates

Zucchini
Water to cover
Pesto Sauce*
Uncolored cheese

Oven 375°

Cut peeled (if zucchini is waxed) or unpeeled zucchini into 3-inch lengths. Split each piece lengthwise. Place in a saucepan. Cover with water and cook until just tender. Drain.

Place cooked pieces in a greased casserole. Spread each piece with pesto sauce and top each with a slice of cheese. Heat in oven until cheese has melted, about 5 minutes.

Yellow

BAKED ACORN SQUASH

No milk, egg, corn, wheat, rye, citrus, or salicylates

Acorn squash
Uncolored butter or allowed margarine
Nutmeg

Oven 375°

Cut squash in half. Scoop out seeds. Place cut side up in a large casserole dish or pan. Pour hot water around the squash so at least half the squash is standing in water. Cover dish and bake for

1 hour. Remove from water. Drain each piece thoroughly. Serve with a generous piece of butter or margarine in each cavity. Sprinkle nutmeg on top.

CARROT RING

No corn, wheat, rye, citrus, or salicylates

Serves 6

6 carrots, grated
Salt
Water
1 cup cooked brown rice

4 ounces uncolored cheese, grated
⅓ cup minced onion
2 eggs, beaten
Salt and pepper to taste

Oven 350°

Bring grated carrots to a boil in salted water. Turn to simmer for 5 minutes. Remove from heat and drain. Combine with other ingredients. Pour into oiled 1½-quart ring mold. Bake in a pan of hot water for 30 minutes. Turn out onto platter. Fill center with peas, either plain or creamed.

CORN PANCAKES

No milk, wheat, rye, citrus, or salicylates

Makes 8 pancakes

1 cup cooked fresh corn
1 egg, well beaten
1 tablespoon pure allowed vegetable oil

¼ cup unbleached flour or oat flour
¼ teaspoon salt

Combine all ingredients and mix well. Drop by spoonfuls onto greased skillet. Turn with spatula when brown and brown other side. Serve with pure maple syrup or Apple or Pear Maple Syrup.*

CORN PUDDING

No milk, wheat, rye, citrus, or salicylates

Serves 6

3 eggs, slightly beaten
1½ teaspoons salt
¼ teaspoon pepper
1 small onion, finely chopped
1 10-ounce package frozen
    corn or 2 cups cooked
    fresh corn

½ cup allowed Soft Bread
    Crumbs*
1 cup scalded milk or
    Chicken Stock*

Oven 350°

In a large bowl combine all the ingredients. Fill a well-greased 1½-quart casserole with mixture. Place casserole in a large pan of hot water and bake for 1¾ hours. Test for doneness by inserting knife in the middle. If knife comes out clean, the pudding is done.

Potatoes, Noodles, and Rice

AU GRATIN POTATOES

No egg, corn, wheat, rye, citrus, or salicylates

Serves 4

2 tablespoons pure allowed
    vegetable oil
2 tablespoons unbleached
    flour or rice flour
1 cup milk
½ teaspoon salt

1 tablespoon minced chives
1 cup grated uncolored
    cheese
2 cups diced cooked potatoes
Paprika

Oven 375°

In a heavy saucepan mix oil and flour. Stir in milk and continue stirring until sauce comes to a boil. Add salt, chives, and ½ cup grated cheese. Stir until cheese has melted.

Place potatoes in a greased 1½-quart casserole dish. Pour sauce over them and stir gently until potatoes are well coated. Spread remaining ½ cup grated cheese on top. Sprinkle paprika over cheese for flavor and color. Bake 15 minutes or until top is bubbling.

BOILED BAKED POTATOES

No milk, egg, corn, wheat, rye, citrus, or salicylates

Serves 4 to 5

12 to 18 small potatoes, peeled	½ cup pure allowed vegetable oil
Salt	2 tablespoons chopped chives
Water	

Oven 500°

Boil potatoes in salted water. Drain, cool, and store in refrigerator. When ready to serve, arrange in shallow baking dish. Cover with oil and sprinkle with chives. Bake for about 10 minutes or until brown.

HOT POTATO SALAD

No egg, corn, wheat, rye, or citrus

Serves 6 to 8

8 medium potatoes	1 cup Mayonnaise* or Eggless Mayonnaise*
Water to cover	
2 cups cubed sharp uncolored cheese	Salt to taste
½ cup chopped onion	⅓ cup sliced green olives

Oven 350°

Scrub potatoes, place in a large pan, and cover with water. Cook until tender. Drain and cool. Peel and cube potatoes and place in a large bowl. Add cheese, onion, mayonnaise, and salt. Toss lightly. Place in a 13x9-inch baking pan. Sprinkle the sliced olives on top. Cover with foil and bake 1 hour.

SCALLOPED POTATOES

No milk, egg, corn, wheat, rye, citrus, or salicylates

Serves 6

6 medium potatoes, pared
   and sliced
4 teaspoons instant minced
   onion
2 teaspoons salt

¼ cup unbleached flour or
   potato flour
¼ cup uncolored butter or
   allowed margarine
1 to 2 cups milk or Chicken
   Stock,* warmed

Oven 350°

Grease a 1½-quart baking dish. Put a layer of sliced potatoes in bottom of dish. Sprinkle 1 teaspoon onion, ½ teaspoon salt, 1 tablespoon flour, and 1 tablespoon shortening on potatoes. Make four layers of potatoes and other ingredients until dish is full. Pour warm milk or stock over potatoes so that they are almost completely covered. Bake for 1 hour 15 minutes or until potatoes are completely cooked.

SWEET POTATOES AND APPLES OR PEARS

No milk, egg, corn, wheat, rye, citrus, or salicylates

Serves 6

4 sweet potatoes or yams
Boiling water
2 cups sliced peeled apples or
   pears
2 tablespoons pure lemon
   juice or unsweetened
   pineapple juice

½ teaspoon cinnamon
1 to 2 tablespoons pure maple
   syrup
¼ cup uncolored butter or
   allowed margarine
½ cup unsweetened apple
   juice or water

Oven 350°

Cook sweet potatoes in their skins in boiling water until nearly done. Cool. Remove skins. Cut into ½-inch slices. Place half the sweet potatoes in a greased 2-quart casserole dish. Place half the sliced apples on top. Layer the rest of the sweet potatoes and apples similarly. Sprinkle lemon juice then cinnamon on top. Drizzle maple syrup over all. Dot with shortening. Pour apple juice or water over all. Cover casserole dish and bake for 45 minutes. Remove cover and continue baking another 15 minutes. About ½ to 1 teaspoon maple syrup per serving.

MACARONI AND CHEESE

No egg, corn, rye, citrus, or salicylates

Serves 6

1 cup uncooked macaroni
2 tablespoons pure allowed
  vegetable oil
2 tablespoons unbleached
  flour

1 cup milk
1 teaspoon salt
1½ cups grated sharp
  uncolored cheese
Paprika

Oven 350°

Cook macaroni according to package directions. Drain and place in greased 2-quart casserole dish. In a heavy saucepan mix oil and flour and slowly add milk. Stir until sauce thickens. Add salt and 1 cup cheese. Stir until cheese is melted. Pour over macaroni. Top with remaining cheese. Sprinkle with paprika. Bake for 15 minutes.

NOODLES ROMANOFF

No egg, corn, rye, citrus, or salicylates

Serves 8

1 8-ounce package noodles
  (whole grain if possible)
Boiling water
Salt
1 12-ounce additive-free
  carton cottage cheese
  (small curd)

1 8-ounce carton sour cream
¾ teaspoon instant minced
  onion
¾ teaspoon dried parsley
  flakes
½ teaspoon salt
Dash of pepper

Cook noodles in boiling salted water according to package directions. Drain and rinse. In a large saucepan combine noodles, cottage cheese, and sour cream. Stir constantly over low heat until mixture is hot. Add onion, parsley, salt, and pepper. Continue to stir over low heat for 2 minutes.

SEASONED RICE

No milk, egg, corn, wheat, rye, citrus, or salicylates

Serves 6

1 cup uncooked brown rice
2⅔ cups water
1 teaspoon salt
1 teaspoon thyme
1 teaspoon dried parsley flakes

1 tablespoon instant minced onion
1 tablespoon uncolored butter or allowed margarine

Combine all ingredients in a heavy saucepan. Bring to a boil. Stir well. Cover and cook over low heat for 50 minutes or until rice is tender and liquid is absorbed.

Others

BAKED BEANS

No milk, egg, corn, wheat, rye, citrus, or salicylates

Serves 5 to 6

1 cup dry navy beans
Water to cover
3 cups water
¼ teaspoon parsley flakes
1 stalk celery with leaves
1 small bay leaf
1 teaspoon instant minced onion
½ teaspoon salt

½ cup Chicken Stock* or Beef Stock*
2 tablespoons pure maple syrup
½ teaspoon paprika
½ cup water
¼ cup unbleached flour or rice flour

Oven 350°

Soak beans in water overnight. Drain. Combine beans, 3 cups

water, parsley, celery, bay leaf, onion, and salt in a large saucepan. Bring to a boil. Simmer 2 hours. Beans should be mealy and tender.

Drain beans. Add stock, pure maple syrup, and paprika. Mix and bake for 15 minutes or until thoroughly heated. Make a paste of water and flour and add as needed to thicken.

BAKED ONIONS

No milk, egg, corn, wheat, rye, citrus, or salicylates

Serves 8

4 large Bermuda onions, peeled and cut in half
4 tablespoons uncolored butter or allowed margarine

¼ cup honey
2 tablespoons water
1 teaspoon paprika
½ teaspoon salt

Oven 350°

Place onions cut side up in a baking pan. Prepare sauce by melting shortening with honey in a saucepan. Stir in water, paprika, and salt. Pour mixture over onions. Cover. Bake 1½ hours. Baste several times during baking. Before serving, sprinkle more paprika on onions if desired.

EGGPLANT ITALIANO

No egg, corn, wheat, rye, citrus, or salicylates

Serves 4 to 6

1 medium eggplant
⅓ cup milk
½ cup allowed Dry Bread Crumbs*
⅓ cup pure allowed vegetable oil
1 cup shredded mozzarella cheese

1 teaspoon oregano
¾ cup Pesto Sauce* or 1 cup Tomato Spaghetti Sauce* or Tomatoless Spaghetti Sauce*
⅓ cup grated Parmesan cheese

Oven 350°

Wash the eggplant and slice into ½-inch rounds. Dip each slice into milk and then into bread crumbs. In a skillet, brown lightly in the oil. Remove from skillet and put eggplant into 1½-quart casserole, overlapping the slices. Sprinkle the shredded mozzarella cheese and oregano over the eggplant and pour the pesto or tomato sauce over all. Top with Parmesan cheese. Bake in oven for 20 to 25 minutes until cheese starts to brown.

CHAPTER FOURTEEN

DESSERTS

You will want to make all desserts as nutritious as possible. Fresh fruit, homemade gelatin molds with fruit, or cheese on whole grain crackers are easy, nutritious desserts. Or try some of the recipes in this chapter. By choosing naturally sweet fruits, you can often cut down the amount of added sweetener necessary.

Cakes

APPLESAUCE OR PEARSAUCE CAKE

No milk, egg, corn, wheat, rye, citrus, or salicylates

Makes 1 9-inch round cake

½ cup uncolored butter or allowed margarine
⅓ cup honey or pure maple syrup
1 egg, slightly beaten, or ½ teaspoon baking powder and 2 tablespoons water or unsweetened juice
1½ cups unsweetened Applesauce or Pearsauce*

2 cups unsifted unbleached flour or 1½ cups potato starch flour
1½ teaspoons cinnamon or allspice
½ teaspoon nutmeg
½ teaspoon salt
1 teaspoon baking soda
1 teaspoon pure vanilla extract
1 cup nuts (optional)

Oven 350°

Cream together shortening and honey or maple syrup. Add egg or egg substitute and applesauce or pearsauce. Mix well. Stir in dry ingredients except nuts. Beat well, using an electric mixer for several minutes. Beat in vanilla. Stir in nuts. Pour into a greased and floured 9-inch round cake pan. Bake about 40 minutes or until a toothpick inserted in the center comes out clean and cake starts to pull away from sides of pan. Cool in pan on wire rack for 5 minutes. Turn out on rack. Serve plain, with Lemon or Orange Sauce,* or cool and frost with desired icing. About 2 teaspoons honey or maple syrup per slice of cake (excluding icing) if cut into eighths.

CAROB CAKE

No milk, corn, rye, citrus, or salicylates

Makes 2 9-inch-round layers

½ cup uncolored butter or allowed margarine, softened
¾ cup honey
2 eggs
⅓ cup carob powder
⅓ cup water
2 cups sifted unbleached flour or sifted whole wheat pastry flour

1 teaspoon baking powder
1 teaspoon baking soda
½ teaspoon salt
⅔ cup buttermilk or milk or water
1½ teaspoons pure vanilla extract
⅔ cup chopped nuts (optional)

Oven 350°

Cream shortening and honey well. Add eggs, beating until fluffy. Blend carob powder with water. Stir into shortening and egg mixture. Combine dry ingredients except nuts. Add to creamed mixture alternately with the buttermilk or other liquid, beating well. Add vanilla and nuts. Mix thoroughly. Bake in two greased and floured 9-inch layer cake pans for 25 to 35 minutes. Cool in pans on wire racks for 10 minutes. Turn out on racks. Cool completely. Ice with desired frosting. About 1 tablespoon honey per slice of cake (excluding icing) if cut into twelfths.

CARROT CAKE

No milk, corn, wheat, rye, citrus, or salicylates

Serves 10 to 12

1 cup unbleached flour and 1 cup sifted whole wheat flour *or* ¾ cup potato flour and ¾ cup rice flour

2 teaspoons baking powder

2 teaspoons baking soda

1 teaspoon cinnamon or allspice

1 cup pure allowed vegetable oil

¾ cup honey or pure maple syrup

3 eggs

2 cups packed grated carrots

1 cup undrained unsweetened crushed canned pineapple

½ cup chopped walnuts

½ cup raisins (optional)

Oven 350°

In a large mixing bowl combine dry ingredients except nuts and raisins. Add oil, honey, and eggs and beat until smooth. Stir in carrots, pineapple, nuts, and raisins and mix thoroughly. Pour into a greased 9x13-inch cake pan and bake for 50 minutes. Wait 10 minutes before removing cake from pan. Cool and frost, if desired. About 1 tablespoon honey or maple syrup per serving.

CUPCAKES

No milk, egg, corn, rye, citrus, or salicylates

Makes 16 cupcakes

1½ cups unbleached flour

2 tablespoons toasted wheat germ

1 tablespoon baking powder

½ teaspoon salt

¼ cup uncolored butter or allowed margarine, softened

⅓ cup honey or pure maple syrup

⅔ cup milk, water, or unsweetened pineapple juice

2 eggs or equivalent egg replacer

1½ teaspoons pure vanilla extract

Oven 350°

Combine dry ingredients in one bowl. In another bowl cream shortening with sweetener. Add liquid and egg or egg replacer. Beat in vanilla. Add flour mixture slowly. Beat for 2 minutes. Spoon batter into paper-lined cupcake pans, filling about two-thirds full. Bake for 20 to 25 minutes or until top springs back when slightly touched. Frost when completely cooled. About 1 teaspoon honey or maple syrup per cupcake.

DESSERT ROLL

No milk, corn, wheat, rye, citrus, or salicylates

Serves 6

CAKE:

4 eggs, separated
½ cup pure maple syrup
1 cup sifted unbleached flour
  or rice flour

¼ teaspoon salt
1 teaspoon baking powder
1 teaspoon pure vanilla
  extract

FILLING:

½ recipe Non-dairy Whipped
  Topping* or 1 cup
  Whipped Topping*

1 tablespoon carob powder
  (optional)

Oven 350°

In a small mixing bowl, beat together egg yolks and maple syrup for several minutes until very light and fluffy. Combine flour, salt, and baking powder and slowly add to egg mixture. In a separate bowl, beat egg whites until stiff. While continuing to beat, add the vanilla. Fold in the egg and flour batter. Prepare a 15x10x1-inch jelly roll pan by lining with aluminum foil and grease. Pour batter into pan and bake for 12 to 15 minutes until lightly browned. Remove from oven and immediately turn cake out onto a piece of foil which has been dusted with a little sifted flour. Remove the top foil. Cut crisp edges off the cake and roll together with foil from narrow end. Allow the cake to cool completely.

Prepare filling. Unroll cake and spread with cream filling. Reroll without foil and chill until ready to serve. About 4 teaspoons maple syrup per slice.

EASY CAROB CAKE

No milk, egg, corn, wheat, rye, or citrus

1 8-inch square cake
or 16 cupcakes

1½ cups sifted unbleached
flour, or 2 cups Scotch-
style oatmeal or oat flour
1 teaspoon baking soda
½ teaspoon salt
2 tablespoons carob powder
1 teaspoon pure vanilla
extract

1 tablespoon apple cider
vinegar
5 tablespoons uncolored
butter or allowed
margarine, melted
½ cup honey
1 cup water

Oven 350°

Combine all dry ingredients. Add vanilla, vinegar, and melted
shortening. Mix well. Stir in honey and water and mix until all ingredients are thoroughly blended. Batter will be thin. Pour into a
lightly greased and floured 8-inch square cake pan. Bake 40 to 45
minutes or until a toothpick inserted in the center comes out
clean. Cool in pan 10 minutes. Carefully remove and cool thoroughly on wire rack. May be iced.

To make cupcakes, fill sixteen cupcake liners two-thirds full
with batter. Bake at 375° for 15 minutes or until a toothpick inserted in the center comes out clean. About 1½ teaspoons honey
per serving.

FRUIT CAKE

No milk, corn, wheat, rye, or citrus

Makes 2 5x9-inch loaves
or 40 cupcakes

1½ cups raisins
1½ cups currants
1½ cups chopped dates
1½ cups chopped dried
apricots

1½ cups chopped walnuts
2 8-ounce cans unsweetened
crushed canned pine-
apple, including juice

1 cup uncolored butter or
    allowed margarine
½ cup pure maple syrup
6 eggs
3 cups whole wheat flour or
    rye flour

1 teaspoon baking powder
1 tablespoon cinnamon
1 teaspoon nutmeg
½ teaspoon allspice
½ cup water

Oven 300°

Combine first six ingredients, mix thoroughly, and let stand 1 hour. Cream together shortening and maple syrup. Add eggs and beat well. Combine dry ingredients and add to shortening mixture alternately with water. Stir in fruits and mix well. Pour into greased 5x9-inch loaf pans or cupcake pans. Bake the loaves 1 hour and 30 minutes and the cupcakes 45 minutes. Remove from pans and cool completely. Store in airtight containers. About ½ teaspoon maple syrup per serving.

GINGERBREAD

No milk, egg, corn, wheat, rye, citrus, or salicylates

Makes 1 8- or 9-inch-
square cake or 16 cupcakes

⅔ cup honey
½ cup melted uncolored
    butter or allowed
    margarine
¾ teaspoon cinnamon or
    allspice

¾ teaspoon nutmeg
1 teaspoon ginger
½ cup boiling water
2½ cups unbleached flour or
    3 cups oat flour
1 teaspoon baking soda

Oven 350°

Combine honey, shortening, and spices. Stir in boiling water. Mix in flour. Add baking soda and stir until thoroughly mixed. Pour into well-greased and lightly floured 8- or 9-inch square cake pan or cupcake tins. Bake 30 to 35 minutes or until a toothpick inserted in the center comes out clean. Let cool 5 minutes in pan. Turn out on wire rack. Serve warm with Lemon or Orange Sauce,* Whipped Topping,* or Non-dairy Whipped Topping.* Re-warm leftovers or serve cold. Great for snacks and lunch boxes. If making cupcakes, fill pans two-thirds full. Bake at 375° about 15 minutes. About 2 teaspoons honey per serving (excluding topping).

OATMEAL CAKE

No milk, corn, wheat, rye, citrus, or salicylates

Makes 1 13x9-inch cake

1 cup rolled oats
½ cup uncolored butter or
   allowed margarine
¾ cup honey
1¼ cups boiling water
1 teaspoon pure vanilla
   extract
2 eggs

1¾ cups unbleached flour or
   oat flour
1 teaspoon baking soda
¾ teaspoon salt
1 teaspoon cinnamon and ¼
   teaspoon nutmeg or ½
   teaspoon extra pure
   vanilla extract

Oven 350°

Place oats, shortening, honey, and boiling water in a large bowl. Stir. Let stand 20 minutes. Beat in vanilla and eggs. Mix together remaining ingredients and beat them into batter. Pour into a greased and floured 13x9-inch pan. Bake 30 to 40 minutes or until a toothpick inserted in the center comes out clean. May be iced but is good plain. About 1 tablespoon honey per slice of cake (excluding icing) if cut into twelfths.

ORANGE OR LEMON CAKE

No milk, corn, rye, or salicylates

Makes 1 9-inch round cake

½ cup uncolored butter or
   allowed margarine,
   softened
½ cup honey
2 eggs
¼ cup milk or pure unsweetened orange juice or
   water
2 tablespoons pure unsweetened orange juice or pure
   lemon juice

2 teaspoons grated uncolored
   unwaxed orange rind or
   lemon rind
½ cup whole wheat flour
1½ cups unbleached white
   flour
½ teaspoon salt
¾ teaspoon baking soda
1 recipe Lemon or Orange
   Sauce* (optional)
1 recipe Orange or Lemon
   Cream Icing* (optional)

Oven 350°

In a large bowl, cream together shortening and honey. Beat in eggs one at a time. Add milk or juice or water and beat. Add more juice and rind and beat well.

Combine flours, salt, and baking soda. Add to creamed mixture a little at a time. Beat well after each addition. Pour into a greased and floured 9-inch round pan and bake for about 25 to 30 minutes or until a toothpick inserted in the center comes out clean. Cool on wire rack for 5 minutes. Remove from pan. Completely cool. If desired, split cake horizontally and fill with lemon or orange sauce. Then ice cake with orange or lemon cream icing. Or serve cake plain. About 2 teaspoons honey per slice of cake (excluding filling and icing) if cut into twelfths.

SNACK-TIME CAKES

No milk, corn, wheat, rye, citrus, or salicylates

Serves 8

Cake and filling recipes from Dessert Roll*

Oven 350°

Prepare cake batter as directed for dessert roll. Take eight paper cups (the type used for hot coffee, but not styrofoam) and oil and dust the insides with unbleached flour or rice flour. Place on a cookie sheet and divide the cake batter evenly into the cups. Bake for 20 to 25 minutes or until lightly browned. Allow to cool completely.

Prepare filling. When ready to fill cakes, run a sharp knife around the cakes and remove from the cups. Split and fill. The cakes can be put back into the paper cups and are then easily packed in a lunch box.

Makes a delicious substitute for store-bought cream-filled spongecake. About 1 tablespoon maple syrup per cupcake.

PINEAPPLE UPSIDE-DOWN CUPCAKES

No milk, egg, corn, rye, citrus, or salicylates

Makes 12 cupcakes

BASIC CAKE:

⅓ cup honey or pure maple syrup

¼ cup uncolored butter or allowed margarine, melted

½ cup milk or water or unsweetened pineapple juice

1⅛ cups unbleached flour

2 tablespoons toasted wheat germ

2 teaspoons baking powder

¼ teaspoon salt

1 teaspoon pure vanilla extract

PINEAPPLE TOPPING:

3 tablespoons uncolored butter or allowed margarine, melted

¼ cup honey or pure maple syrup

1 cup drained unsweetened crushed canned pineapple

Oven 375°

To prepare the cake batter beat together honey or maple syrup, melted shortening, and liquid. In another bowl combine all dry ingredients and add to other mixture. Beat for 1 minute. Add vanilla and beat for another minute.

To prepare topping combine shortening, honey or maple syrup, and pineapple. Distribute pineapple mixture evenly among 12 cupcake liners. Pour cake batter on top. Bake for about 20 minutes. Let cool before removing from cupcake liners.

To pack in a lunch box wrap well and include a spoon. About 2⅓ teaspoons honey or maple syrup per cupcake.

Icings

CAROB CREAM ICING

No egg, corn, wheat, rye, citrus, or salicylates

Makes 3 cups or enough
icing for 1 8- or 9-inch
cake

1½ cups pure whipping cream
1 tablespoon sifted carob powder
2 to 3 tablespoons honey or pure maple syrup

Whip cream. Beat in carob and honey or maple syrup. Spread
on cooled cake. Leftover cake must be covered well and refrigerated.

MAPLE CREAM ICING

No egg, corn, wheat, rye, citrus, or salicylates

Makes 3 cups or enough
icing for 1 8- or 9-inch
cake

1½ cups pure whipping cream
2 to 3 tablespoons pure maple syrup

Whip cream. Beat in maple syrup. Spread on cooled cake. Leftover cake must be covered well and refrigerated.

ORANGE OR LEMON CREAM ICING

No egg, corn, wheat, rye, or salicylates

> Makes 3 cups or enough
> icing for 1 8- or 9-inch
> cake

1½ cups pure whipping cream
3 tablespoons pure unsweetened frozen thawed orange juice
    concentrate or pure lemon juice
1½ tablespoons honey (add 1½ tablespoons more if using
    lemon)

Whip cream. Beat in orange or lemon juice and honey. Spread on cooled cake. Leftover cake must be covered and refrigerated. Delicious on Orange Cake* or Lemon Cake.*

PEPPERMINT CREAM ICING

No egg, corn, wheat, rye, or citrus

> Makes 3 cups or enough
> icing for 1 8- or 9-inch
> cake

1½ cups pure whipping cream
½ to 1 teaspoon oil of peppermint extract
3 tablespoons honey

Whip cream. Beat in ½ teaspoon peppermint extract. Beat in honey. Taste. Add more peppermint if desired. Spread on cooled cake. Leftover cake must be covered well and refrigerated.

VANILLA CREAM ICING

No egg, corn, wheat, rye, citrus, or salicylates

Makes 3 cups or enough
icing for 1 8- or 9-inch
cake

1½ cups pure whipping cream
3 tablespoons honey
1½ teaspoons pure vanilla extract

Whip cream. Beat in honey and vanilla. Spread on cooled cake. Leftover cake must be covered well and refrigerated.

FLUFFY ICING

No milk, corn, wheat, rye, citrus, or salicylates

Makes enough icing
for 1 8- or 9-inch cake

⅔ cup honey
2 egg whites
½ teaspoon pure vanilla extract

In the top of a double boiler mix together honey and egg whites. Place over simmering water and beat with an electric mixer on medium-high speed for 10 to 12 minutes until stiff peaks form. Remove from heat and blend in vanilla.

CAROB FLUFFY ICING

No milk, corn, wheat, rye, citrus, or salicylates

Combine 2 or 3 tablespoons carob powder with the Fluffy Icing* recipe when blending in vanilla. Mix as indicated above.

PINEAPPLE FLUFFY ICING

No milk, corn, wheat, rye, citrus, or salicylates

Mix 3 to 4 tablespoons unsweetened pineapple juice into Fluffy Icing* recipe just before removing from heat.

NON-DAIRY MAPLE ICING

No milk, egg, corn, wheat, rye, citrus, or salicylates

Makes 3 cups or enough icing for 1 8- or 9-inch layer cake

2 envelopes unflavored
  gelatin
½ cup cold water

¾ cup pure maple syrup
¾ cup boiling water
¼ cup ice water

Soften gelatin in cold water. In a heavy saucepan add maple syrup to boiling water. Continue boiling over medium heat until syrup sheets from the edge of a spoon. Remove from heat. Stir in softened gelatin. Cool 10 to 15 minutes. Beat with an electric mixer until thick and fluffy, about 10 minutes. Slowly beat in ice water and continue beating until desired consistency is reached. Spread immediately on cooled cake.

Looks and tastes like a boiled icing but contains no common allergy-causing food.

Brownies and Squares

BUTTERSCOTCH SQUARES

No milk, egg, corn, wheat, rye, citrus, or salicylates

Makes 16 squares

⅔ cup pure maple syrup or
  honey
½ cup uncolored butter or

allowed margarine,
melted

1 egg, slightly beaten, or ¼
cup Apricot Egg
Replacer* plus 1
teaspoon baking powder
1 teaspoon pure vanilla
extract
¼ cup toasted wheat germ
(optional)

1¼ cups unbleached flour *or*
2 cups oat flour
1 teaspoon baking powder
½ teaspoon salt
½ to 1 cup chopped nuts or
dates

Oven 350°

Add maple syrup or honey to melted shortening. Stir well. Cool. Add egg or egg replacer and vanilla and beat until creamy. Add dry ingredients except nuts or dates and mix well. Fold in nuts or dates. Pour into a well-greased 13x9-inch pan. Smooth batter into corners with spoon. Bake 20 to 25 minutes until toothpick inserted in the center comes out clean. Cool. Cut into squares. May be frozen. Great for lunch box. About 2 teaspoons honey or maple syrup per square.

CAROB FUDGE BROWNIES

No milk, corn, rye, citrus, or salicylates

Makes 16 brownies

¾ cup unbleached flour
¼ cup toasted wheat germ
1 teaspoon baking powder
¼ teaspoon salt
½ cup sifted carob powder
½ cup uncolored butter or
allowed margarine,
melted

⅔ cup honey
2 eggs, well beaten
1 teaspoon pure vanilla
extract
½ cup chopped nuts

Oven 350°

Combine flour, wheat germ, baking powder, and salt and mix well. Add carob powder to melted butter. Stir in honey. Blend carob mixture with beaten eggs. Add flour mixture and blend thoroughly. Stir in vanilla and nuts and mix well. Spread in a greased 8-inch square pan. Bake 25 minutes. Brownies are done when a toothpick inserted in the center comes out clean. Cool. Cut into 16 squares. About 2 teaspoons honey per brownie.

PEANUT CAROB OAT SQUARES

No milk, egg, corn, wheat, rye, citrus, or salicylates

Makes 25 squares

½ cup uncolored butter or
   allowed margarine
½ cup honey
¼ cup carob powder
¼ cup water
¼ teaspoon salt

1 teaspoon pure vanilla
   extract
1 cup additive-free peanut
   butter
3 cups rolled oats

Combine first five ingredients in a heavy saucepan. Bring to a boil over medium heat and continue boiling for 1 minute. Remove from heat. Stir in vanilla and peanut butter, beating until well mixed. Mix in oats. Press into a 9-inch square pan. Cool in refrigerator until firm. Cut into squares. May be stored in refrigerator or tightly covered container. About 1 teaspoon honey per square.

PINEAPPLE NUT SQUARES

No milk, egg, corn, rye, citrus, or salicylates

Makes 16 2-inch squares

1⅓ cups whole wheat flour
1 teaspoon baking powder
¼ teaspoon salt
½ to ¾ cup honey
2 eggs or equivalent egg
   replacer

¾ cup drained unsweetened
   crushed canned pine-
   apple, reserve liquid
½ teaspoon pure vanilla
   extract
½ cup chopped nuts

Oven 350°

Combine flour, baking powder, and salt. Add remaining ingredients and mix thoroughly. Pour into a greased 8-inch square pan. Bake for 35 to 40 minutes until slightly browned. Cool and cut into squares. About 1½ to 2 teaspoons honey per square.

Piecrusts

WHEAT PIECRUST

No milk, egg, corn, rye, citrus, or salicylates

Makes 1 8- or
9-inch piecrust

1 cup unsifted unbleached
  flour
2 tablespoons toasted wheat
  germ or unsifted un-
  bleached flour

¾ teaspoon salt
⅓ cup pure allowed vege-
  table oil
2 tablespoons cold milk or ice
  cold water

Oven 450°

Mix flour, wheat germ, and salt together. In a cup measure oil and liquid but do not mix. Add to the flour mixture. Stir until well mixed. With your hands form a smooth ball. Place on a sheet of waxed paper and flatten a little. Cover with another sheet of waxed paper and roll out with a rolling pin to desired size and thickness. Peel off top paper. With paper on top of dough, place in piepan and carefully peel off paper. Fit into pan and press dough around edges. If baking only the crust, prick in several spots with a fork. Bake for 10 to 12 minutes, or until lightly browned. Double recipe for a two-crust pie.

COCONUT CRUST

No milk, egg, corn, wheat, rye, citrus, or salicylates

Makes 1 8- or
9-inch piecrust

3 tablespoons uncolored butter or allowed margarine
1½ cups shredded unsweetened coconut
1 tablespoon honey

Oven 350°

Butter pie plate using 1 tablespoon shortening. Melt remaining shortening and combine thoroughly with coconut and honey, using your fingers if necessary. Pour into piepan and press mixture around the sides and bottom until evenly distributed. Bake in oven 8 to 10 minutes until lightly browned. Cool and fill.

This is good using a Carob* or Vanilla Pudding* for the filling.

CORN FLAKE CRUST

No milk, egg, wheat, rye, citrus, or salicylates

Makes 1 8- or
9-inch piecrust

1 cup crushed additive-free, sugar-free, corn flakes
¼ cup uncolored butter or allowed margarine, melted
1 tablespoon honey
1½ teaspoons cinnamon

Mix together all ingredients. Press mixture in bottom of pan to form crust. May be baked at 350° for 5 minutes.

GRAHAM CRACKER PIECRUST

No milk, egg, corn, rye, citrus, or salicylates

Makes 1 8- or
9-inch piecrust

1½ cups crumbs Graham Crackers*
½ cup uncolored butter or allowed margarine, melted
1 tablespoon honey
1 teaspoon cinnamon (optional)

Mix together all ingredients. Pat firmly into piepan. May be baked at 350° for 10 to 12 minutes. Cool. Fill with any desired filling. Especially good for ice cream pies or cheese cake.

NUT CRUST

No milk, egg, corn, wheat, rye, citrus, or salicylates

Makes 1 8- or
9-inch piecrust

1⅓ cups finely chopped nuts (walnuts or pecans)
2 tablespoons butter or allowed margarine, melted

Oven 350°

Mix together the nuts and shortening. Press against the sides and bottom of piepan, using the back of a spoon. Bake for 12 minutes. Cool before filling.

RICE PIECRUST

No milk, egg, corn, wheat, rye, citrus, or salicylates

Makes 1 8-inch piecrust

¾ cup rice flour
½ teaspoon salt
3 tablespoons pure allowed vegetable oil
¼ cup cold water

Oven 350°

In a small bowl combine flour and salt. Add oil and water. Mix thoroughly and shape into a ball. Place in the middle of an 8-inch piepan. Gently flatten the dough and press it up the sides of the pan. Bake for 15 to 20 minutes.

RYE CRUMB CRUST

No milk, egg, corn, wheat, citrus, or salicylates

Makes 1 8- or
9-inch piecrust

1½ cups Ry-Krisp cracker crumbs
½ cup uncolored butter or allowed margarine, melted
3 tablespoons pure maple syrup or honey
1 teaspoon cinnamon (optional)

Oven 350°

Mix cracker crumbs with shortening, syrup, and cinnamon. Pat firmly into piepan. Bake for 5 to 7 minutes. Cool. Fill with desired filling.

Pies

APPLE OR PEAR PIE

No milk, egg, corn, rye, citrus, or salicylates

Makes 1 8- or 9-inch pie

Double recipe Wheat
  Piecrust*
5 cups peeled, sliced apples or
  pears
½ teaspoon cinnamon

2 tablespoons unbleached
  flour
¼ to ½ cup honey
1 tablespoon uncolored
  butter or allowed mar-
  garine (optional)

Oven 350°

Line pie plate with bottom crust. Combine apples or pears with cinnamon and flour and toss lightly until thoroughly mixed. Pour half of the fruit into the bottom crust and pour ⅛ to ¼ cup honey on top. Add the remaining fruit and remaining honey. Dot with shortening. Cover with top crust, seal, and cut slits to let steam escape. Bake for 35 to 40 minutes until lightly browned and juices are bubbly. Cool before serving. About 2 to 4 teaspoons honey per one-sixth pie.

BANANA CREAM PIE

No corn, wheat, rye, citrus, or salicylates

Serves 6

Cover baked 8- or 9-inch allowed piecrust with 2 medium bananas. Pour Vanilla Cream Pie* filling on top and bake with Meringue Topping* or chill and serve plain or with pure whipped cream.

BLUEBERRY PIE

No milk, egg, corn, rye, citrus, or salicylates

Makes 1 8- or 9-inch pie

Double recipe Wheat
  Piecrust*
4 cups fresh or canned or
  frozen (thawed) blue-
  berries
1 tablespoon water
1 tablespoon pure lemon
  juice (optional)

¼ cup honey
3½ tablespoons minute
  tapioca *or* 4 to 5 tablespoons unbleached flour
2 tablespoons uncolored
  butter or allowed mar-
  garine

Oven 375°

Prepare piecrust. Combine berries, water, lemon juice, and honey in a heavy saucepan. If using tapioca, add tapioca and let stand 10 minutes. Cook over medium heat until berries are tender. If not using tapioca, add flour. Stir until filling thickens. Cool. Pour into prepared pie shell. Dot with shortening. Cover with top crust. Slit top crust with knife in several places. Bake for about 30 minutes or until crust is golden brown. About 2 teaspoons honey per one-sixth pie.

BLUEBERRY TURNOVERS

No milk, egg, corn, rye, citrus, or salicylates

Makes 10 to 12 small
or 5 to 6 large turnovers

1 cup fresh or canned or
  frozen (thawed) blue-
  berries
2 tablespoons water or juice
  from berries
1 to 2 teaspoons honey
  (optional)

1 teaspoon pure lemon juice
  (optional)
1 tablespoon cornstarch or
  potato starch flour mixed
  with 1 tablespoon cold
  water
1 recipe Wheat Piecrust*

Oven 425°

Combine blueberries, water, honey, and lemon juice in a saucepan. Cook until blueberries are tender. Add cornstarch or potato starch flour mixed with water to thicken filling. Continue cooking just until filling thickens.

Roll out piecrust between waxed paper as thin as possible. Cut into squares or circles. Put small amount of filling on piecrust. Fold over. Seal edges by pressing them together. Prick top of each with a fork.

Place on a greased cookie sheet. Bake for 10 to 12 minutes until lightly browned. Serve hot or cold. May be frozen.

CHERRY PIE

No milk, egg, corn, rye, or citrus

Makes 1 8- or 9-inch pie

Double recipe Wheat
  Piecrust*
2 1-pound cans tart unsweetened cherries
⅔ cup honey
½ teaspoon cinnamon

2½ to 3 tablespoons minute tapioca
1 tablespoon uncolored butter or allowed margarine (optional)

Oven 425°

Line piepan with bottom crust. Drain cherries, reserving liquid. Mix cherries in a bowl with the honey, cinnamon, tapioca, and ¼ cup reserved cherry juice. Pour into bottom crust and dot top with shortening. Cover top with crust and cut slits to let steam escape. Bake in oven for 40 to 45 minutes, until lightly browned. Cool before cutting. About 5 teaspoons honey per one-sixth pie.

ICE CREAM PIE

No egg, corn, wheat, rye, citrus, or salicylates

Makes 1 8- or 9-inch pie

1 recipe Graham Cracker Piecrust* or other allowed piecrust
½ gallon allowed ice cream, one or more flavors

Prepare crust. Soften ice cream and fill piecrust. Freeze until firm. If using several flavors, soften one at a time, spread in pie-crust, freeze, soften another, and spread on top of frozen first layer.

LEMON MERINGUE PIE

No milk, corn, wheat, rye, or salicylates

Makes 1 8- or 9-inch pie

½ cup honey
6 tablespoons potato starch
  flour or rice flour
⅛ teaspoon salt
1½ cups hot water
3 egg yolks (save whites for
  meringue)
2 tablespoons uncolored

butter or allowed mar-
  garine
1 teaspoon grated uncolored
  unwaxed lemon rind
⅓ cup pure lemon juice
1 recipe allowed piecrust,
  baked
Meringue Topping*

Oven 325°

In a large saucepan combine honey, flour, and salt. Stir in hot water gradually. Cook over high heat, stirring continuously till mixture boils. Reduce heat and continue cooking and stirring 2 more minutes. Remove from heat.

Add a little of the hot mixture to the egg yolks. Then add egg yolks to hot mixture. Bring to boiling and cook 2 minutes, stirring constantly. Add shortening and lemon rind. Slowly stir in lemon juice. Pour into baked 8- or 9-inch piecrust. Prepare meringue topping. Pile lightly on pie filling and spread out completely to cover the filling. Bake until lightly browned, about 15 to 20 minutes. With meringue, about 5 teaspoons honey per one-sixth pie.

PEACH PIE

No milk, egg, corn, rye, or citrus

Makes 1 8- or 9-inch pie

Double recipe Wheat
  Piecrust*
4 to 5 cups sliced fresh or
  frozen (thawed) peaches

½ cup honey
½ teaspoon cinnamon
¼ cup unbleached flour or
  rice flour

Oven 425°

Line piepan with bottom pastry. Toss the peaches slightly with the honey, cinnamon, and flour. Pour peaches into crust and cover with remaining pastry. Seal edges and cut vents in top to let steam escape. Bake for 35 minutes until juices are bubbly and crust is lightly browned. Cool before serving. About 4 teaspoons honey per one-sixth pie.

PEACH CHIFFON PIE

No milk, corn, wheat, rye, or citrus

Makes 1 8- or 9-inch pie

1 envelope unflavored gelatin
½ cup water
¼ cup plus 2 teaspoons pure maple syrup

1 cup puréed fresh or frozen (thawed) peaches
3 eggs, separated
1 recipe allowed piecrust, baked

Combine gelatin, water, ¼ cup maple syrup, peaches, and egg yolks in a medium saucepan and bring to a boil over medium heat, stirring constantly. Chill mixture until it mounds slightly when stirred. Beat egg whites until fluffy. Slowly add 2 teaspoons maple syrup and continue to beat until the whites stand in stiff peaks. Fold the chilled mixture gently into the egg whites and mix thoroughly. Pour into the baked piecrust and refrigerate for several hours until set. May be served topped with fresh peach slices. About 2 teaspoons maple syrup per one-sixth pie.

PUMPKIN WHIP PIE

No egg, corn, wheat, rye, citrus, or salicylates

Makes 1 8- or 9-inch pie

1 recipe allowed piecrust, baked
1 envelope unflavored gelatin
¾ cup milk
½ cup plus 1 tablespoon pure maple syrup

1½ cups canned pumpkin
½ teaspoon salt
½ teaspoon cinnamon
½ teaspoon ginger
¼ teaspoon nutmeg
1 cup pure whipping cream

Combine in a medium saucepan all ingredients except whipping cream and 1 tablespoon maple syrup. Cook over medium heat, stirring constantly, until mixture boils. Place pan over ice cubes or in refrigerator, stirring occasionally, until mixture thickens and mounds slightly. Whip cream and sweeten with 1 tablespoon maple syrup. Fold pumpkin mixture into whipped cream and mix thoroughly. Pour into baked piecrust and refrigerate 2 to 3 hours until filling is set. About 4 teaspoons maple syrup per one-sixth pie.

STRAWBERRY PIE

No milk, egg, corn, wheat, rye, or citrus

Makes 1 8- or 9-inch pie

1 recipe allowed piecrust
1 quart fresh strawberries
1 cup water
½ cup honey
3 tablespoons cornstarch or
   arrowroot flour

Bake single piecrust and cool. Wash and hull strawberries. Measure out 1 cup berries and place in saucepan with ¾ cup water and honey. Bring to a boil and cook for 5 minutes, mashing berries slightly. Combine the remaining water with the cornstarch or arrowroot flour to form a paste. Add this slowly to the strawberry mixture until thickened. Cook for 1 minute. Remove from heat. Place the remaining berries in the baked piecrust, cutting berries in half or quarters if very large. Pour thickened sauce over the strawberries and refrigerate until set, about 3 hours. Serve plain or top with whipped cream. About 4 teaspoons honey per one-sixth pie.

VANILLA CREAM PIE

No corn, wheat, rye, citrus, or salicylates

Makes 1 8- or 9-inch pie

3 tablespoons cornstarch or
   arrowroot
⅓ cup pure maple syrup or
   honey
½ teaspoon salt
2⅓ cups milk
2 egg yolks, slightly beaten
1 tablespoon pure allowed
   vegetable oil
1½ teaspoons pure vanilla
   extract
1 recipe allowed piecrust,
   baked

In a heavy saucepan combine cornstarch or arrowroot, sweetener, and salt. Add milk. Stir constantly over medium heat until sauce comes to a boil. Stir 1 minute longer. Remove from heat and very slowly pour in egg yolks, stirring vigorously. Add oil and vanilla and blend well. Cover and cool. Pour into baked piecrust. Chill thoroughly. May be served with pure whipped cream or with Meringue Topping.* About 2½ teaspoons sweetener per one-sixth pie (excluding topping).

MERINGUE TOPPING

No milk, corn, wheat, rye, or citrus

Makes topping for 1
8- or 9-inch pie

¼ teaspoon cream of tartar
3 egg whites (at room temperature)
2 tablespoons honey or pure maple syrup
½ teaspoon pure vanilla extract

Oven 325°

In a mixing bowl combine cream of tartar and egg whites. Beat until almost thick enough to hold a peak. Add honey or maple syrup gradually, beating until stiff but not dry. Beat in vanilla. Pile lightly on pie filling and spread out to cover. Bake for 15 to 20 minutes.

Fruits

APPLE OR PEAR CRISP

No milk, egg, corn, wheat, rye, citrus, or salicylates

Serves 4

5 or 6 apples or pears
½ cup oat flour
¼ cup uncolored butter or allowed margarine
1 tablespoon pure maple syrup

Oven 375°

Peel, core, and slice apples or pears and place in a deep pan or dish. Mix together oat flour, shortening, and maple syrup, working quickly so it does not become oily. Spread mixture on top of fruit. Bake for 30 minutes or until fruit is done and the topping is beginning to brown. May be served warm or cold. Good plain, with whipped cream, or a spoonful of allowed ice cream on each portion. Less than 1 teaspoon maple syrup per serving.

BAKED APPLES OR PEARS

No milk, egg, corn, wheat, rye, or salicylates

Serves 4

4 large apples or pears, cored, peeled, and cut in sixths
¼ cup honey
1 tablespoon pure maple syrup
2 tablespoons pure lemon juice
½ teaspoon cinnamon
½ teaspoon ginger
¼ teaspoon nutmeg

Oven 350°

Place apples or pears in baking dish. Combine remaining ingredients and pour over fruit. Bake 30 to 40 minutes. Fruit should be barely tender. Serve slightly warm or cold. About 4 teaspoons honey and maple syrup per serving.

FRUIT AMBROSIA

No milk, egg, corn, wheat, or rye

Serves 4

4 large oranges
2 ripe bananas
¾ cup shredded unsweetened coconut

With a sharp knife cut off all rind and inner white membrane from oranges. Cut sections out of orange, catching juice in a bowl. Peel and cut bananas into slices. Add coconut and toss lightly.

A cup of drained unsweetened canned pineapple chunks may also be added to this mixture.

CHAPTER FIFTEEN

PUDDINGS AND FROZEN DESSERTS

Puddings and ice creams are usually milk products but this chapter has some milk-free recipes your child will enjoy. Puddings and ice cream are easily made from scratch with honey or pure maple syrup. Puddings may be thickened with arrowroot or tapioca rather than cornstarch.

Puddings

VANILLA PUDDING

No egg, corn, wheat, rye, citrus, or salicylates

Serves 6

¼ cup cornstarch or potato
   starch flour
¼ teaspoon salt
2¼ cups milk
¼ cup honey or pure maple
   syrup

2 tablespoons uncolored
   butter or allowed mar-
   garine
1 teaspoon pure vanilla
   extract

In a large saucepan combine cornstarch or potato starch and salt. Add milk slowly and stir until smooth. Stir in honey or maple syrup. Cook over medium heat, stirring constantly until mixture boils. For cornstarch pudding, continue stirring and boil 1 minute longer. Remove from heat. For potato starch pudding, remove from heat as soon as pudding thickens. Stir in shortening and vanilla and mix well. Refrigerate in a covered container. About 2 teaspoons honey or maple syrup per serving.

CAROB PUDDING

No egg, corn, wheat, rye, citrus, or salicylates

Serves 6

Vanilla Pudding*
2 to 4 tablespoons carob powder

Prepare vanilla pudding as directed above. Add carob powder when vanilla is added. Stir until well mixed and carob is melted. Refrigerate in a covered container. About 2 teaspoons honey or maple syrup per serving.

CREAMY MAPLE PUDDING

No corn, wheat, rye, citrus, or salicylates

Serves 6

1 envelope unflavored gelatin
¼ cup cold water
⅓ cup pure maple syrup
3 eggs, separated

1 teaspoon pure vanilla
  extract
1 cup pure whipping cream,
  whipped

Sprinkle gelatin over cold water. Heat maple syrup to boiling point and stir in softened gelatin until dissolved. Beat egg yolks well. Gradually add hot syrup to egg yolks, beating continuously. Return syrup and egg mixture to heat and cook for several minutes, stirring constantly. Cool. Add vanilla. Refrigerate until thickened. Whip cream and fold into pudding. Beat egg whites until stiff and fold into pudding. Chill until set. About 1 tablespoon maple syrup per serving.

LEMON OR ORANGE PUDDING

No egg, corn, wheat, rye, or salicylates

Serves 6

Vanilla Pudding*
6 tablespoons pure lemon juice or pure unsweetened frozen
    (thawed) orange juice concentrate

Prepare vanilla pudding as directed above. Substitute lemon
juice or orange juice for vanilla extract. About 2 teaspoons
honey or maple syrup per serving.

PINEAPPLE PUDDING

No milk, egg, corn, wheat, rye, citrus, or salicylates

Serves 4

1 20-ounce can unsweetened chunk or crushed pineapple,
    drained, reserving juice
1½ tablespoons arrowroot
1 banana, sliced (optional)

Measure out 1 cup drained crushed or chunk pineapple and set
aside. Liquefy rest of pineapple and juice in blender. Pour into a
heavy saucepan. Add arrowroot powder and mix well. Cook over
medium heat, stirring constantly until pudding thickens. Remove
from heat. Stir in crushed or chunk pineapple and banana slices.
Chill.

MAPLE APPLE OR PEAR PUDDING

No milk, eggs, corn, wheat, rye, or citrus

Serves 6

3 tablespoons minute tapioca
⅛ teaspoon salt
2 tablespoons pure maple
    syrup
⅓ cup cold water
½ cup chopped dates

½ cup raisins
¼ cup chopped nuts
1½ cups sliced apples or
    pears, peeled if waxed
1½ cups boiling water

In the top of a double boiler, combine tapioca, salt, maple syrup, and cold water. Let stand 5 minutes. Add remaining ingredients and mix well. Cook over boiling water until pudding is thickened and fruit is tender. Serve warm with allowed topping or just plain. About 1 teaspoon maple syrup per serving but recipe is high in natural fruit sugars too.

MILKLESS COCONUT PUDDING

No milk, corn, wheat, rye, citrus, or salicylates

Serves 4

2 cups shredded unsweetened coconut
3 cups boiling water

1 tablespoon unflavored gelatin
3 egg yolks
3 tablespoons honey

Put coconut into a heatproof bowl. Pour the boiling water over the coconut and allow to sit until lukewarm. Drain coconut through a fine sieve or cheesecloth, reserving all liquid. Squeeze the coconut until thoroughly drained. Liquid should measure 2 cups. If necessary, add water to make the 2 cups.

Pour coconut liquid into a saucepan and mix with the other ingredients. Cook over medium heat until very hot and gelatin is dissolved. Do not boil. Pour into serving dishes and refrigerate 3 to 4 hours until set.

One-half cup of the drained coconut can be stirred into the pudding when partially set. About 2 teaspoons honey per serving.

LEMON PUDDING CAKE

No corn, wheat, rye, or salicylates

Serves 8

½ cup unbleached flour or sifted whole wheat flour or ⅝ cup potato starch flour
½ teaspoon baking powder
¼ teaspoon salt

4 eggs
½ cup honey
⅓ cup pure lemon juice
1 tablespoon uncolored butter or allowed margarine, melted

1 teaspoon grated uncolored   Whipped Topping*
    unwaxed lemon peel   (optional)
1½ cups milk

Oven 350°

Mix together flour, baking powder, and salt. Set aside. In a large bowl beat eggs with electric mixer on high speed. Slowly beat in honey. Continue beating for 5 minutes. At low speed beat in lemon juice, butter or margarine, and lemon peel. Stir in flour mixture. Stir in milk until just mixed. Pour into a greased 8-inch square pan. Place in shallow pan in oven. Pour 1 inch hot water into pan. Bake about 50 minutes. Cake is done when lightly browned and center springs back when touched. Cool slightly. Serve warm with whipped topping if desired. About 1 tablespoon honey per serving.

Frozen Desserts

CANTALOUPE ICE CREAM

No egg, corn, wheat, rye, citrus, or salicylates

Serves 6 to 8

1¾ cups pure whipping   3 tablespoons honey
    cream   ⅛ teaspoon cinnamon
1½ cups cubed cantaloupe   ⅛ teaspoon nutmeg

Put ¾ cup whipping cream and other ingredients in a blender and mix until smooth. Pour into freezer trays until partially frozen. Whip remaining cream until stiff and fold into frozen mixture. Pour back into freezer trays and freeze until firm. About 1 teaspoon honey per serving.

GRAPE ICE

No milk, egg, corn, wheat, rye, or citrus

Serves 4

1 envelope unflavored gelatin
¼ cup cold water
2 cups unsweetened grape juice
2 tablespoons honey (optional)

Soften gelatin in cold water. Heat grape juice and stir in softened gelatin and honey until both are well dissolved. Cool. Pour into a 9-inch square pan and freeze until frozen around the edges. In a chilled bowl beat the partially frozen grape ice until smooth but not melted. Return to pan. Cover tightly with foil. Freeze until firm. Zero to 1½ teaspoons honey per serving.

MAPLE ICE CREAM

No egg, corn, wheat, rye, citrus, or salicylates

Serves 8

2 cups pure whipping cream
1 cup milk
½ cup non-instant dry milk
   powder

¼ cup pure maple syrup
1 cup additive-free peanut
   butter (optional)

In a large mixing bowl combine 1 cup whipping cream and milk. Beat in dry milk powder until well dissolved. Beat in maple syrup. Beat in peanut butter. In another bowl whip remaining cream until stiff. Fold into milk mixture. Freeze in a shallow pan until partially frozen. Return to mixing bowl and beat until smooth but not melted. Return to freezer. Freeze until firm. About 1½ teaspoons maple syrup per serving.

ORANGE ICE CREAM

No egg, corn, wheat, or rye

Serves 4 to 6

1 cup milk
1 cup pure whipping cream
½ cup pure unsweetened
    frozen (thawed) orange
    juice concentrate

3 tablespoons grated un-
    colored unwaxed orange
    rind
1 teaspoon pure lemon juice
½ cup non-instant dry milk
    powder (optional)

Combine all ingredients and beat well. Freeze in a covered shallow container until partially frozen. Beat with an electric mixer till smooth. Return to shallow container. Cover tightly. Freeze until firm.

The advantage of this ice cream is that it contains no extra sweetener, but depends on the natural sweetness of the orange juice. Great for the child who doesn't tolerate honey or maple syrup.

PAPAYA ICE

No milk, egg, corn, wheat, rye, citrus, or salicylates

Serves 6

1 envelope unflavored gelatin
¼ cup cold water
2 tablespoons honey

1 cup water
1 ripe papaya, peeled and
    puréed

Soften gelatin in cold water. Add honey to 1 cup water and boil gently for 5 minutes over medium heat. Dissolve softened gelatin in hot honey syrup. Remove from heat. Fold in puréed papaya. Freeze in a 9-inch square pan until frozen around the edges. Beat partially frozen papaya ice in a chilled bowl until smooth but not melted. Return to pan. Cover tightly with foil. Freeze until firm. About 1 teaspoon honey per serving.

PINEAPPLE ICE

No milk, egg, corn, wheat, rye, citrus, or salicylates

Serves 4

1 envelope unflavored gelatin
¼ cup cold water
1 20-ounce can unsweetened crushed or chunk pineapple,
    drained well, reserving 1 cup juice
2 tablespoons honey (optional)

Soften gelatin in cold water. Heat pineapple juice. Stir in honey
and softened gelatin until both are well dissolved. Purée pineapple
in blender and fold into juice and gelatin mixture. Freeze in a
9-inch square pan until frozen around the edges. Beat partially
frozen pineapple ice in a chilled bowl until smooth but not melted.
Return to pan. Freeze until firm. Zero to 1½ teaspoons honey per
serving.

PINEAPPLE ICE CREAM

No egg, corn, wheat, rye, citrus, or salicylates

Serves 4

1 6-ounce can frozen pure
    unsweetened (thawed)
    pineapple juice concen-
    trate
1 cup milk

1 cup pure whipping cream
⅔ cup non-instant dry milk
    powder (optional)
⅛ teaspoon pure vanilla
    extract

Combine all ingredients in a blender. Turn on highest speed
until smooth. Pour into a shallow container and chill in freezer
until partially frozen. Beat with an electric mixer until smooth but
not melted. Freeze in a covered container until firm.

This ice cream contains no extra sweetening agent and can be
enriched with extra milk powder.

PUMPKIN ICE CREAM

No egg, corn, wheat, rye, citrus, or salicylates

Serves 8 to 10

1½ pints pure whipping
    cream
⅔ cup pure maple syrup

1 cup canned pumpkin
¼ teaspoon cinnamon
¼ teaspoon nutmeg

Combine 1½ cups whipping cream with other ingredients in a saucepan. Bring to a boil and immediately remove from heat. Cool. Add remaining cream and mix in thoroughly.

Pour into freezer trays and freeze until partially set. Scoop into a bowl and beat until light. Pour back into trays and freeze until firm. About 4 teaspoons maple syrup per serving.

STRAWBERRY ICE CREAM

No egg, corn, wheat, rye, or citrus

Makes almost 2 quarts

1 quart (4 cups) strawberries
½ cup honey
½ cup non-instant dry milk
    powder (optional)

1 cup milk
1½ teaspoons pure vanilla
    extract
2 cups pure whipping cream

Wash strawberries well. Remove stems. Crush. Add honey and mix well. Add milk powder to milk. Combine with strawberry mixture. Add vanilla. Freeze until almost frozen. Whip cream. Beat frozen strawberry mixture until smooth. Fold in whipped cream. Freeze until firm. About 1 tablespoon honey per serving.

VANILLA ICE CREAM

No corn, wheat, rye, citrus, or salicylates

Serves 6 to 8

1 envelope unflavored gelatin
2 cups cold milk
⅓ cup honey
2 eggs, separated
⅛ teaspoon salt

2 teaspoons pure vanilla
    extract
2 cups pure whipping cream
    or half and half cream

Sprinkle gelatin over cold milk in top of double boiler. Place over boiling water and stir until gelatin is dissolved. Add honey and stir until dissolved. Remove from heat. Add egg yolks and salt. Beat well with an electric mixer. Place again over boiling water and cook, stirring constantly until mixture coats spoon. Remove from heat. Cool. Stir in vanilla and cream. Pour into shallow pans and freeze until almost firm. Beat egg whites until stiff. Place frozen mixture in chilled bowl and beat until smooth. Fold in egg whites. Return to shallow pans and freeze until firm. About 2 teaspoons honey per serving.

CAROB ICE CREAM

No corn, wheat, rye, citrus, or salicylates

Serves 6 to 8

Vanilla Ice Cream*
6 to 8 tablespoons carob powder

Prepare ice cream as above but dissolve carob powder in hot milk containing the dissolved gelatin. About 2 teaspoons honey per serving.

WATERMELON SHERBET

No milk, corn, wheat, rye, or salicylates

Serves 8 to 10

1 envelope unflavored gelatin
½ cup cold water
½ cup pure maple syrup
1 cup hot water

2 cups watermelon pulp
1 tablespoon pure lemon juice
2 egg whites
¼ teaspoon salt

Sprinkle gelatin over cold water. Set aside. Combine maple syrup and hot water in saucepan and bring to a full boil. Continue to cook until the syrup reaches the thread stage (230°). Meanwhile, chop watermelon in blender on low speed for 15 seconds. Remove syrup from heat and stir in softened gelatin, fruit, and lemon juice. Chill until the mixture thickens. Whip the egg whites together with the salt until stiff peaks form. Fold gently but thoroughly into the gelatin mixture. Pour into two refrigerator trays and freeze until mushy. Beat the mixture until light and pour back into refrigerator trays. Freeze until firm. About 1 tablespoon maple syrup per serving.

Others

CAROB MOUSSE

No corn, wheat, rye, citrus, or salicylates

Serves 8

⅔ cup carob powder
⅓ cup water
⅓ cup pure maple syrup
¼ teaspoon salt

3 eggs, separated
2 cups pure whipping cream
1 teaspoon pure vanilla
  extract

In the top of a double boiler combine carob powder, water, maple syrup, salt, and slightly beaten egg yolks. Stir well. Cook over boiling water for 3 minutes. Let cool. Whip cream. Beat egg whites until stiff. Add vanilla to carob mixture and fold in cream and egg whites until thoroughly mixed. Pour into 2-quart mold or individual dishes. Chill thoroughly. About 2 teaspoons maple syrup per serving.

CREAM PUFFS

No corn, rye, citrus, or salicylates

Makes 12 to 14 cream puffs

CREAM PUFFS:

2 tablespoons toasted wheat germ

About 1 cup unbleached flour

½ cup uncolored butter or allowed margarine

1 cup boiling water

⅛ teaspoon salt

4 eggs

BANANA WHIPPED FILLING:

2 cups pure whipping cream

1 tablespoon pure vanilla extract

5 medium-sized very ripe bananas, diced

Oven 400°

Put wheat germ in bottom of measuring cup and add enough flour to make 1 cup. In a heavy saucepan melt shortening in boiling water. Bring to a rolling boil. Add flour and salt. Stir vigorously over medium heat until mixture forms a ball. Remove from heat. Cool slightly. Beat in eggs, one at a time, until dough is stiff.

Drop dough by heaping tablespoonfuls 3 inches apart on lightly greased cookie sheet. Bake until golden brown and puffy, about 30 minutes. Remove from oven and cool.

Prepare filling by whipping cream until stiff. Stir in vanilla. Fold in diced bananas. Split cream puffs and fill with banana filling. This recipe contains no added sweeteners.

COMPANY CHEESE CAKE

No corn, wheat, rye, or salicylates

Serves 6

1 envelope unflavored gelatin

¼ cup cold water

1 egg, separated

3 tablespoons honey

½ cup milk

¼ teaspoon salt

1 cup additive-free cottage cheese

1 tablespoon pure lemon juice
¼ teaspoon pure lemon extract or ½ teaspoon grated unwaxed uncolored lemon rind

½ cup pure whipping cream, chilled and whipped
1 recipe Corn Flake Crust* or any allowed piecrust, baked

Soften gelatin in cold water. In the top of a double boiler, beat egg yolk slightly, add honey, milk, and salt. Cook over boiling water until mixture coats the spoon. Add gelatin to custard and stir until dissolved. Place cottage cheese in a blender on highest speed until smooth and creamy. Remove top of double boiler from heat. Add cottage cheese, lemon juice, and lemon extract or rind to custard. Cool until custard begins to thicken. Whip cream or evaporated milk and beat egg white until stiff. Fold both into custard.

Prepare corn flake crust or piecrust. If using corn flakes, place most of the crumbs in the bottom of an 8- or 9-inch piepan or 1½-quart mold. Add cheese mixture. Sprinkle remaining crumbs on top and chill thoroughly. Unmold when ready to serve. Or pour cheese mixture into baked pie shell and chill. About 1½ teaspoons honey per serving.

EASY CHEESE CAKE

No egg, corn, wheat, rye, citrus, or salicylates

Serves 8

1 recipe Graham Cracker Piecrust* or any allowed piecrust, baked
1 cup boiling water
1 envelope unflavored gelatin
¼ cup honey

2 8-ounce packages cream cheese, softened
1 teaspoon pure vanilla extract
1 cup sour cream (optional)
Fresh fruit (optional)

Prepare piecrust in a 9-inch piepan. Cool if baked. In a large bowl pour boiling water over gelatin and stir until completely dissolved. Add honey and stir well. With an electric mixer beat in cream cheese and vanilla until smooth. Pour cheese mixture into crust. Chill in refrigerator until firm. Top, if desired, with sour cream or sliced fresh fruit. About 2 teaspoons honey per serving.

GRAPE JUICE SPONGE

No milk, corn, wheat, or rye

Serves 6

2 packages unflavored gelatin
3 tablespoons cold water
2 cups heated unsweetened
   grape juice

¼ cup honey
1 tablespoon pure lemon juice
3 egg whites, beaten

Soften gelatin in cold water. Dissolve in heated grape juice. Add honey and lemon juice and stir well.

Chill until partly set. Fold in beaten egg whites and mix thoroughly. Refrigerate. Serve with Whipped Topping* or just plain. About 2 teaspoons honey per serving.

PINEAPPLE FLUFF

No corn, wheat, rye, or salicylates

Serves 6

1 envelope unflavored gelatin
¼ cup cold water
3 eggs, separated
1 teaspoon pure lemon or
   pure orange extract
2 tablespoons pure lemon
   juice or pure unsweet-
   ened orange juice

2 tablespoons honey
½ teaspoon salt
⅔ cup drained unsweetened
   crushed canned pine-
   apple
½ cup pure whipping cream

Soften gelatin in cold water. In the top of a double boiler, beat egg yolks. Add lemon or orange extract, lemon or orange juice, honey, and salt. Cook over boiling water, stirring constantly until mixture thickens and coats spoon. Remove from heat. Add softened gelatin. Stir until dissolved. Add pineapple and refrigerate until mixture begins to thicken. Whip cream. Beat egg whites until stiff. Fold each into pineapple mixture. Refrigerate in a covered container or pour into a 2-quart mold and chill. Or pour into your favorite piecrust. Chill. About 1 teaspoon honey per serving.

LEMON DELIGHT DESSERT

No corn, wheat, rye, or salicylates

Serves 4 to 6

1 envelope unflavored gelatin   ½ teaspoon salt
⅓ cup water   ¼ cup honey
3 eggs, separated   ⅓ cup sour cream
⅓ cup pure lemon juice

Soften gelatin in water. In top of double boiler mix egg yolks, lemon juice, salt, honey, and gelatin. Cook over simmering water, stirring constantly. When mixture begins to coat spoon remove from stove. Chill until mixture starts to thicken. Stir in sour cream. In a small bowl beat egg whites until they begin to hold their shape. Continue to beat until egg whites become stiff but not dry. Fold egg whites into lemon mixture. Spoon into individual dishes or large bowl and refrigerate. About 1 tablespoon honey per serving.

PLAIN YOGURT

No egg, corn, wheat, rye, citrus, or salicylates

Makes 1 quart

2 cups milk
1⅓ cups non-instant or instant dry milk powder
2 cups water
3 tablespoons plain yogurt (must contain live culture)

In a 2-quart saucepan combine milk, milk powder, and water. Mix well and bring just to a boil over medium heat, stirring occasionally to prevent sticking.

Cool to room temperature. Add small amount of cooled milk to yogurt and stir until smooth. Add this to remaining milk mixture and stir well.

Pour into yogurt-maker cups and set on base. Leave for 5 to 7 hours or until thickened (pudding texture). Refrigerate.

This yogurt is much tastier than commercial varieties. Add fruit if desired.

Some milk-sensitive individuals can tolerate a little yogurt even if they can't drink milk.

PINEAPPLE YOGURT

No egg, corn, wheat, rye, citrus, or salicylates

Serves 2

1 cup Plain Yogurt*
½ cup well-drained unsweetened crushed canned pineapple
½ teaspoon pure vanilla extract

Combine ingredients and serve.

VANILLA YOGURT

No egg, corn, wheat, rye, citrus, or salicylates

Serves 2

1 cup Plain Yogurt*
1 teaspoon pure vanilla extract
1 teaspoon honey

Combine ingredients and serve. About ½ teaspoon honey per serving.

CHAPTER SIXTEEN

SNACKS AND BEVERAGES

Snacks and beverages should be as nutritious as possible. Some easily prepared, nutritious snacks are cheese on whole grain crackers, raw vegetables or fruits with a dip, cottage cheese, a cold piece of meat, nuts, seeds, popcorn, nut butters on celery, and so forth. If you have time, homemade pizza, cookies, and quick breads made with nutritious ingredients are tasty and filling.

Cookies

CAROB COOKIES

No milk, egg, corn, rye, citrus, or salicylates

Makes about 3 dozen cookies

½ cup uncolored butter or allowed margarine, softened
⅓ cup honey
¼ cup water
2 tablespoons toasted wheat germ
1 cup unbleached flour

¼ cup carob powder
1 teaspoon baking powder
¼ teaspoon baking soda
¼ teaspoon salt
1½ teaspoons pure vanilla extract
½ cup chopped walnuts or pecans

Oven 400°

Cream together shortening and honey. Mix in water. Combine dry ingredients except nuts and add to creamed mixture, mixing thoroughly. Add vanilla and nuts and stir well. Drop by teaspoonfuls onto a greased cookie sheet. Bake 8 to 10 minutes. Remove from cookie sheet and let cool. About ½ teaspoon honey per cookie.

CARROT-RAISIN COOKIES

No milk, egg, corn, rye, or citrus

Makes 5 dozen cookies

1 cup whole wheat flour or
    oat flour
2 cups rolled oats
½ cup wheat germ
    (optional)
1½ teaspoons baking powder
1 teaspoon salt
¾ cup honey
½ cup uncolored butter or
    allowed margarine,
    softened

2 eggs or an extra teaspoon
    baking powder plus ¼
    cup water
1½ cups packed finely grated
    carrots
1 cup raisins
½ cup chopped walnuts or
    pecans

Oven 350°

Combine all ingredients thoroughly in a large bowl. Drop by teaspoonfuls onto an ungreased cookie sheet and bake 12 minutes or until slightly browned. Remove from cookie sheet immediately and let cool. Store in an airtight container. About ½ teaspoon honey per cookie.

FRUIT DROP COOKIES

No milk, egg, corn, rye, citrus, or salicylates

Makes 3½ dozen cookies

½ cup uncolored butter or allowed margarine
½ cup honey
2 eggs, slightly beaten, or equivalent egg replacer
1 cup chopped dates
1 cup coarsely grated apples or pears
1 cup rolled oats
½ cup chopped nuts

1½ cups whole wheat flour
¼ cup toasted wheat germ
½ teaspoon cinnamon
½ teaspoon baking powder
¼ teaspoon salt
3 tablespoons water or unsweetened fruit juice (apple, pineapple, or pear)

Oven 350°

Cream shortening and honey. Add eggs or egg replacer and mix thoroughly. Stir in rest of ingredients. Drop by teaspoonfuls onto a greased cookie sheet. Bake for 15 minutes until lightly browned. Remove from cookie sheet immediately and cool thoroughly before storing. About ½ teaspoon honey per cookie.

GINGER COOKIES

No milk, egg, corn, rye, citrus, or salicylates

Makes about 3 dozen cookies

¾ cup pure allowed vegetable oil or uncolored butter or allowed margarine, softened
½ cup pure maple syrup
1¾ cups unbleached flour

¼ cup toasted wheat germ
2 teaspoons baking soda
½ teaspoon salt
½ teaspoon cinnamon
2 teaspoons ginger

Oven 350°

In a large bowl cream together shortening and maple syrup. In a small bowl mix flour, wheat germ, soda, salt, cinnamon, and ginger. Combine contents of both bowls and stir well. Drop by teaspoonfuls onto ungreased cookie sheet 3 inches apart. Flatten each ball with a fork or the palm of your hand. Bake for about 15 minutes. Remove from cookie sheet and let cool. About ⅔ teaspoon maple syrup per cookie.

LEMON AND DATE MACAROONS

No milk, corn, wheat, rye, or salicylates

Makes 5 dozen cookies

1 cup uncolored butter or allowed margarine, softened
¾ cup honey
2 eggs
¼ cup pure lemon juice
¾ cup chopped dates

½ cup chopped nuts
1 cup sifted unbleached flour or rice flour or oat flour
½ teaspoon salt
1 teaspoon baking soda
3 cups rolled oats

Oven 350°

Cream shortening and honey together. Mix in eggs and lemon juice. Beat thoroughly. Stir in dates and nuts. Add flour, salt, and soda. Mix well. Add oats and mix thoroughly. Measure level tablespoons of dough and put on well-greased cookie sheet. Press mounds flat. Bake for 12 to 15 minutes. Remove from cookie sheet and let cool. About ½ teaspoon honey per cookie.

OATMEAL COOKIES

No milk, egg, corn, wheat, rye, citrus, or salicylates

Makes about 40 cookies

¾ cup uncolored butter or allowed margarine, softened
½ cup honey
1 egg (optional)
¼ cup milk or water
1 teaspoon pure vanilla extract or 1 teaspoon pure orange extract and 1 teaspoon grated un-

colored unwaxed orange rind
1 cup unbleached flour or oat flour
1 teaspoon salt
½ teaspoon baking soda
3 cups rolled oats
½ cup raisins, chopped nuts, or unsweetened flaked coconut (optional)

Oven 350°

Cream together shortening and honey. Beat in egg and liquid. Add vanilla or orange extract and rind. Mix in flour, salt, and baking soda. Work in oats. Add raisins, nuts, or coconut, if desired. Drop from teaspoon onto a greased (and floured if making recipe without egg) cookie sheet. Bake for about 12 minutes or until cookies are lightly browned. Let cookies cool on cookie sheet for 1 minute. Remove and let cookies cool completely. About ½ teaspoon honey per cookie.

PEANUT BUTTER COOKIES

No milk, egg, corn, rye, citrus, or salicylates

Makes 3½ dozen cookies

½ cup pure maple syrup or honey

½ cup pure allowed vegetable oil or uncolored butter or allowed margarine, softened

1 teaspoon pure vanilla extract

1 cup additive-free peanut butter

1½ cups unbleached flour

¼ cup toasted wheat germ

¼ teaspoon salt

½ teaspoon baking soda

½ teaspoon baking powder

Oven 375°

In a large bowl combine maple syrup, shortening, and vanilla. Beat until well mixed. Add peanut butter and beat together. In a small bowl mix together flour, wheat germ, salt, soda, and baking powder. Combine contents of both bowls and mix well. Drop dough from teaspoon onto ungreased cookie sheet and press flat with a fork. Bake for about 15 minutes. Remove from cookie sheet and let cool completely. About ½ teaspoon maple syrup or honey per cookie.

PINEAPPLE DROP COOKIES

No milk, egg, corn, rye, citrus, or salicylates

Makes 5 dozen cookies

1 cup uncolored butter or
    allowed margarine,
    softened
¾ cup pure maple syrup or
    honey
2 cups slightly drained
    unsweetened crushed
    canned pineapple
2 teaspoons baking powder

½ teaspoon baking soda
2 cups unbleached flour and
    2 cups whole wheat flour
2 tablespoons toasted wheat
    germ
1 teaspoon salt
1½ teaspoons pure vanilla
    extract

Oven 400°

Cream shortening and honey or maple syrup. Add pineapple.
Mix well. Add dry ingredients to creamed mixture. Blend in vanilla. Drop by teaspoonfuls onto greased cookie sheet. Bake for 8
to 10 minutes. Remove from cookie sheet. Let cool completely.
About ¾ teaspoon maple syrup or honey per cookie.

PUMPKIN COOKIES

No milk, egg, corn, wheat, rye, citrus, or salicylates

Makes 3½ dozen

1½ cups whole wheat flour
    or rye flour
½ teaspoon baking powder
½ teaspoon baking soda
¼ teaspoon cinnamon
¼ teaspoon nutmeg
1 teaspoon salt
½ cup uncolored butter or
    allowed margarine,
    softened

⅓ cup pure maple syrup
1 egg or equivalent egg
    replacer
½ cup pure unsweetened
    apple juice
1 teaspoon pure vanilla
    extract
1 cup canned pumpkin
1 cup chopped nuts

Oven 350°

Blend together all dry ingredients except nuts and set aside.

Cream together shortening and maple syrup. Add egg or egg replacer, apple juice, vanilla, and pumpkin. Stir in dry ingredients and then chopped nuts. Drop by teaspoonfuls onto ungreased cookie sheet and bake 15 minutes. Remove from cookie sheet and let cool completely. About ½ teaspoon maple syrup per cookie.

REFRIGERATOR COOKIES

No milk, egg, corn, rye, citrus, or salicylates

Makes 4 dozen cookies

1 cup pure allowed vegetable oil or uncolored butter or allowed margarine, softened

¾ cup pure maple syrup or honey

2 teaspoons pure vanilla extract

½ cup toasted wheat germ

2 cups unbleached flour

1 cup whole wheat flour

2 teaspoons baking powder

1 teaspoon salt

1 teaspoon baking soda

1 cup chopped nuts (optional)

Oven 400°

In a large bowl cream together shortening and maple syrup or honey. Stir in vanilla. In another bowl combine dry ingredients except nuts. Combine contents of both bowls and then add nuts. Dough will be very firm. Wrap in waxed paper and chill 4 hours or overnight. When ready to bake, shape dough into walnut-size balls and place on greased cookie sheet. Flatten each ball with a fork. If the edges crumble, press together.

Or chilled dough may be rolled on a lightly floured surface till ¼ inch thick and cut into desired shapes. Cookies may be decorated with nuts, dried fruits, raisins, or seeds. Bake for 8 to 10 minutes. About ¾ teaspoon honey or maple syrup per cookie.

VANILLA COOKIES

No milk, egg, corn, rye, citrus, or salicylates

Makes 2½ dozen cookies

1 egg or ½ teaspoon extra baking powder and 2 tablespoons water
½ cup uncolored butter or allowed margarine, softened
⅓ cup pure maple syrup or honey
1 teaspoon pure vanilla extract

2 tablespoons toasted wheat germ
1 cup unbleached flour
½ teaspoon salt
1 teaspoon baking powder
½ cup finely chopped nuts
Unsweetened shredded coconut

Oven 350°

In a large bowl cream together egg or extra baking powder and water, shortening, and maple syrup or honey. Add vanilla and mix well. Stir together the dry ingredients except nuts and gradually add to batter. Stir in nuts. Drop by teaspoonfuls onto greased cookie sheet or into a bowl of coconut. Then place ball on cookie sheet. Space about 2 inches apart. Bake for 12 to 15 minutes. Remove from cookie sheet and cool on wire rack. About ½ teaspoon maple syrup or honey per cookie.

Crackers

CHEESE WAFERS

No egg, corn, rye, citrus, or salicylates

Makes 50 wafers

½ cup uncolored butter or allowed margarine, softened
2 cups shredded uncolored natural Colby or uncolored sharp cheese

1 cup unbleached flour
1 teaspoon salt
1 teaspoon onion powder (optional)
⅛ teaspoon pepper

Oven 350°

Cream shortening and cheese together until well blended. Add remaining ingredients and beat well. Work mixture with your hands and form into 2 logs about 1½ inches in diameter. Wrap and chill till firm. Using a sharp knife, cut into ⅛-inch slices. Place on ungreased cookie sheet and bake for 12 minutes.

Before baking, crackers may be garnished with nut halves, sesame seeds, herbs, Parmesan cheese, and so forth.

COTTAGE CHEESE CRACKERS

No egg, corn, wheat, rye, citrus, or salicylates

Makes about 2 dozen
2-inch crackers

1⅛ cups rice flour or 1½ cups unbleached flour
¾ teaspoon salt
½ cup uncolored butter or allowed margarine, softened
½ cup additive-free cottage cheese

Oven 450°

In a large bowl mix flour and salt. Add softened shortening and cottage cheese. Cut in with pastry blender until well blended. Wrap dough in waxed paper and refrigerate for at least 1 hour.

On a well-floured board roll out dough ⅛-inch thick. Cut out crackers with a 2-inch cookie cutter and place on ungreased baking sheet. Prick each cracker with a fork.

Bake for 12 to 15 minutes until lightly browned. Remove from baking sheet and cool on a rack.

For a more flavorful cracker, Parmesan cheese may be sprinkled on crackers before baking.

GRAHAM CRACKERS

No milk, egg, corn, rye, citrus, or salicylates

Makes 28 1½-inch
squares

1 cup graham flour or whole
   wheat flour
1 cup unbleached flour
1 teaspoon salt
½ teaspoon cinnamon
   (optional)

1 teaspoon baking powder
¼ cup uncolored butter or
   allowed margarine
⅓ cup honey
¼ cup water or milk

Oven 400°

Mix together dry ingredients. Cut in shortening. Add honey and water or milk. Mix well. Roll dough out between two pieces of waxed paper to ¼-inch thickness. Cut into 1½-inch squares. Prick with a fork. Bake on an ungreased cookie sheet in the upper one third of the oven until golden brown, about 15 to 18 minutes. Watch crackers carefully to be sure bottoms don't burn. About ½ teaspoon honey per cracker.

OATMEAL CRACKERS

No milk, egg, corn, wheat, rye, citrus, or salicylates

Makes 1 to 1½ dozen crackers

1 cup oat flour
½ teaspoon salt
¼ teaspoon baking soda
4 tablespoons cold water

2 tablespoons pure allowed
   vegetable oil
1 tablespoon cold water (if
   needed)

Oven 375°

In a small bowl combine flour, salt, and baking soda. Add water and oil and mix well. Add 1 tablespoon more of cold water if needed to make a soft dough. Shape into a ball. Roll dough as thin as possible on a board sprinkled with oat flour. Cut with a cookie cutter or cut into rectangles with a sharp knife. Place on a

lightly greased cookie sheet. Bake for 3 minutes, turn once and bake 3 minutes longer or until lightly brown and crisp.
Nutritious served with peanut butter for breakfast.

Others

CHEESY POPCORN

No egg, wheat, rye, citrus, or salicylates

Makes about 2 quarts popcorn

¼ cup pure allowed vegetable oil
⅓ cup corn for popping
3 tablespoons uncolored butter or allowed margarine

2 tablespoons grated Parmesan cheese
⅛ teaspoon onion or garlic salt (optional)
Salt to taste

Heat oil in 2½-quart saucepan until one corn kernel dropped in pops. Add corn. Cover and shake until corn stops popping. Remove from heat.

In a small saucepan melt shortening. Stir in grated cheese and onion or garlic salt. Pour over hot popcorn. Mix popcorn lightly. Add additional salt to taste.

CORN CHIPS

No milk, egg, wheat, rye, citrus, or salicylates

Makes 96 corn chips

12 all-corn tortillas
Pure allowed vegetable oil
Salt

Cut each tortilla into eighths. Heat about 1 inch of oil in skillet to 375°. Fry just a few pieces at a time, turning occasionally until crisp and lightly browned. Drain on paper towel. Sprinkle lightly with salt.

POTATO CHIPS

No milk, egg, corn, wheat, rye, citrus, or salicylates

Baking potatoes
Cold water
Pure allowed vegetable oil
Salt

Peel as many potatoes as desired. Cut paper-thin rounds from the potatoes using a potato peeler. Drop the slices into cold water. When all the potatoes have been cut up, drain off the water and rinse twice with fresh cold water. Spread out onto paper towels and pat the tops dry with additional towels.

In a skillet or saucepan heat oil (at least 1½ to 2 inches deep) to 370°. Drop the potato slices into the oil, making sure the slices do not overlap and are not too crowded. Fry for about 30 seconds or until lightly browned. Quickly remove from the oil with a fork or slotted utensil and drain on paper towels. Salt immediately.

These taste exactly like commercial potato chips and do not require a lot of work. Be careful when you are frying them as they will overcook very quickly and have a burned flavor.

PRETZELS I

No milk, egg, corn, rye, citrus, or salicylates

Makes about 36 4-inch pretzels

1 package dry yeast or 1 cake compressed yeast	2½ to 3 cups unbleached flour
1 teaspoon pure maple syrup or honey (optional)	6 cups boiling water
1¼ cups warm water	2 tablespoons baking soda
1 tablespoon salt	Salt (either regular table or coarse salt)
½ cup toasted wheat germ	

Oven 475°

Dissolve yeast and maple syrup or honey in warm water. Set in a warm place until bubbly. Add salt. Gradually stir in wheat germ and enough flour until dough is stiff. Place on a floured surface and knead for about 5 minutes or until dough is smooth and elastic. Place in a greased bowl, turning dough once to coat the top. Cover and set in a warm place until double in bulk, about 1 hour. Punch down. Rolling pieces of dough between your hands to about the thickness of a pencil, form sticks or pretzel shapes. Drop several pretzels at a time into boiling water to which soda has been added. When pretzels float to the top, continue boiling for about 30 to 60 seconds. Drain with a slotted spoon and place on well-greased cookie sheet. Sprinkle well with salt. Bake for about 12 minutes (depending on thickness) or until golden brown. Pretzels will be chewy. May be served with butter and eaten like a bread stick. Store in covered container.

PRETZELS II

No milk, corn, rye, citrus, or salicylates

Makes 24 pretzels

½ recipe White Bread* dough (enough for 1 loaf)
1 egg yolk
1 tablespoon milk or water
Salt (either regular table or coarse salt)

Oven 375°

Allow white bread dough to rise once and then firmly punch down. Cut off walnut-sized pieces of dough and roll on a board with the palms of your hands into thin long round strips about ¼ inch in diameter and 14 to 16 inches long. Twist into pretzel shapes and place on a greased cookie sheet. Do *not* allow to rise. Combine the egg yolk and milk or water and brush tops of pretzels with this mixture. Place in the middle of a preheated oven for 15 minutes until golden brown. Remove from oven and immediately brush again with egg yolk mixture and sprinkle with salt. Allow to cool and store.

PRETZELS III

No milk, corn, wheat, citrus, or salicylates

Makes 24 pretzels

All-Rye Bread* recipe
1 egg yolk
1 tablespoon milk or water
Salt (either regular table or coarse salt)

Follow directions in Pretzels II recipe.

GELATIN SNACKS

No milk, egg, corn, wheat, rye, citrus, or salicylates

Makes 16 snacks

3 envelopes unflavored gelatin
½ cup cold water
1½ cups unsweetened allowed fruit juice (for example, grape, orange, pineapple, see note below)

Sprinkle gelatin over cold water. Heat juice over low heat. Add gelatin, stirring constantly until well dissolved.

Pour into a 9-inch square pan, so that the depth of the liquid is about ½ inch. Chill thoroughly.

Cut out desired shapes with metal cookie cutters, pressing down firmly on the gelatin. Shapes may be decorated with a little icing or left plain. Refrigerate.

Note: Lemon juice, papaya juice, lime, unsweetened grapefruit juice, and unsweetened cranberry juice may also be used but will probably need some honey or may be mixed with one of the naturally sweeter fruit juices. The Lemonade* recipe may be used.

ICE CREAM CONES

No milk, corn, rye, citrus, or salicylates

Makes 1 dozen small cones

½ cup uncolored butter or
   allowed margarine
⅜ cup pure maple syrup
2 eggs, beaten
⅛ teaspoon salt

¼ teaspoon pure vanilla
   extract
½ cup unbleached flour
1 tablespoon toasted wheat
   germ
2 tablespoons water

Melt shortening. Set aside until cool. Gradually beat maple
syrup into beaten eggs. Add shortening, salt, vanilla, flour, and
wheat germ and mix thoroughly. Thin batter with water.

Batter may be cooked on a waffle iron preset on medium heat
or on a greased griddle. Spread 2 tablespoons batter thin. Cook 1
to 2 minutes until golden brown on both sides. Or drop 2 tablespoons batter onto a greased and floured cookie sheet, spreading
the batter thin until a 5-inch circle is formed. Bake at 300° for 10
to 12 minutes or until golden brown.

After batter has been cooked, remove from waffle iron, griddle,
or baking sheet and immediately shape into cones. Secure pointed
end of cone with toothpicks until cool. Remove toothpicks. Store
unused cones well wrapped in the refrigerator until needed.

ICE CREAM SANDWICHES

No egg, corn, rye, citrus, or salicylates

Makes 9 squares

2½ cups crumbs Graham
   Crackers*
¾ cup uncolored butter or
   allowed margarine,
   melted

2 tablespoons honey
1½ teaspoons cinnamon
   (optional)
1 quart allowed ice cream

Mix cracker crumbs with shortening, honey, and cinnamon.
Press half the mixture in the bottom of a well-greased 8x8-inch

cake pan. Place in freezer. Chill the remaining crumbs. Soften ice cream. Spread over bottom layer of crumbs until about ½-inch thick. Sprinkle remaining crumbs on top and press them lightly into the soft ice cream. Freeze until firm. To unmold, place pan in hot water. Unmold onto a large piece of foil. Cut immediately into squares. Wrap in foil and return to freezer.

PEANUT BUTTER POPSICLES

No egg, corn, wheat, rye, or citrus

Makes 12 small popsicles

1 cup boiling water
1 envelope unflavored gelatin
2 tablespoons carob powder
¼ cup pure maple syrup or
    honey

1 cup additive-free peanut
    butter
1 cup milk

In a medium-sized bowl, pour boiling water over gelatin and carob powder. Stir until dissolved. Add maple syrup or honey. Using an electric mixer or blender beat in peanut butter until smooth. Add milk and beat until well blended. Pour into 12 3-ounce paper cups. Place in freezer until partially frozen. Insert plastic spoons or ice cream sticks and freeze until firm. One teaspoon sweetener per popsicle.

POPSICLES

No milk, egg, corn, wheat, rye, citrus, or salicylates

Makes 12 popsicles

24 ounces unsweetened allowed fruit juice (for example, orange, grape, pineapple, see note below)
12 3-ounce paper cups
12 plastic spoons

Pour juice into paper cups. Place a spoon in each cup. Freeze until hard, about 12 hours. To remove popsicles, run hot water over the outside of the cup. Spoon serves as a handle and may be reused.

Note: Lemon juice, papaya juice, lime, unsweetened grapefruit juice, and unsweetened cranberry juice may also be used but will probably need some honey or may be mixed with one of the naturally sweeter fruit juices. The Lemonade* recipe may be used.

LEMON YOGURT POPSICLES

No egg, corn, wheat, rye, or salicylates

Makes 4 popsicles

1 cup Plain Yogurt*
2 tablespoons pure lemon juice
2 teaspoons honey
1 teaspoon grated unwaxed uncolored lemon rind (optional)
4 3-ounce paper cups
4 plastic spoons

Combine ingredients. Pour into paper cups. Insert a plastic spoon for a handle in each. Freeze until firm. Unmold from cup. About ½ teaspoon honey per popsicle.

ORANGE YOGURT POPSICLES

No egg, corn, wheat, or rye

Makes 6 popsicles

1 cup Plain Yogurt*
½ cup pure unsweetened frozen (thawed) orange juice concentrate
1 teaspoon pure vanilla extract
6 3-ounce paper cups
6 plastic spoons

Combine ingredients. Pour into paper cups. Insert a plastic spoon for a handle in each. Freeze until firm. Unmold from cup.

SNOW CONES

No milk, egg, corn, wheat, rye, citrus, or salicylates

Unsweetened allowed fruit juices (pineapple, grape, orange, grapefruit, etc.)

Pour allowed fruit juice into an ice cube tray. Freeze. Remove frozen cubes from tray and store in freezer container or plastic bag in the freezer. Remove frozen cubes as needed and place several at a time in blender. Grind into small chips. Serve immediately.

TOASTED SEEDS

No milk, egg, corn, wheat, rye, citrus, or salicylates

Makes ½ cup seeds

½ cup seeds from watermelon, cantaloupe, or pumpkin
1 teaspoon pure allowed vegetable oil
Salt or onion salt

Oven 350°

Separate seeds from pulp. Wash well. May be stored in a covered container in the refrigerator for several days while collecting more seeds. Wash all seeds again. Drain well. Mix with oil and several dashes of salt or onion salt. Spread on cookie sheet. Toast in oven 10 to 15 minutes or until lightly browned, turning seeds every 5 minutes to prevent scorching.

FRUIT FRITTERS

No milk, egg, corn, wheat, rye, citrus, or salicylates

Makes 2 cups batter

1 cup unbleached flour or
   rice flour
2 tablespoons toasted wheat
   germ (optional)
1½ teaspoons baking powder
¼ teaspoon salt
2 tablespoons honey
1 egg or equivalent egg
   replacer

½ cup unsweetened fruit
   juice (apple, pineapple,
   pear, or peach)
Pure allowed vegetable oil
Sliced pineapple (if canned,
   drain thoroughly and pat
   dry)
Peeled and sliced peaches
Peeled, cored, and sliced
   apples

Combine dry ingredients. Add honey and egg or egg replacer. Mix thoroughly. Add juice until you get a fairly thin batter, using more if necessary. Dip fruit slices into batter until thoroughly coated and drop into hot oil. Fry in 3 inches of oil at 370° until lightly browned on one side. Turn and continue to cook until other side is browned. Remove from oil and drain on paper towels. Serve warm.

FRUIT LEATHER

No milk, egg, corn, wheat, rye, citrus, or salicylates

Makes 6 squares

Oven 170°

These snacks can be made from any number of fruits—apples, peaches, pears, plums, apricots, or nectarines. You can even try mixtures of any of these to produce different flavors. Try to pick ripe, sweet-tasting fruits so no sweetener is even necessary.

Wash thoroughly and core or pit as necessary 5 or 6 large pieces of fruit. There is no need to peel but cut off any bruises or blemishes. Cut into chunks and put into a blender. Put onto high speed and blend until smooth, adding more pieces until you have approximately 2 cups puréed fruit. Lightly grease an 11x17-inch jelly roll pan. Pour fruit onto the pan and spread evenly. Put into the oven and leave the door slightly ajar to let moisture escape. Leave in the oven until the fruit has dried evenly all over and can be lifted from the pan. Turn out onto a board and cut into 5- to 6-inch squares. These can be rolled into sticks or stacked with sheets of plastic wrap in between each square. Store in an airtight container.

These are excellent as snacks and keep for several days or weeks. They are high in natural fruit sugars so use sparingly.

FRUIT SNACKS

No milk, egg, corn, wheat, rye, or citrus

Makes 25 snacks

1 cup chopped dried apricots
1 cup raisins or currants
½ cup finely chopped nuts (pecans, walnuts, or almonds)
½ cup toasted wheat germ or ground nuts
1 cup shredded unsweetened coconut
¼ cup honey

Mix all ingredients together. Form into balls, adding more honey if necessary to make the balls keep their shape. Store in covered container to keep moist. About ½ teaspoon honey per snack.

STUFFED DATES

No milk, egg, corn, wheat, rye, citrus, or salicylates

Slit dates lengthwise. Insert part of a walnut or a whole nut if dates are large. Or fill date with cream cheese. Keep in covered container in refrigerator.

RICE CAKE SNACKS

No milk, egg, corn, wheat, rye, citrus, or salicylates

Rice cakes (purchased at health foods stores)

Oven 350°

Spread each cake with uncolored butter or allowed margarine. Sprinkle with one of the following: onion salt, celery salt, or grated Parmesan cheese. Place on a flat pan. Heat for 2 or 3 minutes.

Or the rice cakes may be spread with uncolored butter or allowed margarine and heated for 2 or 3 minutes in oven. Spread with peanut butter and serve warm.

ZUCCHINI SNACK SQUARES

No milk, corn, wheat, rye, citrus, or salicylates

Makes 24 squares

3 cups thinly sliced zucchini, peeled if waxed
¾ cup potato starch flour *or* 1 cup unbleached flour
1½ teaspoons baking powder
1 teaspoon salt
2 tablespoons instant minced onion
1 tablespoon dried parsley flakes
½ teaspoon dried oregano
Dash of pepper
1 clove garlic, finely chopped
½ cup pure allowed vegetable oil
4 eggs, slightly beaten
½ cup grated Parmesan cheese (optional)

Oven 350°

Combine all ingredients. Pour into a greased 11½x8x2-inch pan. Bake until golden brown, about 40 minutes. Cut into squares. Serve warm. Reheat leftovers or serve cold.

PIZZA CRUST

No milk, egg, corn, rye, citrus, or salicylates

Makes 2 12-inch crusts
or 3 9-inch crusts

1 package dry yeast or 1 cake compressed yeast
1½ cups warm water
3 to 3½ cups unbleached flour *or* 2 cups whole

wheat flour and 1 to 1½ cups unbleached flour
1 teaspoon salt
1 tablespoon pure allowed vegetable oil

Dissolve yeast in warm water. Stir in about half the flour. Add salt. Beat well with an electric mixer for several minutes. Add oil. Work in enough remaining flour until dough is no longer sticky. On a floured surface, knead dough for 5 to 8 minutes.

Place in a lightly greased bowl, turning dough to coat the top. Cover with a damp cloth and let rise in a warm place until double in bulk, about 1 hour. Punch down. Divide dough into desired number of pieces. Roll each piece into a circle. Place on oiled pizza pans or in cake pans. Turn up the edges. Fill and proceed as in desired pizza recipe.

Dough may be made earlier in the day. Place in refrigerator where it will slowly rise. If it hasn't doubled in bulk, remove from refrigerator and let continue to rise in a warm place.

TOMATO OR PESTO PIZZA

No milk, egg, corn, rye, citrus, or salicylates

Makes 2 12-inch pizzas

1 recipe Pizza Crust*
1 recipe Pesto Sauce* *or* 2 cups Tomato Spaghetti Sauce* *or* 2 cups Tomatoless Spaghetti Sauce*
½ pound ground beef or Italian Sausage*
8 ounces mozzarella cheese, shredded

Oven 350°

Prepare pizza crust. Prepare pesto or spaghetti sauce. Brown ground beef or sausage in a heavy skillet. Drain off excess grease. Add sauce and heat through. Spread sauce over pizza crust and top with mozzarella cheese. Bake for 20 to 25 minutes until crust is lightly browned.

PEANUT BUTTER LOG

No milk, egg, corn, wheat, rye, or citrus

Makes 2 8-inch logs

1 cup additive-free peanut butter

½ cup rolled oats *or* 1 cup toasted wheat germ

½ cup raisins or currants

½ cup finely chopped dates

1 cup finely chopped nuts

Combine first four ingredients thoroughly. Form into 2 logs 1½ inches in diameter. Roll in chopped nuts, pressing nuts into roll until completely covered. Roll each in waxed paper and refrigerate for 2 to 3 hours. Cut into slices with a sharp knife. These can also be made into small individual balls.

CHEESE BALL I

No egg, corn, wheat, rye, citrus, or salicylates

Makes 1 13-ounce ball

1 8-ounce package cream cheese, softened

5 ounces uncolored sharp cheese, grated

Garlic salt

Dried parsley flakes

Chopped walnuts, pecans, or peanuts

Mix thoroughly cream cheese and sharp cheese with pastry blender or with hands until cheeses are completely blended. Sprinkle garlic salt over the cheese mass and blend it in, using either a pastry blender or your hands. Continue adding garlic salt until desired taste is reached.

Shape cheese into a ball and roll in parsley and chopped nuts until well coated. Refrigerate until serving time. Spread on crackers, bread, or vegetables.

CHEESE BALL II

No egg, corn, wheat, rye, citrus, or salicylates

Makes 1 14-ounce ball

1 8-ounce package cream
  cheese, softened
2 ounces Roquefort cheese
4 ounces uncolored sharp
  cheese, grated
1 teaspoon additive-free soy
  sauce

1 teaspoon instant minced
  onion
2 tablespoons milk
Dried parsley flakes
Chopped nuts

Blend cheeses, soy sauce, onion, and milk together, using your hands. Form into a ball or log and roll in parsley flakes and nuts. Serve with vegetables, crackers, or Potato Chips.*

TOFU CHEESE SPREAD

No milk, egg, corn, wheat, rye, citrus, or salicylates

Makes ¼ cup

4 tablespoons Tofu (soy cheese)
4 tablespoons chopped chives
1 teaspoon salt

Blend ingredients thoroughly. Serve on crackers or spread on celery stalks.

Tofu is a pure soybean product rich in protein found in the produce department of most supermarkets.

CELERY STUFFERS

No milk, egg, corn, wheat, rye, citrus, or salicylates

Use one of the following to fill crisp celery ribs:

Peanut butter
Cottage cheese
Cream cheese or Cream Cheese and Pineapple Spread*
Tuna Salad Sandwich Spread*

Cheese Sandwich Spread*
Peanut Butter Spread*
Tofu Cheese Spread*

Beverages

APPLE LEMONADE

No milk, egg, corn, wheat, or rye

Makes about 2 cups

2 cups pure unsweetened apple juice
4 tablespoons pure lemon juice

Combine juices. Chill. Serve over ice. Contains no added sweetener.

BANANA MILK SHAKE

No corn, wheat, rye, citrus, or salicylates

Makes 2 cups

1 cup milk
1 banana
½ cup Vanilla Ice Cream*

Combine all ingredients in a blender and blend on low speed for 30 to 45 seconds or until smooth. Pour into thermos for lunch box. Shake again before drinking.

CAROB MILK SHAKE

No corn, wheat, rye, citrus, or salicylates

Makes 1½ cups

1 cup milk
½ cup Vanilla Ice Cream*
2 tablespoons Carob Syrup*

Combine milk and ice cream in a blender. Blend at low speed and pour in syrup while mixing. You can add more ice cream to make a thicker shake. Pour into thermos for lunch box. Shake again before drinking.

CRANBERRY JUICE

No milk, egg, corn, wheat, rye, or citrus

Serves 4

1 pound washed fresh or
    frozen (thawed) cran-
    berries
2 cups water
2 to 3 tablespoons honey

2 cloves (optional)
1 tablespoon pure lemon
    juice (optional)
Water

In a large saucepan combine berries and water. Bring to a boil, reduce heat, cover, and simmer until skins burst, about 5 minutes. Strain through cheesecloth. Return juice to pan and bring to a boil. Add honey and cloves and simmer for 2 more minutes. Cool. Add lemon juice if desired. Remove cloves. Add enough water to cranberry juice to make 2 cups liquid. Serve chilled. About 2 teaspoons honey per serving.

CRANAPPLE OR CRANGRAPE JUICE

No milk, egg, corn, wheat, rye, or citrus

Serves 4

2 cups Cranberry Juice*
2 cups unsweetened apple juice or grape juice

Combine desired juices. Serve chilled with ice cubes or hot in mugs.

EGG NOG

No corn, wheat, rye, citrus, or salicylates

Serves 2

    2 cups very cold milk
    2 eggs
    1 tablespoon honey
    ½ teaspoon pure vanilla extract

Combine ingredients and mix well in a blender or with an electric mixer. Serve at once. About 1½ teaspoons honey per serving.

NO-MILK EGG NOG

No milk, corn, wheat, rye, citrus, or salicylates

Serves 2

    2 cups pure unsweetened orange juice or pineapple juice
    1 to 2 eggs
    2 teaspoons pure lemon juice (optional)

Combine ingredients and mix well in a blender or with an electric mixer. Serve over cracked ice.

FRUIT JUICE FIZZ

No milk, egg, corn, wheat, rye, citrus, or salicylates

Serves 2

    4 ounces unsweetened grape juice or pure unsweetened
        orange juice or pineapple juice
    4 ounces soda water

Combine juice and soda water. Serve over ice cubes.
Choose a brand of soda water containing as few additives as possible.

HOT APPLE CIDER

No milk, egg, corn, wheat, rye, or citrus

Serves 2

2 cups unsweetened apple cider or apple juice
2 cloves
1 2-inch stick cinnamon

Heat ingredients in heavy saucepan until hot but not boiling. Let stand for 10 minutes. Remove cloves and cinnamon. Serve in mugs.

HOT CAROB DRINK

No egg, corn, wheat, rye, citrus, or salicylates

Serves 2

2 cups milk
3 tablespoons carob powder
2 teaspoons honey (optional)

Combine all ingredients in a saucepan and stir until well mixed. Heat and continue stirring until carob powder is dissolved and mixture is desired temperature.

LEMONADE

No milk, egg, corn, wheat, rye, or salicylates

Makes 7 8-ounce servings

6 to 8 ounces pure lemon juice
½ cup honey
6 cups cold water
1 uncolored unwaxed lemon, sliced (optional)

In a blender combine lemon juice and honey on high speed. Mix sweetened lemon juice with cold water in a large pitcher. Add lemon slices, if desired. Serve over ice. About 3½ teaspoons honey per 8-ounce serving.

PAPAYA JUICE

No milk, egg, corn, wheat, rye, citrus, or salicylates

Makes 1¾ cups

2 cups sliced, peeled papayas
1 cup unsweetened pineapple juice
1 tablespoon pure lemon juice (optional)
1 cup water

Place papayas in a heavy saucepan with pineapple juice, lemon juice, and water. Bring mixture to a boil. Reduce heat and simmer until papayas are soft. Purée in a blender. Pour through a sieve. Chill juice. Serve over ice or use in Papaya Gelatin* or Papaya Popsicles.*

CHAPTER SEVENTEEN

SWEET TREATS

All commercial candy is out. It's full of artificial colorings, flavorings, and sugar. Don't go overboard in making candy at home, but if your child doesn't seem bothered by honey, maple syrup, or natural fruit sugars you might use some of the candy recipes in this chapter for special occasions. We have tried to make many of these recipes more nutritious than usual by adding non-instant dry milk powder, wheat germ, nutritious fruits, peanut butter, and nuts.

Be *very careful* handling hot maple syrup and honey.

CANDIED NUTS

No milk, egg, corn, wheat, rye, citrus, or salicylates

Makes 2 cups

½ cup pure maple syrup or honey
¼ cup water
1 tablespoon uncolored butter or allowed margarine
1¼ cups whole nuts

Combine maple syrup or honey with water in a small heavy saucepan. Bring to a boil. Cook over medium heat until a bit of syrup dropped into very cold water forms a firm ball when shaped with your fingers. Remove syrup from heat and quickly stir in half the nuts. Drain nuts with slotted spoon and spread onto greased plate. Repeat with remaining nuts. When cool, separate nuts as desired.

This easy-to-make candy offers more protein and less sweeteners than most other candies.

CARAMEL POPCORN

No milk, egg, wheat, rye, citrus, or salicylates

Makes 3 quarts popcorn

2 cups honey
⅓ cup water
¼ cup uncolored butter or allowed margarine
¼ teaspoon salt

½ cup corn for popping
¼ cup pure allowed vegetable oil
1 cup salted additive-free peanuts

Combine in a saucepan honey, water, butter or margarine, and salt. Bring to a boil over medium heat, stirring constantly. Continue to cook, stirring occasionally, until candy reaches 280°.

While caramel is cooking, heat oil in 2½-quart saucepan until one corn kernel dropped in pops. Add corn. Cover and shake until corn stops popping. Remove from heat. Place in a large bowl and mix with peanuts. When caramel is done, quickly pour syrup over popcorn and nuts while stirring briskly until all kernels are covered. Spread on two greased baking sheets and allow to cool. Break into bite-size pieces and store in a tightly covered container.

COCONUT CANDY BARS

No egg, corn, wheat, rye, citrus, or salicylates

Makes 20 bite-sized bars

2 cups unsweetened shredded coconut
½ cup honey
1 tablespoon milk
3 tablespoons non-instant dry milk powder

Combine all ingredients until well mixed. Shape the mixture into small logs about 2 inches long. Chill in refrigerator for 1 hour. Eat as snacks or wrap for holiday candies. Slightly more than 1 teaspoon honey per piece.

CREAMY CANDY

No egg, corn, wheat, rye, citrus, or salicylates

Makes about 1½ dozen balls

1 cup pure maple syrup
¼ teaspoon salt
1 cup pure whipping cream

½ teaspoon pure vanilla extract
1 cup unsweetened shredded coconut (optional)

Combine all ingredients except vanilla in a saucepan. Bring to a boil, stirring constantly. Continue to boil over medium-low heat, stirring frequently, until the temperature reaches soft ball stage (234°). Immediately remove from heat, add vanilla, and allow to cool until thermometer reads 110°. Quickly stir until candy becomes thick. Drop by teaspoonfuls onto waxed paper. To shape, knead gently and roll until the candy forms a neat ball. Let cool or roll in shredded unsweetened coconut while still warm. About 1 tablespoon maple syrup per ball.

MAPLE SUCKERS

No egg, corn, wheat, rye, citrus, or salicylates

Makes 1½ dozen lollipops

Cook Creamy Candy* until hard ball stage (254°). Place lollipop sticks 4 inches apart on greased baking sheet. Pour candy over one end of stick to form a disc. Let cool until firm. About 1 tablespoon maple syrup per lollipop.

HONEY CAROB FUDGE

No milk, egg, corn, wheat, rye, citrus, or salicylates

Makes 24 ounces or
64 pieces

½ cup carob powder
¾ cup milk or water
¾ cup honey
¼ cup uncolored butter or
   allowed margarine
1 teaspoon pure vanilla
   extract

1 cup chopped nuts
¼ cup toasted wheat germ
   (optional)
1½ to 1¾ cups non-instant
   dry milk powder or
   potato starch flour

In a heavy saucepan combine carob, liquid, honey, and shortening. Bring to a rolling boil over medium heat and continue boiling for 2 minutes. Remove from heat and cool. Stir in vanilla, nuts, and wheat germ. Work in milk powder or potato starch flour until candy is thick. Pour into a greased 8-inch square pan. Cover and refrigerate until firm. Cut into pieces. Keep refrigerated. About ½ teaspoon honey per piece.

HONEY VANILLA FUDGE

No milk, egg, corn, wheat, rye, citrus, or salicylates

Makes 10 ounces or 64
1-inch-square pieces

1 cup honey
⅔ cup milk or pure half and
   half cream or Soy Milk*
   or Nut Milk*
¼ cup uncolored butter or
   allowed margarine

1½ teaspoons pure vanilla
   extract
½ cup chopped walnuts or
   pecans or peanuts

Grease sides of heavy saucepan with a little shortening. Combine honey, milk, and shortening in saucepan over medium heat. Stir until honey dissolves and mixture comes to a boil. Reduce heat to low or honey will scorch. Let boil over low heat until soft

ball stage (234°) is reached. This may take an hour or so. Remove from heat. Let stand until temperature reaches 110° or bottom of pan is comfortably warm. Add vanilla. Beat until creamy and thickened. Stir in nuts. Pour into well-greased 8-inch square pan. Refrigerate. When firm, cut into 1-inch-square pieces. About ¾ teaspoon honey per piece.

PEANUT BRITTLE

No milk, egg, corn, wheat, rye, citrus, or salicylates

Makes about 90 1-inch pieces

1⅓ cups pure maple syrup
⅔ cup water
¼ cup uncolored butter or allowed margarine
1 cup shelled peanuts

In a medium saucepan combine maple syrup and water. Cook over medium heat until boiling. Add shortening and continue cooking, stirring frequently. When soft ball stage (234°) is reached, add peanuts. Continue cooking and stirring frequently until hard ball stage (250°) is reached. Pour immediately onto a well-greased cookie sheet, spreading the candy around. When completely cool and candy is hard, loosen and crack into bite-sized pieces. About ⅔ teaspoon maple syrup per piece.

PEANUT BUTTER FUDGE

No milk, egg, corn, wheat, rye, citrus, or salicylates

Makes about 1 pound
or 24 1-inch-square pieces

1 cup pure maple syrup
⅔ cup milk or Soy Milk* or Nut Milk*
¼ teaspoon salt
2 tablespoons uncolored butter or allowed margarine

1 teaspoon pure vanilla extract
½ cup smooth or crunchy additive-free peanut butter
¾ cup chopped walnuts or pecans or peanuts

Combine maple syrup, milk, salt, and shortening in a heavy saucepan. Bring to a boil over medium heat. Cook to soft ball stage (234°), stirring occasionally. Remove from heat. Add vanilla and peanut butter and beat with an electric mixer until fudge begins to stiffen. Fold in nuts. Turn into lightly greased 8½x4½-inch loaf pan. Cool. Cut into pieces. About 4 teaspoons maple syrup per piece.

PINEAPPLE-ORANGE CANDY

No milk, egg, corn, wheat, or rye

Makes 18 pieces

1 uncolored unwaxed orange
1 cup drained crushed unsweetened canned or fresh pineapple
⅜ cup maple syrup or honey

3 tablespoons uncolored butter or allowed margarine
½ cup unsweetened shredded coconut or chopped nuts

Peel orange, saving one half of the peelings. Cut orange in half. Discard seeds. Place orange pieces, peelings, and pineapple in blender. Liquefy fruit. Add maple syrup and mix well. Place in a heavy saucepan. Add shortening. Cook over medium heat until boiling. Reduce heat to low. Continue cooking, stirring frequently, as it thickens. Test for soft ball stage (234°) by dropping small amounts of candy into ice cold water. When candy can be pressed into soft balls, it is done. Remove from heat. Stir in half the coconut or half the nuts. Drop by teaspoonfuls into a bowl of remaining coconut or nuts. Form into balls. Refrigerate until firm. About 1 teaspoon honey or maple syrup per piece.

POPCORN BALLS

No milk, egg, wheat, rye, citrus, or salicylates

Makes 12 to 15 balls

Follow recipe for Caramel Popcorn.* After spreading popcorn on baking sheet, let cool until you can handle it and form into balls using your hands. Butter hands to prevent sticking. Wrap each ball in waxed paper and store. About 1 tablespoon honey per ball.

SWEET POTATO CANDY

No milk, egg, corn, wheat, rye, citrus, or salicylates

Makes 60 balls

1 cup mashed cooked sweet
    potato
¼ teaspoon salt
1 cup flaked unsweetened
    coconut
1½ cups finely chopped nuts
¾ cup finely minced dates
1 teaspoon pure vanilla
    extract

4 teaspoons honey
½ cup potato starch flour *or*
    1½ to 2 cups non-
    instant dry milk powder
Chopped nuts (optional)
Flaked unsweetened coconut
    (optional)

Mix together first seven ingredients. Then mix in either potato starch flour or milk powder, adding a little at a time until candy is stiff. Shape into balls and roll in extra chopped nuts and/or extra coconut. Chill until firm. Balls keep well in the refrigerator.

CHAPTER EIGHTEEN

HOLIDAY AND BIRTHDAY
SUGGESTIONS

If a child has behavior problems, they usually are exaggerated at holiday and party times. Anticipation and excitement coupled with eating foods that are high in sugars, artificial ingredients, and items to which your child is sensitive lead to tears, tantrums, and a trying time for all.

To overcome this holiday trauma you can do several things that will ease the situation. Talk with your child about the coming holiday or party and explain that he won't be able to eat some things that he has in the past. List the foods that he can have, especially the ones that he likes best. If he understands the situation you have a good chance of getting his co-operation.

Providing special food for holidays and birthdays while taking care of diet needs may seem to be an impossible task. For some holidays such as Halloween and Easter, candy and sweets are a main attraction, especially for children. Some rethinking must be done to come up with ideas that still lend a festive holiday feeling but are nutritious and follow dietary needs of family members.

First of all a positive attitude is imperative. If you are the cook in the family, you must be determined to serve attractive, nutritious meals and snacks that everyone can eat. Do this cheerfully so others in the family will come to meals in the right frame of mind. This is especially important at the beginning of the diet, at least until positive results are seen. Remember how much better everyone will feel and behave than before and you will see that it is worth the extra effort.

Second, don't feel that you must have a wide variety of food. A simple menu carefully prepared is far better than a lot of dishes that leave you harried and frustrated. Select the things on the diet your family enjoys the most and take special care when shopping to buy the best quality meats, fruits, and vegetables you can afford. Add garnishes such as parsley or fruit slices to platters of meats or casseroles to make a pleasing appearance. Top cookies or cakes with nuts, raisins, coconut, or dried fruit bits. Vegetables can be served with simple sauces or just lemon juice to give a different taste.

Third, plan menus ahead and do as much preparation beforehand as possible. Don't tackle more than you can handle. A freezer can be used to store cookies, cakes, pies, or even casseroles that you make days or weeks in advance. Ask for helpers in the kitchen. Small children can do things to help and this gives them a good feeling about themselves. If you are having close friends or relatives in for dinner, maybe they would be willing to bring a dish to ease the cooking chores. Pick something they can make that will still be on the diet, like vegetable dishes, relish trays, or tossed salads.

Fourth, don't abandon all your old recipes thinking you can't use them. If you will review holiday menus you have used in the past, you will probably find that many recipes are fine to use as they are. Even if they have forbidden ingredients don't be afraid to try a substitution. One thing we have found working on this book is that recipes are far more flexible than you might imagine. Try an egg replacer in baked items. To replace wheat, a rye, rice, or oat flour may work. Add nutrition to wheat recipes by using whole wheat or add wheat germ to unbleached flour. Milk can be omitted by substituting water or fruit juice if flavoring and sweetening are needed.

Any fruits can usually be substituted by using another fruit. Pears instead of apples, dates instead of raisins, or pineapple instead of oranges or lemons. For extra nutrition try adding chopped fruit or nuts to cakes and cookies. Unsweetened coconut ground to a fine powder in the blender replaces powdered sugar. Honey or pure maple syrup can replace sugar in recipes with minor adjustments. Use the minimum amount of sweetener to reduce your family's taste for sweets and let the natural sweetening come through.

Try these substitutions in your recipes long before the holiday or birthday dinner to give you time to redo them if necessary. Look through the recipes given in this book to give you some ideas as to how we have substituted ingredients in ordinary recipes. Be adventurous.

Fifth, at birthday and holiday times try to keep what your child eats within your control. Offer to bring snacks and treats to parties at your child's school and make things that will keep him on the diet but will be enjoyed by everybody.

Serve holiday dinners at your house as opposed to going out. This way you can be sure that the diet will be continued. If this is not practical, perhaps the hostess will understand your problem and provide some alternative foods for your child or you can offer to bring a dish your child likes and can eat.

If none of these ideas works for you and avoiding forbidden food isn't practical, explain to your child ahead of time that he may eat whatever is served but must return to the diet the following day. As he gets used to the diet and realizes how much better he feels, this will become easier. In fact, you may be surprised by how responsible and careful he will be regarding his own diet.

Here are some holiday suggestions beginning with Thanksgiving and Christmas. You'll have to adapt the menus and recipes to your child's own diet.

At Thanksgiving, a turkey dinner is a must at our house. A typical menu using recipes found in this book could go something like this.

Roast Turkey with Rice Stuffing*
Cranberry Sauce*
Mashed Potatoes with Homemade Gravy or Baked Potatoes
Sweet Potatoes and Apples or Pears*
Spinach Supreme* and/or Lima Beans with Mushrooms*
No-knead Whole Wheat Refrigerator Rolls*
Pumpkin Whip Pie*

This menu may be similar to what you have been serving for years at Thanksgiving at your house. Some things you may have purchased already prepared will have to be made at home now.

The cranberry sauce, rolls, and pie certainly can be made the day before and refrigerated. Even the vegetables can be cooked and then drained and refrigerated until the other ingredients are added the next day.

Don't use instant mashed potatoes, packaged stuffings, or prepared gravies, as these are usually full of additives or questionable ingredients. Mashed potatoes may be mashed with the cooking water instead of milk.

The turkey should not be the self-basting type. Stuff it right before roasting. Once the bird is in the oven this leaves you time to do the vegetables.

Again, don't plan more things than you can manage. Cut the menu down if necessary to what you can handle.

Christmas, being exciting for children, should be special. Cookies and cakes have become a tradition at our house and are used for entertaining and gift-giving. These can also be served at your child's school for their Christmas party. Let the teacher know ahead of time that you are willing to bring the refreshments. Bake a variety of wholesome cookies or use slices of goodies like Fruit Cake* or Date and Nut Bread.* The drinks can be simple—unsweetened fruit juice over ice served with holiday cups and napkins. These things can be eaten and enjoyed and they keep your child on his diet without his even realizing it.

Christmas dinner could be prepared using the following menu:

Pot Roast*
Scalloped Potatoes*
Broccoli Casserole* and/or Baked Acorn Squash*
Tossed Salad with Thousand Island Dressing*
White Bread*
Carrot Cake*

The salad and dressing, bread, and dessert should be prepared well in advance. The roast and potatoes are both to be done in the oven with little or no tending. If you don't have space to cook the vegetables in the oven, prepare buttered beans and/or carrots on the stove. Even though the menu is varied you have a hearty holiday meal for family and guests that can be handled relatively easily.

An open house for friends and neighbors can be a great way to start the new year. Include the children as well as the adults. Homemade cheese balls, nuts, pretzels, Potato Chips,* Cheesy Popcorn,* and raw vegetable trays with dip can be placed around the room. For the children make Egg Nog* and/or fruit juice and for the adults a mulled wine. Serve these in punch bowls and let everyone help himself. Your children can be recruited to watch and refill the food or drinks when necessary. Choose items your child can eat so he feels that he and the other children are a part of the party, yet everything is nutritious and adheres to his diet.

Valentine's Day is another time when you can offer to serve snacks at school. Cupcakes with icing that has been tinted pink or red with a "safe" homemade coloring would be fine. If you are an artist with icing, make a heart outline in red on top of plain white icing. The same thing can be done with iced cookies. A cranberry or fruit drink served in decorated cups will continue the Valentine theme.

Easter is one of the holidays that seem to revolve around candy. As your family gets accustomed to not eating all the commercial candy, you will find more suitable substitutes. One alternative could be to make candylike sweets from the Fruit Snacks* or Coconut Candy Bars* recipes in this book. There are also candy recipes such as Caramel Popcorn* or Creamy Candy,* but these are very high in sugars and we recommend making them only occasionally and in very small batches.

Wrapping these treats in colored cellophane will give them the appearance of commercial candy and satisfy youngsters. Plastic eggs can be bought and filled with coins or tiny inexpensive gifts to replace some candy. Dye hard-cooked eggs using the "safe" colorings in Chapter Six.

For a school party treat, make Easter baskets from school milk cartons. Ask the teacher to save one milk carton for each child. Wash, rinse, and air dry. Cut the top portion off the carton at the crease. Staple a paper handle over the top of the basket and then cover with crepe paper, strips of colorful gift wrap, or construction paper. Fill with Easter basket grass and small candies or treats for each child, using safe items your youngster can eat. This

may seem like a lot of trouble but it really isn't and the children
love them. Remember it's all worth it if your child is doing well on
his diet.

For Easter dinner serve:

Broiled Lamb Chops*
Au Gratin Potatoes*
Asparagus and Egg Casserole* and/or Carrot Ring*
Waldorf Salad*
High Protein Bread*
Vanilla Ice Cream* with Carob Fudge Sauce*

Again do as much preparation as possible ahead of time so you
are not rushed at the last minute. Make the salad, bread, and dessert the day before. The asparagus casserole can be made earlier
and refrigerated; potatoes once in the oven need no watching. The
only last-minute cooking would be for the lamb chops.

Fourth of July is an ideal time for a picnic. For the menu serve:

Grilled Hamburgers on Sandwich Buns*
Relish Tray with Vegetable Dip*
Hot Potato Salad*
Molded Vegetable Salad
Watermelon Fruit Basket

The watermelon fruit basket is made by cutting a whole watermelon in half lengthwise. Scoop out the pulp, remove seeds, and
cut into 1-inch chunks. Cut up a variety of other fruits such as
honeydew melon, strawberries, raspberries, cantaloupe, grapes,
blueberries, sweet cherries, bananas, and pineapple. Just before
the picnic, fill the melon half with the fruit by adding small
amounts of each fruit until filled. This way you won't have to toss
the fruit and possibly bruise it. Chill and serve.

The buns, vegetable salad, and relish tray can be prepared prior
to the picnic. Make the hot potato salad, cover with foil, and refrigerate until time for cooking.

At Halloween, candy is a main attraction. Instead of handing
out the usual "junk food" at trick-or-treat time, give apples, small
boxes of raisins, small bags of popcorn, potato chips, or if you're
really ambitious homemade doughnuts.

If your child wants to go out to trick-or-treat, let him, but ex-

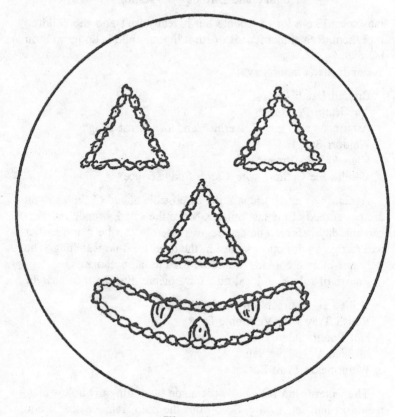

Illustration #1

plain again that he can't eat most of what he gets and make sure
you have plenty of treats on hand that are allowed. Maybe he
would like to trade in his treats for a penny apiece. He probably
only wants to take part in the fun and this sometimes is as important as staying on the diet.

You might have a Halloween party for your child. The menu
could include:

Pumpkin Face Cake
Yeast Doughnuts*
Popcorn, Nuts, or Toasted Seeds*
Hot Apple Cider*
Witches' Brew Punch

Have the guests come in costume. Decorate the room with black and orange streamers and balloons. Paper skeletons and witches, ghosts made from old sheets, Indian corn and corn stalks will complete the decorations. Create a centerpiece by cutting a pumpkin face and place a candle or small light inside.

Serve all the food buffet-style and let everyone help himself. The pumpkin face cake is a double-layer cake with icing colored with carrot juice. Make the face by outlining the eyes, nose, and mouth with raisins or nuts. (Illustration #1) The witches' brew punch is a simple fruit punch mixture of your favorite flavors. Drop small pieces of dry ice into the punch to make it bubble and smoke.

Activities include bobbing for apples, pin the nose on the pumpkin, a treasure hunt, or ghost stories.

Birthday Ideas

Birthdays for children are always looked forward to with much excitement. This sometimes leads to many behavior problems that make these occasions times of frustration and anxiety for the rest of the family.

For a very small child a simple family party would be best. If you wish, invite one or two of his friends to join in the celebration with a treat of allowed ice cream or fruit ice and cake.

As your child gets older and a party with several children seems more in order, try to build it around a special interest. Take some friends from the ball team to a local ball game with ice cream and cake afterward. A luncheon party followed by a trip to the movies could be just right for your youngster.

There are many excursion-type parties you can plan if you do a little exploring. Zoos, airports, or TV stations sometimes will arrange tours for youngsters and this takes care of any entertainment. Serve the children their homemade treats before or after and you have a different type of party that the children will remember. Include the birthday child in the planning. This is just as much fun as the party itself. You may find he has some very good ideas of his own.

Of course, the traditional type of birthday party with ice cream, cake, games, and favors will always be a hit. Invite only the number of children you can handle or recruit some helpers. Neighborhood teen-agers are great for this type of thing. Some teen-agers who may play piano or guitar well enough to lead a sing along or do magic acts or crafts can even help with entertainment.

Games can be the old stand-bys that everyone knows how to play. There are numerous books available at the local library that are loaded with party ideas and games. Look these over and come up with ideas that make both you and your child happy. Decorations of balloons and crepe paper streamers work fine. Novelty and craft stores are full of decorations, trimmings, and inexpensive favor-type materials that can make things easy.

The food should be something that all children will like. It must be homemade to make sure that it is safe but this is done easily and usually can be prepared ahead of time. Commercial ice creams are full of forbidden ingredients. Preservatives, artificial colorings, and flavorings abound, so to be sure you should make your own ice cream or fruit ice. Follow any of the recipes in this book and you will make delicious homemade ice cream with a minimum amount of work.

An ice cream maker could be a good investment for the family. It not only makes a fairly large quantity of ice cream at one time but is also fun to watch. Follow directions carefully for success.

Birthday cakes now are going to have to be homemade. The usual two-layer cake can be decorated with purchased plastic decorations. Put them on immediately before serving to eliminate any possible transfer of contaminating chemicals from the plastic. If you are handy and artistic, try your hand at some of the more elaborate icing designs.

If your child is sensitive to most grains, try a gelatin cake. Make any allowed gelatin recipe and pour into a cake pan and chill until very firm. Unmold onto a plate and cover completely with a whipped cream frosting. Chill until just before serving. Cut just like a regular cake and don't forget the candles!

Since you will be doing more party-type baking, you may want to invest in some specialty baking pans. There are several available through large department stores or mail order catalogues. They may be a worth-while purchase.

Here are several birthday party ideas:

Hobo Lunch

Menu

Beef Stew*
Wheat Biscuits*
Fruit Wedges
Birthday Pie

At a back-yard picnic table make the centerpiece a kettle containing hearty beef stew full of vegetables. Serve this with homemade biscuits and fresh fruit wedges.

Instead of a cake for dessert make your child's favorite pie. To prepare the pie to hold candles, omit the top crust and bake as usual until 10 minutes before filling is done. Remove from oven and make small mounds of meringue directly on the pie filling. Return to oven and bake for the additional 10 minutes or until lightly browned. Make enough so that there will be a mound for each small birthday candle.

For decorations use a checkered tablecloth and either paper plates and cups or mismatched plates and hobo-type tin cups. A favor package can be wrapped hobo-style in a red bandana for each child.

Winter Snow Party

Menu

Snowman Cake
Fruit Ice
Hot Carob Drink*

Place a mirror in the middle of the table with coconut around the edges for snow. Make little snowmen out of small styrofoam balls and set them on the mirror "lake." These can also be used for party favors.

For the snowman cake, bake one 8-inch round cake and one 8-inch square cake to make into a snowman with a hat. Cut the

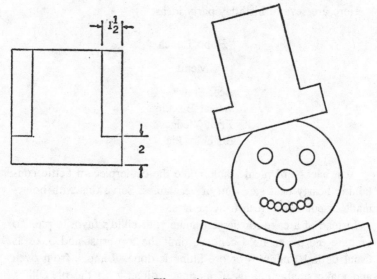

Illustration #2

square cake as indicated in the diagram below and cover with a tinted icing, using any color that is convenient. Ice the round layer with white icing and cover with coconut. Make a face with nuts and raisins and lay next to the hat as shown. (Illustration #2)

Skating at a rink or a nearby frozen lake or sled riding on a neighborhood hill is a full afternoon of fun. Serve the refreshments before or after.

Outer Space Party

Menu

Moon Missile Cake
Ice Cream or Fruit Ice
Martian Munchies
Rocket Fuel

Build a robot centerpiece by using any handy boxes for the head and body and paper towel cores for arms and legs. Cover it all with aluminum foil and make the facial features with black construction paper. Decorate with balloons and streamers in various colors. Shop for novelty items like tiny robots, astronauts, jet planes, and rockets for favors.

The missile cake can be made by cutting a 9x9-inch cake, following the diagram below. Rearrange pieces as indicated and ice all around. Decorate using nuts, raisins, or colored icing. (Illustration #3)

Serve any flavor homemade ice cream or fruit ice that is allowed. Martian munchies are made by tossing together nuts, currants, chopped dates, and unsweetened coconut. Serve in nut cups and pass bowls of extra for refills. Rocket fuel drinks are only fruit juice or a combination of juices served over crushed ice.

Luau Party

Menu

Fruit Boat
Sweet and Sour Meatballs*
Rice
Tossed Salad
Coconut Cake

Seat your guests at a low table surrounded by cushions instead of chairs. You can improvise a table by placing sheets of plywood on bricks. Cover the top with a colorful cloth. Add co-ordinated napkins and plates. If the party is held outdoors, patio torches or large candles are great for lighting.

A centerpiece using fresh fruit and flowers ringed with candles would be appropriate. Paper leis can be made or purchased for each guest. Add Hawaiian background music with a phonograph or tape unit.

The dinner starts out with a fruit boat made from whole fresh pineapples that have been cut in half lengthwise leaving the tops on. Hollow out the pineapples and cut the meat into chunks. Mix with a variety of other fresh fruit and refill each pineapple half. Serve as a first course giving each person one half. Sweet and sour meatballs served over rice and a tossed salad make up the rest of the menu.

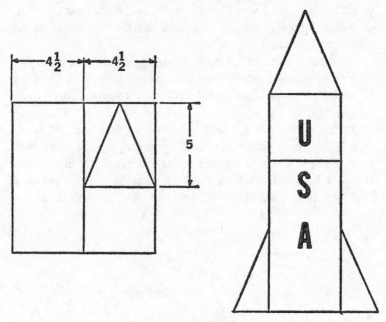

Illustration #3

For dessert make your child's favorite cake and frosting and cover the outside completely with unsweetened shredded coconut.

Wild West Party

Menu

Sloppy Joes* on Sandwich Buns*
Cole Slaw
Carrot and Celery Sticks
Ice Cream
Deputy Badge Cake
Juice or Milk

The table can be decorated with paper plates, cups, and napkins in a cowboy motif. Inexpensive cowboy hats and deputy badges are used for favors. The centerpiece is made to look like a corral by using toy building logs for a fence and adding barnyard animals from the toy box.

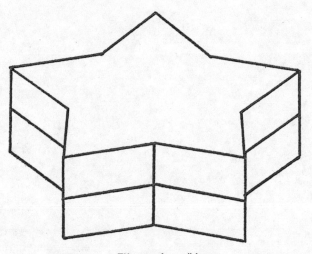

Illustration #4

A deputy badge cake is an 8- or 9-inch layer cake put together with icing between layers. Before icing the outside cut into a star shape. Ice on all sides and edge with colored icing or nuts. Write U S MARSHAL (child's name) on the top with icing as shown. Cut into wedges and serve with ice cream. (Illustration #4)

THE BASIC DIET

Avoid:
  Artificial colors and flavors
  Preservatives (BHA, BHT, sodium nitrite, MSG)
  Sugar (molasses, brown sugar, white sugar, turbinado, and raw
    sugar)
  Bleached white flour
  Chocolate, coffee, cocoa, tea, cola drinks, diet cola drinks

Limit:
  Serve no more than 16 ounces of milk per day
  Honey and pure maple syrup
  Pasta products (spaghetti, macaroni, noodles, lasagne)
  Fruits high in natural sugars—raisins, dates, dried fruits, grapes,
    plums, and prunes

Use freely:
  Whole grain flours and cereals
  Fresh fruits
  Fresh vegetables
  Nuts and seeds
  Uncolored cheese, meat, eggs, fish, beans
  Water
  Carob instead of chocolate
  Brown rice

Serve:
  3 meals a day plus 2 to 3 small high protein snacks

Use only if absolutely necessary:
  Artificial sweeteners

APPENDIX B

THE COMMON FOODS
ELIMINATION DIET*

Here are menus, suggested recipes, and a diet diary example for
the Common Foods Elimination Diet. Milk, eggs, corn, wheat,
chocolate, rye, citrus, sugar, and artificial colors, flavors, and preservatives are avoided in all forms for a week or until the child
has been better for two days. Then, one day at a time, each food
is reintroduced and the child's behavior is observed.

On food items followed by "2x," double the recipe, reserving
leftovers for another meal or snack.

DAY 1

Meal	Foods	Symptoms
Breakfast	Hamburger or chopped steak (no bun) or Homemade Sausage Patties*	Tired, draggy, fussy all morning
	Fried potatoes (in pure safflower oil)	
	Unsweetened applesauce	
	Unsweetened pineapple juice or tomato juice	

* Before starting this diet, please be certain to check detailed suggestions
and precautions for its use, beginning on page 22.

Meal	Foods	Symptoms
Snack	Apple or pear (peeled if waxed)	
Lunch	Plain hamburger with Tomato Catsup*	Irritable, seems worse, misses all his favorite foods
	Allowed potato chips (no preservatives, fried in pure safflower oil) or Potato Chips*	
	Grape Gelatin* with allowed fruit (pears, peaches, pineapple, apple, or grapes) (2x)	
	Carrot sticks	
	Unsweetened grape juice	
Snack	Shelled peanuts, carrots, celery	
Dinner	Fried Chicken*	Irritable; very difficult day
	Potatoes (2x) or Seasoned Rice*	Hate the diet already—how will we survive another week?
	Peas (2x)	
	Candle Salad* or tossed salad with allowed dressing	
	Peanut Carob Oat Squares*	
	Ice water	
Bedtime Snack	Rice Cake Snacks* or Tofu Cheese Spread* on rice crackers	

DAY 2

Breakfast	Oatmeal with honey or pure maple syrup or Oat or Rice Pancakes*	Irritable, short attention span
	Broiled pork chops	
	Pears or peaches (fresh or water packed)	
	Unsweetened pineapple juice or ice water	
Snack	Gelatin Snacks* (grape or pineapple) (2x)	

Meal	Foods	Symptoms
Lunch	Pea Soup* or Chicken Soup* (rice)	Bad morning
	Leftover cold Fried Chicken*	
	Allowed potato chips or Potato Chips*	
	Fresh grapes or leftover Grape Gelatin*	
	Leftover Peanut Carob Oat Squares*	
	Ice water or unsweetened pineapple juice	
Snack	Tofu Cheese Spread* on rice cake or peanut butter on celery	Better?
	Hot Apple Cider* or cold unsweetened apple juice or Popsicles* (allowed juice) (pineapple, cranberry, grape)	
Dinner	Tomato Spaghetti Sauce* on rice	
	Lettuce salad with allowed dressing	
	Green beans with allowed safflower margarine	
	Pineapple Ice* or melon in season	
	Ice water	
Bedtime Snack	Peanuts, walnuts, or pecans or leftover Peanut Carob Oat Squares*	Went to bed easily

DAY 3

Meal	Foods	Symptoms
Breakfast	Granola Bars* or fried potatoes (in pure safflower oil)	Angry about no eggs—really misses them
	Homemade Sausage Patties*	
	Banana or fresh peach	
	Unsweetened pineapple juice or ice water	
Snack	Leftover Gelatin Snacks* or leftover cold Fried Chicken* leg	
	Celery with peanut butter	

Meal	Foods	Symptoms
Lunch	Cold Fried Chicken* Pumpkin* or Zucchini Bread* with allowed margarine or jam Carrot sticks Raw apple or pear (unwaxed) Leftover Peanut Carob Oat Squares* Ice water or tomato juice	Seems nice and calm; good morning, played well by himself
Snack	Popsicles* (allowed juice) Raw vegetables with Zippy Curry Dip*	
Dinner	Fish (baked or broiled) Baked potato or sweet potato Asparagus or green beans Allowed Fruit Cup* Maple Apple Pudding* or Baked Apples or Pears* Ice water or unsweetened pine- apple juice	Better day today
Bedtime Snack	Unsweetened pineapple chunks or other fruit Peanuts, cashews, or walnuts	Went to bed easily

DAY 4

Meal	Foods	Symptoms
Breakfast	Lamb chops or hamburger Pumpkin* or Zucchini Bread* with allowed margarine or jam Unsweetened applesauce Unsweetened grape juice or ice water	Slept longer last night, dark circles almost gone
Snack	Rice Cake Snacks* or Pumpkin* or Zucchini Bread* Peanuts, walnuts, sunflower seeds Ice water or Popsicles* (allowed juice)	

Meal	Foods	Symptoms
Lunch	Tuna Salad* or Chicken Sandwich Spread* on rice cakes or lettuce Carrots, celery Peaches (fresh or water packed) Pumpkin* or Zucchini Bread* with allowed margarine Ice water or unsweetened grape juice	Good morning, can't believe how sunny his disposition is
Snack	Tofu Cheese Spread* on rice crackers or peanut butter and allowed jam between two rice crackers or cold Fried Chicken* Carrots, celery, cherry tomatoes	
Dinner	Beef Stew* or Skillet Dinner* (2x) Carrot Cake* or Gingerbread* or fresh melon Ice water or Papaya Juice* sweetened with honey	Good day
Bedtime Snack	Tofu Cheese Spread* or peanut butter on celery Popsicles* (allowed juice)	

DAY 5

Repeat menus for Day 1   Great all day

DAY 6

Repeat menus for Day 2   Good day, happy, good concentration

DAY 7

Repeat menus for Day 3 or Day 4   Diet is helping— told us how good he feels, is very affectionate

Meal	Foods	Symptoms

DAY 8 — Reintroduce Eggs

Meal	Foods	Symptoms
Breakfast	Scrambled eggs (omit milk, scramble in a little safflower oil) Fried potatoes Unsweetened applesauce Unsweetened pineapple juice or ice water	Good before breakfast: then angry, irritable, crying. Eggs?
Snack	Hard-cooked egg, unsweetened pineapple juice	Worse after egg, draggy
Lunch	Hard-cooked egg Potato Chips* Grape Gelatin* with allowed fruit Carrots Unsweetened grape juice	Just awful, back to old self. STOP SERVING EGGS
Snack	Shelled peanuts, carrots, celery	
Dinner	Fried Chicken* (2x) Potatoes (2x) Peas (2x) Candle Salad* or tossed salad with allowed dressing Ice water	
Bedtime Snack	Rice Cake Snacks* or Tofu Cheese Spread* on rice cakes	What an awful day, a little better tonight

DAY 9 — Reintroduce Sugar

He seems okay this morning so we will introduce sugar. If he had not been okay, wait another day.

Meal	Foods	Symptoms
Breakfast	Oatmeal with brown sugar (no milk) Broiled pork chops Pears or peaches (fresh or water packed) with sugar sprinkled on top Unsweetened pineapple juice	Surprised us by not wanting sugar; felt guilty encouraging him to eat it
Snack	Sugar cubes, Gelatin Snacks* (grape or pineapple) (2x) Walnuts or cashews	Irritable, hyperactive, nose running, dark circles under eyes are back
Lunch	Sugar cubes Pea Soup* or Chicken Soup* (rice) Cold Fried Chicken* Allowed potato chips or Potato Chips* Fresh grapes or Grape Gelatin* Peanut Carob Oat Squares* Ice water or unsweetened pineapple juice	Irritable, can't concentrate, very hopped up STOP SUGAR
Snack	Tofu Cheese Spread* on rice cake or peanut butter on celery Hot Apple Cider* or cold unsweetened apple juice	Wish we never had to give him back these foods—he was doing so well
Dinner	Tomato Spaghetti Sauce* on rice Lettuce and tomato salad with allowed dressing Green beans with allowed safflower margarine Pineapple Ice* or melon in season Ice water	

Meal	Foods	Symptoms
Bedtime Snack	Peanuts, walnuts, or pecans or leftover Peanut Carob Oat Square*	

DAY 10 — Reintroduce Corn

Meal	Foods	Symptoms
Breakfast	Corn on cob with allowed margarine Homemade Sausage Patties* Granola Bars* Banana or fresh peach Unsweetened pineapple juice or ice water	Seems okay today, so we will return corn; reaction to sugar only lasted 12 hours or so
Snack	Popcorn popped in pure safflower oil	Okay
Lunch	Popcorn Cold Fried Chicken* Pumpkin* or Zucchini Bread* with allowed margarine or jam Carrot sticks Raw apple or pear (unwaxed) Tomato juice or ice water	Okay
Snack	Popcorn Raw vegetables with Zippy Curry Dip*	Okay
Dinner	Corn on the cob with allowed safflower margarine Fish (baked or broiled) Asparagus or green beans Allowed Fruit Cup* Maple Apple Pudding* or Baked Apples or Pears* Ice water or unsweetened pineapple juice	After dinner, legs ache, nose streaming, very unreasonable, can't sit down to watch TV STOP CORN
Bedtime Snack	Unsweetened pineapple chunks or other fruit Peanuts, cashews, or walnuts	

Meal	*Foods*	*Symptoms*

DAY 11 — Reintroduce Wheat

Meal	Foods	Symptoms
Breakfast	Whole wheat pancakes (no milk, sugar, or eggs) with pure maple syrup and allowed margarine or Cream of Wheat cereal (no milk or sugar) Lamb chop or hamburger Unsweetened apple juice Unsweetened grape juice or ice water	Is okay this morning
Snack	Leftover pancake or spread banana with peanut butter and roll in honey, wheat germ, and coconut Peanuts, walnuts, sunflower seeds	Restless, hard to concentrate?
Lunch	Tuna Salad* or Chicken Sandwich Spread* on rice cakes or lettuce Spaghetti added to Chicken Soup* Peaches (fresh or water packed) Pumpkin* or Zucchini Bread* with allowed margarine Ice water or unsweetened grape juice	Dark circles are back
Snack	Leftover Chicken Soup* with spaghetti or another banana prepared as above	Legs ache, hopped up STOP WHEAT
Dinner	Beef Stew* or Skillet Dinner* Carrot Cake* or Gingerbread* or fresh melon Ice water or Papaya Juice* sweetened with honey	
Bedtime Snack	Tofu Cheese Spread* or peanut butter on celery Popsicles* (allowed juice)	

Meal	*Foods*	*Symptoms*
	DAY 12 — Reintroduce Rye	
Breakfast	Hamburger or chopped steak (no bun) or Homemade Sausage Patties* Natural Ry-Krisp crackers with allowed margarine and jam Fried potatoes in pure safflower oil Unsweetened applesauce Unsweetened pineapple juice or tomato juice	Seems fine this morning, great morning
Snack	Ry-Krisp cracker with peanut butter Apple or Pear (peeled if waxed)	
Lunch	Ry-Krisp cracker with allowed margarine and jam Plain hamburger with Tomato Catsup* Allowed potato chips or Potato Chips* Grape Gelatin* with allowed fruit Carrot sticks Unsweetened grape juice	Fine, seems okay
Snack	Shelled peanuts, carrots, celery Ry-Krisp crackers with peanut butter	Still fine; maybe he isn't sensitive to rye. Keeping fingers crossed
Dinner	Fried Chicken* (3x) Potatoes (2x) Peas (2x) Candle Salad* or tossed salad with allowed dressing Ry-Krisp cracker with allowed margarine Fruit in season	Great day
Bedtime Snack	Ry-Krisp cracker with peanut butter or Tofu Cheese Spread*	Good night. Not sensitive to rye. Hooray!

Meal	Foods	Symptoms

DAY 13 — Reintroduce Citrus

		He only likes oranges so will just try these
Breakfast	Oatmeal with honey or pure maple syrup or Oat or Rice Pancakes*	Good morning
	Broiled pork chops	
	Fresh orange sections	
	Unsweetened pineapple juice or ice water	
Snack	Fresh-squeezed orange juice	
	Allowed nuts or cold Fried Chicken* leg	
Lunch	Pea Soup* or Chicken Soup* (rice)	
	Leftover cold Fried Chicken*	
	Allowed potato chips or Potato Chips*	
	Fresh orange sections	
	Leftover Peanut Carob Oat Squares*	
	Ice water or unsweetened pineapple juice	
Snack	Fresh-squeezed orange juice	Good afternoon
	Tofu Cheese Spread* on rice cake or peanut butter on celery	
Dinner	Tomato Spaghetti Sauce* on rice	Great evening, good night
	Fruit salad with fresh orange sections	
	Green beans with allowed safflower margarine	
	Pineapple Ice* or melon in season	
	Ice water	
Bedtime Snack	Peanuts, walnuts, or pecans or leftover Peanut Carob Oat Square*	Hooray again! He's not sensitive to oranges
	Fresh-squeezed orange juice	

Meal	Foods	Symptoms

DAY 14 — Reintroduce Chocolate

Meal	Foods	Symptoms
Breakfast	Granola Bars* or fried potatoes (in pure safflower oil) Homemade Sausage Patties* Banana or fresh peach Unsweetened pineapple juice or ice water Piece of unsweetened chocolate	Okay this morning
Snack	Leftover Gelatin Snacks* or leftover cold Fried Chicken* leg Celery with peanut butter Piece of unsweetened chocolate	After snack, nose is streaming, irritable, mad at the world STOP CHOCOLATE
Lunch	Cold Fried Chicken* Pumpkin* or Zucchini Bread* with allowed margarine or jam Carrot sticks Raw apple or pear (unwaxed) Leftover Peanut Carob Oat Squares* Ice water or tomato juice	
Snack	Popsicles* (allowed juice) Raw vegetables with Zippy Curry Dip*	
Dinner	Fish (baked or broiled) Baked potato or sweet potato Asparagus or green beans Allowed Fruit Cup* Maple Apple Pudding* or Baked Apples or Pears* Ice water or unsweetened pineapple juice	
Bedtime Snack	Unsweetened pineapple chunks or other fruit Peanuts, cashews, or walnuts	

Meal	Foods	Symptoms

DAY 15 — Introduce Food Colorings

Meal	Foods	Symptoms
Breakfast	Lamb chops or hamburger Pumpkin* or Zucchini Bread* with allowed margarine or jam Unsweetened applesauce Mix all food colors together: add ½ teaspoon to grape juice or ice water	Okay this morning After drinking colored ice water, became very hopped up, silly, dark circles under eyes STOP COLORS
Snack	Rice Cake Snacks* or Pumpkin* or Zucchini Bread* Peanuts, walnuts, sunflower seeds	
Lunch	Tuna Salad* or Chicken Sand- wich Spread* on rice cakes or lettuce Carrots, celery Peaches (fresh or water packed) Pumpkin* or Zucchini Bread* with allowed margarine Ice water or unsweetened grape juice	
Snack	Tofu Cheese Spread* on rice crackers or peanut butter and allowed jam between two rice crackers or cold Fried Chicken* Carrots, celery, cherry tomatoes	Bad afternoon
Dinner	Beef Stew* or Skillet Dinner (2x) Carrot Cake* or Gingerbread* or fresh melon Ice water or Papaya Juice* sweetened with honey	Better this evening
Bedtime Snack	Tofu Cheese Spread* or peanut butter on celery Popsicles* (allowed juice)	

Meal	*Foods*	*Symptoms*
	DAY 16 — Reintroduce Milk	
		Hooray! Last day. Seems okay this morning
Breakfast	Hamburger or chopped steak (no bun) or Homemade Sausage Patties*	
	Fried potatoes (in pure safflower oil)	
	Unsweetened applesauce	
	Glass of milk	
Snack	Glass of milk	Tired this morning? Not sure
	Apple or pear (peeled if waxed)	
Lunch	Plain hamburger with Tomato Catsup*	
	Allowed potato chips or Potato Chips*	
	Grape Gelatin* with allowed fruit	
	Glass of milk	
Snack	Shelled peanuts, carrots, celery	Irritable, crying, temper tantrum, fighting with brother
	Glass of milk	
		STOP MILK
Dinner	Fried Chicken*	
	Potatoes or Seasoned Rice*	
	Peas	
	Candle Salad* or tossed salad with allowed dressing	
	Peanut Carob Oat Square*	
Bedtime Snack	Rice Cake Snacks* or Tofu Cheese Spread* on rice cakes	Awful evening but we're done. Hooray! P.S. He wet the bed

CONCLUSIONS: This child seems sensitive to eggs, sugar, corn, wheat, chocolate, colors, and milk. He seemed to do fine on rye and oranges. If any reaction had been doubtful, that particular elimination diet should be repeated.

APPENDIX C

HOW TO FOLLOW AN ELIMINATION DIET

To use this chart, just follow the arrows. When you come to a diamond shaped box, answer the question and follow the appropriate arrow.

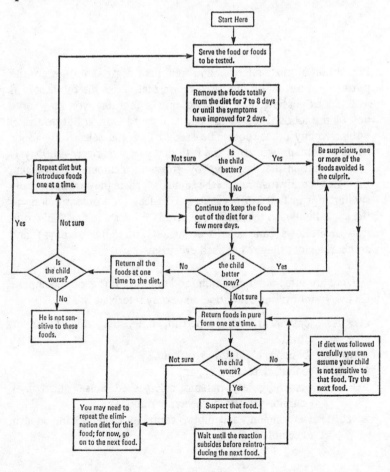

A FIVE-DAY ROTATION DIET

Prevention of more allergies and treatment of present ones are the purposes of a rotation diet. A rotation diet varies the foods served as much as possible. For example, on the first day, you may serve any of the foods listed in the column under Day 1, but you may not serve any other food. The second day you select only foods listed in column two. After the fifth day you start over with Day 1.

The rotation diet is set up by grouping members of the same biological family together on the same day, since they are chemically similar. For instance, asparagus, garlic, leek, and onions belong to the same family, so they must be served on the same day. This rotation diet allows cane and beet sugars (on different days) and saccharin, since they're not used every day.

Here are some other common food families. For a more complete list ask your librarian for a food taxonomy reference book.

CITRUS: lemon, orange, grapefruit, lime, tangerine, kumquat, citron

BANANA: banana, plantain, arrowroot

PALM: coconut, date, date sugar

PARSLEY: carrot, celery, parsnip, celery seed, anise, dill, fennel, cumin, parsley, caraway, coriander

MELON: watermelon, cucumber, cantaloupe, pumpkin, squash, zucchini

	Day 1	Day 2	Day 3	Day 4	Day 5
Meat, fish, poultry	Chicken, eggs, pheasant, capon Cornish hens Tuna	Pork Shrimp, lobster, crab	Lamb Duck Scallops, clams, oysters	Turkey Halibut, sole, turbot, flounder	Beef Salmon, trout
Vegetables	Lettuce Onion, garlic, chives, leeks, asparagus Artichoke	Carrots, celery, parsley, parsnips	White potato, tomato, eggplant Spinach, beets Green pepper	Yams Legumes—peas, green beans, soy, lima beans Cucumber, squash, pumpkin, zucchini	Cabbage, broccoli, Brussels sprouts, cauliflower, radish Corn
Fruit	Apples, pears, quince Papaya Rhubarb Figs, breadfruit	Citrus—orange, lime, lemon, grapefruit, tangerine, kumquat Banana, plantain, mango	Berries—raspberry, strawberry, blackberry Pineapple Avocado	Cantaloupe, watermelon Grapes, raisins Coconuts, dates Blueberry, cranberry	Apricot, peach, plum, prune Nectarine, cherry
Starch	Wheat, rye Buckwheat	Arrowroot Barley	Oats Tapioca	Rice, rice flour Soy flour	Cornstarch, corn meal
Beverages	Apple juice Maté tea Papaya juice	Orange or grapefruit juice Lemonade (sweetened with honey)	Tomato juice Unsweetened pineapple juice Sassafras tea	Unsweetened grape juice Tea	Milk Pure cocoa Coffee
Nuts, seeds	Pecan, walnut Sunflower seeds	Cashews, pistachio Sesame seeds	Brazil nuts Macadamia nuts	Peanuts Filberts Melon seeds	Almond
Oils	Sunflower oil Walnut oil	Sesame oil Olive oil Cottonseed oil	Safflower oil Avocado oil Uncolored safflower oil margarine	Peanut oil Soy oil Uncolored soy oil margarine	Uncolored butter Corn oil Uncolored corn oil margarine
Sweeteners	Cane sugar	Honey (orange, grapefruit, tangelo) Barley malt syrup	Beet sugar	Saccharin Date sugar	Maple syrup
Miscellaneous	Bakers' yeast Cider vinegar Mushrooms	Allspice, cloves Dill, cumin, caraway, coriander, fennel Olives	Cinnamon, bayleaf, basil, sassafras, oregano, thyme, rosemary, peppermint, spearmint Nutmeg, mace	Carob Egg replacer Wine vinegar Cream of tartar	Chocolate White distilled vinegar Pure vanilla extract

LEGUME: lentil, pea, chick pea, bean (kidney, pinto, navy, string), licorice, soybean, peanut, clover honey, carob, alfalfa

CASHEW: cashew, pistachio, mango

APPLE: apple, pear, quince

BUCKWHEAT: buckwheat, rhubarb

WALNUT: English walnut, black walnut, pecan, hickory nut, butternut

ONION: onion, garlic, asparagus, chive, leek

POTATO: potato, tomato, eggplant, red and green pepper, chili pepper, paprika, cayenne

PLUM: plum, cherry, peach, apricot, nectarine, almond, wild cherry

MUSTARD: mustard, turnip, radish, horseradish, cabbage, watercress, cauliflower, Brussels sprouts, rutabaga

LAUREL: avocado, cinnamon, bay leaf, sassafras

GRASS: wheat, corn, rice, oats, barley, rye, wild rice, cane, sorghum

BOVID: milk products, beef, lamb

BIRD: chicken, turkey, eggs, duck

MOLLUSKS: clam, scallop, oyster, abalone, snail

CRUSTACEANS: crab, lobster, shrimp, crayfish

FRESHWATER FISH: sturgeon, herring, salmon, whitefish, bass, perch

SALTWATER FISH: salmon, trout, tuna, sole, flounder, herring, cod, sea bass, anchovy

NATURAL FOODS CONTAINING SALICYLATES

Some hyperactive children may be bothered by natural salicylates.

Avoid

Almonds
Apples, apple cider, cider vinegar
Apricots
Blackberries
Boysenberries
Cherries
Cloves
Cranberries
Cucumbers, cucumber pickles
Currants
Gooseberries
Grapes, wine, wine vinegar
Green peppers
Mint
Nectarines
Oil of winter-green
Oranges
Peaches
Plums, prunes
Raisins
Raspberries
Strawberries
Tea
Tomatoes

May have as substitutes

Bananas
Coconuts
Dates
Figs
Grapefruit
Lemons
Limes
Melons
Papayas
Pears
Pineapples
Pomegranates
Tangerines

Drugs with salicylates include:
Aspirin
Aspirin compounds

Medications with aspirin added
Liniments

As a substitute for aspirin white Tylenol® tablets may be used if your doctor approves.

SHOPPING INFORMATION

Here is a suggested shopping list you can consult for the Basic Diet or the various elimination diets. If you can't locate the brands mentioned, you should be able to find similar ones in your area. If you have any doubts or questions about products, contact the manufacturer. Ingredients do change from time to time so always read labels carefully.

Dairy Products	Brand Names	Comments
Butter, margarine	Land o' Lakes Unsalted Sweet Butter	A milk product, never colored.
	Land o' Lakes Lightly Salted Butter	A milk product, may contain vegetable dye (annatto).
	Willow Run Margarine	Soy margarine, natural vegetable color; contains no milk or corn.
	Downey's Natural Honey Butter	A milk product, just honey and butter, may contain vegetable dye (annatto) at some times of the year.

	Downey's Cinnamon Honey Butter	Same as natural but contains cinnamon.
	Hain's Soy & Liquid Wheat Germ Oil Margarine	Soy margarine, contains wheat, citric acid, natural vegetable color; contains no milk or corn.
	Hain's Safflower Oil Margarine	Safflower margarine, contains no milk or corn.
Cheese	County Line Colby Sharpy, Old World Series	Milk products, no coloring added.
	Kraft white cheeses such as Parmesan, Brick, Munster, Swiss, Mozzarella, Monterey Jack	Milk products, no dye added.
	Kraft yellow cheeses	Milk products, natural vegetable dye.
	Michigan Brand Cottage Cheese	A milk product, no stabilizers added.
Ice cream	Shiloh Farms	A milk product. Read label.

Flours

Unbleached, naturally matured	Harrington Hogson's Mill Pillsbury Unbleached White Elam's Unbleached White	A wheat product, B vitamins added.
Whole wheat or rye		Read labels.

Other types of flours	Cellu, Elam's	Look for rice, potato starch, oat flour, Scotch-style oatmeal, arrowroot, tapioca.
Mixes	Jolly Joan Rice, Potato, Corn	Read labels.
Baked loaves	Catherine Clark's Brownberry Natural Wheat[1]	Contains sugar.
	Catherine Clark's Natural Raisin Cinnamon[1]	Contains corn syrup, milk, no preservatives.
	Pepperidge Farm Sprouted Wheat[1]	Contains honey, brown sugar, molasses, no preservatives.
	Pepperidge Farm Whole Wheat[1]	Contains milk, molasses, corn syrup, calcium propionate.
	Pepperidge Farm Honey Brand[1]	Contains molasses, caramel color, no preservatives.

Cereals

Cold	Post Grape Nuts	Wheat.
	Popeye Puffed Wheat	Wheat.
	Popeye Puffed Rice	Rice.
	El Molino Puffed Rice	Whole brown rice.
	Quaker Puffed Wheat	Citric acid, B vitamins.
	Quaker Puffed Rice	Citric acid, B vitamins.
	Olde Mill Maple Nut Granola	Contains wheat, rye, corn, pure maple syrup.
	Sovex Honey Almond Granola	Contains oats, wheat, honey.

[1] These brands seem preferable to most of the commercial baked loaves. However, they do contain sugar in one form or other and there may be other problem ingredients like milk and corn you can't use. So read the labels.

Hot	Quaker Old Fashioned or Quick Oats	Oats only.
	Quaker Cream of Whole Wheat	Wheat only.
	Wheatena	Wheat only.
	Quaker Cream of Rice	Rice only.
	Con Agra Cream of Rye	Rye only.

Chocolate and Carob

Chocolate	Baker's Unsweetened Chocolate	Pure chocolate.
	Hershey's Baking Chocolate, Unsweetened	Pure chocolate.
	Hershey's Cocoa	Pure cocoa.
Carob powder	El Molino Cara Coa Carob Powder	Vanilla, oil of orange, lemon, cinnamon, and coriander.

Snacks

Crackers	Ralston Purina Original Ry-Krisp	Rye only.
	Rice Cakes, Rice Crackers	Brown rice, no preservatives.
Popcorn		Choose plain popcorn. Pop in pure allowed oil.
Potato chips and corn chips	Charles Chips	Cottonseed oil, contains no preservatives.
	Jay's Natural Potato Chips	Corn or cottonseed oil, contains no preservatives.
	Hain's Natural Potato Chips	Pure safflower oil.
	Health Valley Corn Chips	Corn, safflower oil.

Beverages

Unsweetened fruit juice	Welch's Grape Juice (bottled)	Sugar-free.
	Dole Pineapple Juice	Sugar-free.
	Also look for unsweetened grapefruit, apple, orange, prune, and tomato juices	
	Minute Maid Frozen Concentrate Orange-grapefruit, Pineapple, Tangerine	Sugar-free.

Miscellaneous Items

Baking powder	Cellu Cereal-free Baking Powder	Corn-free.
Egg replacer	Jolly Joan Egg Replacer	Contains no eggs. Read label.
Extracts	McCormick's Pure Vanilla, Lemon, Orange, or Peppermint	Pure extracts in alcohol.
Gelatin	Knox Unflavored	Made exclusively from beef.
Hot dogs, sausage	Shiloh Farms	No nitrites. Read label.
Imitation catsup	Hain's	Contains tomato, honey, cider vinegar, natural spices.
Mayonnaise	Hain's Eggless Mayonnaise	Read label.
Oils	Hain's, Golden Harvest	Pure oils, no preservatives. Look for safflower, corn, sunflower, soy, and walnut.

	Puritan Oil	No preservatives. Made from sunflower and soy oils.
Peanut butter, nut butters, jams	Smuckers Natural Peanut Butter	Peanuts, salt only.
	Shedd's Peanut Butter	Peanuts, salt only.
	Elam's Peanut Butter	Wheat germ and peanuts only.
	Hain's Jams	Read labels.
	Hain's Cashew, Almond, Sesame Butters	Contains just nuts or seeds.
Salad dressings	Hain's	Check labels.
Salt		Choose sea salt without dextrose.
Soy milk	CHO Free Soy Milk	Corn, milk, and sugar-free.
Tofu cheese		Soy cheese, no milk; look in the produce area of your store.
Vinegar	Heinz Apple Cider Vinegar	No corn or wheat.
	Heinz Wine Vinegar	No corn or wheat.
	Heinz Distilled White Vinegar	May contain corn, rye, or barley.
	Heinz Malt Vinegar	Contains barley.
Yeast	Red Star Dry Yeast	No preservatives.
	Fleischmann's Compressed Yeast Cakes	Contains cereal starch (corn), no preservatives.

APPENDIX G

SOME COMMONLY USED
ADDITIVES

Not all additives are bad for you. But it's difficult for the concerned consumer to know which additives may cause problems in sensitive individuals, which ones have been poorly tested for safety, and which ones are harmless or even beneficial.

Part of the problem is the unfamiliar technical names that are confusing and hard to pronounce and so they inspire distrust. And there are so many additives to keep straight with such varied functions. But to keep this subject in perspective, natural foods are also made of many chemicals with strange names. Some of these natural chemicals are toxic in large amounts, can cause cancer and birth defects in test animals, while others may cause allergic problems in sensitive people. So just because Mother Nature produces a chemical doesn't ensure its safety. For instance, some people are allergic to aspirin but they also tend to be sensitive to the salicylate chemical found naturally in some fruits and vegetables.

For the sensitive person, another problem is determining whether a reaction is caused by the food itself or by one of the additives. No one sits down to a bowl of BHT or a plate of sodium nitrite, so it's not always obvious what the problem is. For instance, if your child reacts to potato chips that are processed with soybean oil with BHT added, but does not react to potatoes or to soybeans, then you come to the conclusion that it must be the BHT. Since it's not always that easy to pinpoint the culprit, you're better off using fresh natural foods where the only problem could be the food itself (some people, however, are bothered by the insecticides and chemical sprays). Or choose brands that don't contain additives. Then you know if your child reacts to a food, that it must be the food itself.

Since it's hard to avoid all additives, here are some of the most common ones and some information about each. For further information, consult Michael F. Jacobson's *Eater's Digest: The Consumer's Factbook of Food Additives* (Doubleday Anchor Books, Garden City, New York, 1972) or Beatrice Trum Hunter's *Fact/ Book on Food Additives and Your Health* (Keats Publishing, Inc., New Canaan, Connecticut, 1972). Or order a great poster called "Chemical Cuisine," available for $1.75 from the Center for Science in the Public Interest, 1755 S Street, N.W., Washington, D.C. 20009.

ARTIFICIAL COLORS: Here are some of the common artificial colors:

Blue No. 1 (Brillian Blue)　　　Red No. 3 (Erythrosine)
Blue No. 2 (Indigotine)　　　　　Red No. 40 (Allura)
Citrus Red No. 2　　　　　　　　Yellow No. 5 (Tartrazine)
Green No. 3 (Fast Green)　　　　Yellow No. 6 (Sunset Yellow)
Orange B

These dyes are derived from processing coal. Many researchers believe they are poorly tested for safety. They may cause hyperactivity and other behavior problems in sensitive individuals and are known to cause other types of allergic reactions. Often labels only state "U. S. Certified Color added" or "artificial color" and do not specify which dye is present. Butter, ice cream, and cheese may be dyed without stating any information.

ARTIFICIAL FLAVORS: This group of compounds is used to flavor foods. A dozen chemicals may be required to imitate one flavor so it's even harder to track down problem-causing components. These flavors are frequently found with artificial colors and lots of sugar. Choose products with natural flavors. Then if a reaction occurs you'll know what food you're dealing with.

BHA AND BHT: These letters stand for butylated hydroxyanisole and butylated hydroxytoluene respectively. These chemicals are widely used as preservatives to prolong shelf life of cereals, oils, and snack foods. They may be present in some oils without appearing on the label if the oils were purchased with the preservatives already added. They cause some sensitive children to become hyperactive and may cause other allergic reactions. These chemicals are believed poorly tested for safety by some researchers.

CAFFEINE: This stimulant is added to soft drinks and occurs naturally in coffee, tea, and cocoa. It disrupts normal blood sugar levels in sensitive individuals. It may cause withdrawal symptoms when removed suddenly from the diet.

CALCIUM PROPIONATE: This chemical is used to inhibit mold growth and occurs naturally in some foods. Allergic reactions have been reported.

CARAMEL COLOR: This color may be derived from heat-treating one of the following: sucrose (cane or beets), dextrose or glucose from corn, molasses and lactose (milk sugar).

CASEIN, SODIUM CASEINATE: Casein is the protein in milk and may cause problems in milk-sensitive people. It's used as a thickening and whitening agent.

CITRIC ACID: This chemical occurs widely in nature. Commercially it is usually made from corn or sugar beet molasses but may also be produced from lemon or pineapple. Some individuals are sensitive to citric acid whether it occurs naturally or is made artificially. Some natural sources of citric acid are oranges, grapefruit, lemons, limes, pineapples, tomatoes, kumquats, and tangerines.

EDTA: This abbreviation stands for ethylenediamine tetraacetic acid and is used to trap metal impurities in foods acquired during processing. EDTA is used by doctors for medical purposes. It is widely found in salad dressings, mayonnaise, processed fruits and vegetables, and soft drinks to name just a few.

ETHYLENE: Although this chemical is not listed on labels, this gas may be used to ripen bananas and sometimes apples, pears, oranges, and tomatoes. Such fruit may cause problems in the chemically sensitive person.

EXTENDERS: These foods are added as fillers because they are usually less expensive than the major ingredient in the product. They may be soy, starch, glucose, breading, or milk casein. Unless the label lists specific information, you won't know which one is present.

LECITHIN: This is a nutritious chemical found widely in nature. Food processors use lecithin as an antioxidant and emulsifier. Soybean is the most common source by far for lecithin used by the food industry.

MALT: May be made from yeast-fermented corn, wheat, or barley.

MODIFIED FOOD STARCH OR FOOD STARCH: May be derived from wheat, corn, sorghum, arrowroot, tapioca, or potatoes.

MONOSODIUM GLUTAMATE (MSG): This is a very widely used chemical in soups, poultry, cheese, sauces, etc., as a flavor enhancer. MSG is no longer added to baby foods. It is known to cause "Chinese Restaurant Syndrome" in sensitive persons. It used to be extracted from soybean or seaweed but is now also derived from wheat, corn, or sugar beets.

NATURAL DYES: Here are some vegetable dyes commonly used that seem preferable to coal tar dyes. Conceivably they could cause problems in sensitive people.
  Annatto (from seeds of annatto tree)
  Paprika (dried pod of a sweet pepper)
  Tumeric (dried herb)
  Saffron (dried plant)
  Grape (grape skins)
  Dehydrated beets
  Riboflavin (may be synthetic or natural)
  Carrot oil (carrots)
  Beta-carotene (may be synthetic or natural)

NATURAL GUMS: Karaya, arabic (acacia) and tragacanth are members of the legume family and are known to cause allergic reactions in some people. Other gums you may encounter are locust bean gum (carob), chicle (chewing gum), guar, ghatti, and carrageen.

These gums are used as thickening agents and stabilizers. Many researchers feel they have been poorly tested for safety.

POTASSIUM IODATE OR POTASSIUM IODIDE: This is the chemical

added to salt to provide iodine, a necessary nutrient. May bother some sensitive people.

QUININE: This flavoring agent is used in beverages and can cause reactions in sensitive people.

SODIUM BENZOATE: This chemical occurs naturally but persons sensitive to aspirin and salicylates may also be sensitive to sodium benzoate.

SODIUM CHLORIDE: This is common table salt. A diet too high in sodium may contribute to high blood pressure. Teach your children to use less salt and cut down on the salt used in cooking.

SODIUM NITRITE AND SODIUM NITRATE: These chemicals are widely used in ham, bacon, hot dogs, smoked fish, and luncheon meats as a preservative and color stabilizer. They have recently come under attack as cancer-causing agents. They are no longer added to baby foods. They may cause joint inflammation, severe headache, and other reactions in sensitive people.

SULFUR DIOXIDE OR SODIUM BISULFITE: These chemicals prevent discoloration of dried fruit and inhibit the growth of bacteria. Dried fruits without this chemical are available and just as tasty even though they look brown and discolored.

VITAMINS AND MINERALS: These chemicals may be added for nutritional reasons or because they perform some other function as an additive. These chemicals may be either natural or synthetic. Some individuals may be sensitive to one or both forms.

Alpha-tocopherol is Vitamin E and prevents oils from becoming rancid.

Beta carotene is the precursor for Vitamin A and is used also as a coloring agent.

Ascorbic acid is Vitamin C and is used also as a color stabilizer and antioxidant. Sodium ascorbate is a more soluble form.

Ferrous gluconate is an iron compound used for its nutritional benefits and also as a coloring agent.

Ergosterol is a natural steroid converted by ultraviolet radiation to Vitamin D.

Niacin, riboflavin, and thiamine are B vitamins. Brewer's yeast and rice are common sources of these vitamins.

BASIC NUTRITION

Here is a brief review of what your child should be eating. The daily food guide below presents foods in four groups on the basis of their similarity in nutrient content. The four groups are:

> The meat group
> The vegetable – fruit group
> The milk group
> The bread – cereal group

Meat Group

Foods included in this group are beef, veal, lamb, pork, liver, heart, kidney, poultry, eggs, fish, and shellfish. Also, dry beans, dry peas, lentils, nuts, seeds, peanuts, and peanut butter. These foods add protein, B vitamins, and minerals to the diet.

Amounts recommended: Choose two or more servings per day. Count as a serving: 2 to 3 ounces lean, boneless cooked meat, poultry, or fish, 2 eggs, 1 cup cooked dry beans, dry peas, or lentils, or ¼ cup peanut butter.

Vegetable-Fruit Group

Foods included in this group are all vegetables and fruits. Particularly important are those that are valuable as sources of vitamin C and vitamin A.

Good sources of vitamin C include oranges, grapefruit, grapefruit juice, cantaloupe, guava, mango, papaya, broccoli, Brussels sprouts, green pepper, sweet red pepper, pineapple juice (if fortified with ascorbic acid), strawberries, and tomatoes.

Fair sources of vitamin C include honeydew melon, lemon, lemonade, watermelon, asparagus tips, raw cabbage, collards, garden cress, kale, mustard greens, potatoes and sweet potatoes cooked in the jacket, spinach, and turnip greens.

Good sources of vitamin A are dark green and deep yellow vegetables and a few fruits—broccoli, cantaloupe, carrots, chard, collards, cress, kale, mango, peaches, pumpkin, spinach, sweet potatoes, tomatoes, turnip greens and other dark green leafy vegetables, and winter squash. Whole milk, liver, and fish are also high in vitamin A.

Amounts recommended are four or more servings each day from this vegetable-fruit group. These servings should include one good source of vitamin C (vitamin C is needed *daily*) or two servings of a fair source, and one serving, at least every other day, of a good source of vitamin A. The remaining servings may be any vegetable or fruit, including those rich in vitamins A and C.

Since citrus fruits may not be allowed, finding a good source of vitamin C that your child likes sometimes is a problem. If your child won't eat non-citrus fruits high in vitamin C, vitamin C tablets that are uncolored and unflavored are another possibility. Check with your doctor as to how much your child should take daily.

Milk Group

Foods included in the milk group are milk—whole, evaporated, skim, dry, and buttermilk—cheese—cottage, cream, Cheddar-type, or natural ice cream, and yogurt. Limit milk consumption to 16 ounces a day.

Part or all of the milk may be skim milk, buttermilk, evaporated milk, or dry milk. Other milk products may replace part of the milk as follows:

1-inch cube Cheddar-type cheese = ½ cup milk
½ cup yogurt = ½ cup milk
½ cup cottage cheese = ⅓ cup milk
2 tablespoons cream cheese = 1 tablespoon milk
½ cup ice cream or ice milk = ⅓ cup milk

If your child is allergic to milk, you will want to be sure he gets other sources of good protein, vitamin A, B vitamins, vitamin D, and calcium. Check with your doctor or his nurse regarding a calcium supplement.

Bread-Cereal Group

All breads and cereals are included in the group, but whole grain products are superior to enriched or restored. This group includes breads, cooked cereals, allowed cold cereals, corn meal, whole grain crackers, flour, soy flour, grits, macaroni, spaghetti, noodles, brown rice, rolled oats, quick breads, and other baked goods if made with whole grain (preferred) or enriched flour. Don't use bleached flours or white rice.

Amounts recommended are four servings or more daily. Count as one serving: 1 slice of bread, 1 ounce cold cereal, ½ to ¾ cup cooked cereal, corn meal, grits, or pasta products.

This group of foods adds essential B vitamins, iron, vitamin E, some protein, and minerals to the diet.

APPENDIX I

EQUIVALENTS AND SUBSTITUTIONS

Here are some common conversions you may need:

Carob–Chocolate–Cocoa
    1 square of unsweetened chocolate = 3 tablespoons carob powder
    1 tablespoon cocoa = 1 tablespoon carob powder

Unsalted Butter–Salted Butter
    Add about ½ teaspoon salt for each stick (½ cup) of un-colored butter used in a recipe

Fresh Onion–Instant Minced Onion
    1 tablespoon instant minced onion = ¼ cup chopped raw onion

Dried Sweet Basil–Fresh Basil
    1 tablespoon dried crushed basil = about 6 to 8 tablespoons fresh chopped basil

Cinnamon–Allspice
    1 teaspoon cinnamon = 1 teaspoon allspice

Lemon Juice–Lemon Extract–Lemon Rind
    2 tablespoons fresh lemon juice = ½ teaspoon lemon extract = 1 teaspoon grated rind

Milk–Water or Juice
    1 cup milk = 1 cup water or juice plus 1 tablespoon fat

Egg–Egg Substitution
    1 egg = 2 tablespoons flour plus ½ teaspoon shortening plus
                   ½ teaspoon baking powder plus
                    2 tablespoons liquid

Sugar–Honey–Maple Syrup

    1 cup sugar = ⅓ to ½ cup honey or pure maple syrup. Reduce other liquids by ¼ cup per cup of honey.

    To prevent overbrowning lower baking temperature about 25°.

    To measure honey or maple syrup, first moisten measuring cup with liquid or oil, then measure sweetener.

Wheat Flour–Other Flours

    1 cup wheat flour = 1¼ cups barley flour

                        1 cup corn flour

                        1⅓ cups oat flour

                        ¾ cup potato flour

                        ¾ cup rice flour

                        1⅓ cups rye flour

                        1⅓ cups soy flour

                        1 cup tapioca

Wheat Flour–Other Thickeners

    1 tablespoon wheat flour = 2 tablespoons rye flour

                                1 tablespoon cornstarch

                                2 teaspoons arrowroot flour

                                2 teaspoons rice flour

                                2 teaspoons minute tapioca

                                2 teaspoons potato starch

All-purpose Flour Without Wheat

    1 cup cornstarch + 2 cups rice flour + 2 cups soy flour + 3 cups potato starch flour

    Use cup for cup as you would wheat flour, but reduce temperature 25° and increase baking time as needed.

Enriched Flour (Cornell Triple-rich Formula)

    For each cup of flour called for put 1 tablespoon soy flour, 1 tablespoon dry milk powder, and 1 teaspoon wheat germ into the bottom of measuring cup. Then fill the cup with unbleached flour.

SUGGESTED READING

Allergy

Crook, William G., M.D. *Are You Allergic,* 1974. Professional Books, P.O. Box 3494, Jackson, Tenn. 38301.
A super guide for any allergic person or child.

Crook, William G., M.D. *Tracking Down Hidden Food Allergy,* 1978. Professional Books, P.O. Box 3494, Jackson, Tenn. 38301.
A well-written, well-illustrated guide with easy-to-follow directions. Makes a great workbook for any group of parents who are trying diet control together.

Frazier, Claude A., M.D. *Coping with Food Allergy.* New York: Quadrangle/The New York Times Book Co., 1974.
A thorough, well-written book on food allergies with many helpful recipes.

Rapp, Doris J., M.D. *Allergies and Your Child.* New York: Holt, Rinehart and Winston, Inc., 1972.
A helpful book with lots of questions (and answers) parents of allergic children might ask.

Diet and Behavior

Abrahamson, E. M., M.D., and Pezet, A. W. *Body, Mind and Sugar.* New York: Avon, 1951.

Breneman, J. C., M.D. *Help Your Bed-wetting Child,* 1978. Galesburg, Mich. 49053.

Cheraskin, E., M.D.; Ringsdorf, W. M.; and Bresher, A. *Psychodietetics.* New York: Bantam Books, 1974.

Cott, Alan, M.D. *The Orthomolecular Approach to Learning Disabilities,* 1977. Academic Therapy Publication, P.O. Box 899, 1539 Fourth Street, San Rafael, Cal. 94901.
An interesting book for parents interested in diet and vitamin therapy for their learning disabled child.

Crook, William G., M.D. *Can Your Child Read? Is He Hyperactive?,* 1975. Professional Books, P.O. Box 3494, Jackson, Tenn. 38301.
A must for every parent with a hyperactive and/or learning disabled child. Lots of helpful information on diet, allergy, medicines, vitamins, and behavior modification.

Dufty, William. *Sugar Blues.* New York: Chilton, 1975.

Feingold, B. F., M.D. *Why Your Child Is Hyperactive.* New York: Random House, 1974.
An interesting story of Dr. Feingold's experiences with his additive and salicylate-free diet and hyperactive children.

Fredericks, Carlton, Ph.D., and Goodman, Herman, M.D. *Low Blood Sugar and You.* New York: Grosset & Dunlap, 1969.

Mackarness, Richard, M.D. *Eating Dangerously: The Hazards of Hidden Allergies.* New York: Harcourt Brace Jovanovich, 1976.

Powers, Hugh, M.D., and Presley, James. *Food-Power: Nutrition and Your Child's Behavior.* New York: St. Martin's Press, 1978.

Randolph, Theron, M.D. *Human Ecology and Susceptibility to the Chemical Environment.* Springfield, Ill.: Charles C. Thomas, 1970.

Smith, Lendon H., M.D. *Improving Your Child's Behavior Chemistry.* Englewood Cliffs, N.J.: Prentice-Hall, 1976.
An entertaining, fascinating book by a popular pediatrician. Par-

ents of hard-to-raise children will identify with the characters in this book and will profit from Dr. Smith's advice.

Speer, Frederick, M.D. *Allergy of the Nervous System.* Springfield, Ill.: Charles C. Thomas, 1970.

A fascinating collection of articles on the effect of allergy on the brain. Written for professionals, but some parents may find it interesting.

Stevens, George E.; Stevens, Laura J.; and Stoner, Rosemary B. *How to Feed Your Hyperactive Child.* Garden City, N.Y.: Doubleday & Co., Inc., 1977.

Von Hilsheimer, George. *Allergy, Toxins, and the Learning-Disabled Child.* San Rafael, Cal.: Academic Therapy Publications, 1974.

Wunderlich, Ray C., M.D. *Allergy, Brains and Children Coping,* 1973. Johnny Reads, Box 12834, St. Petersburg, Fla. 33733.

An interesting, well-written book by a pediatrician based on his experiences with allergic, hyperactive, learning disabled, and other problem children.

Diet and Health

Coffin, Lewis, M.D. *The Grandmother Conspiracy Exposed.* Santa Barbara, Cal.: Capra Press, 1974.

A well-written, thought-provoking book by a pediatrician who is concerned about the effect of diet on the health of today's children.

Davis, Adelle. *Let's Have Healthy Children.* New York: Harcourt Brace Jovanovich, 1951.

Goldbeck, Nikki, and Goldbeck, David. *The Supermarket Handbook: Access to Whole Foods.* New York: Harper & Row, 1973.

Hunter, Beatrice Trum. *Fact/Book on Food Additives and Your Health.* New Canaan, Conn.: Keats Publishing, Inc., 1972.

Jacobson, Michael F. *Eater's Digest: The Consumer's Factbook of Food Additives.* Garden City, N.Y.: Doubleday Anchor Books, 1972.

LaLeche League. *The Womanly Art of Breastfeeding.* Danville, Ill.: Interstate Printers, 1958.

Lappe, Frances Moore. *Diet for a Small Planet*. New York: Ballantine Books, 1971.

Null, Gary, and Null, Steven. *How to Get Rid of the Poisons in Your Body*. New York: Arco Publishing, 1977.

Ott, John N., Ph.D. *Health and Light*. Old Greenwich, Conn.: Devin-Adair Co., 1973.
A fascinating account of the effects of light on animals and plants and how modern lighting, building, and television may affect our health adversely.

Pryor, Karen. *Nursing Your Baby*. New York: Harper & Row, 1963.

Reuben, David, M.D. *Everything You Always Wanted to Know About Nutrition*. New York: Simon & Schuster, 1978.
This question-and-answer book about nutrition is a must for families who are interested in improving their diets.

Williams, Roger J. *Nutrition Against Disease*. New York: Pitman Publishing Corp., 1971.

Wood, Curtis, Jr. *Overfed but Undernourished*. New York: Tower Publications, 1971.

Wunderlich, Ray C., M.D. *Improving Your Diet,* 1976. Johnny Reads, Inc., Box 12834, St. Petersburg, Fla. 33733.

Helpful Cookbooks

Davis, Adelle. *Let's Cook It Right*. New York: Signet, 1947.

Dworkin, Stan, and Dworkin, Floss. *The Good Goodies: Recipes for Natural Snacks 'N' Sweets*. Emmaus, Pa.: Rodale Press, Inc., 1974.

Emerling, Carol G., and Jonckers, Eugene O. *The Allergy Cookbook*. New York: Barnes & Noble Books, 1969.

Farmilant, Eunice. *The Natural Foods Sweet-tooth Cookbook*. Garden City, N.Y.: Doubleday & Co., Inc., 1973.

Kees Beverly. *Cook with Honey*. Brattleboro, Vt.: The Stephen Greene Press, 1973.

Lansky, Vicki. *The Taming of the C.A.N.D.Y. Monster*. Wayzata, Minn.: Meadowbrook Press, 1978.

Little, Billie. *Recipes for Allergics*. New York: Grosset & Dunlap, 1971.

Martin, Faye. *Naturally Delicious Desserts and Snacks*. Emmaus, Pa.: Rodale Press, 1978.
A beautifully illustrated, well-written cookbook with lots of yummy desserts and snacks all made with honey, maple syrup, or molasses. Expensive but worth the price for families who must have their desserts.

Opton, Gene, and Hughes, Nancie. *Honey Feast*. San Francisco, Cal.: Apple Pie Press, 1974.

Parkhill, Joe. *The Wonderful World of Honey, A Sugarless Cookbook*. Lenexa, Kansas: Cookbook Publishers Inc., 1977.

Shattuck, Ruth R. *Creative Cooking Without Wheat, Milk and Eggs*. Cranbury, N.J.: A. S. Barnes and Co., Inc., 1974.

Vaughan, Beatrice. *Real Old-time Yankee Maple Cooking*. Brattleboro, Vt.: The Stephen Greene Press, 1969.

Other Sources of Information

Allergy Awareness Newsletter
Marilyn Sondy, Editor
1609 Mills Avenue
N. Muskegon, Mich. 49445
The Allergy Awareness Newsletter is an interesting, informal newsletter written by a dedicated mother of an allergic family.

Allergy Information Association
Room 7, 25 Poynter Drive
Weston, Ontario, Canada M9R 1K8
The Allergy Information Association is a superb volunteer organization dedicated to helping allergy sufferers. They are also concerned with the relationship of diet to behavior. They publish an interesting newsletter and offer helpful recipes—$10 for membership, $5 for information kit.

Association for Children with Learning Disabilities (ACLD)
5225 Grace Street
Pittsburgh, Pa. 15236
The purpose of this national organization is to improve the educational opportunities of children with learning disabilities.

Center for Science in the Public Interest (CSPI)
1755 S Street N.W.
Washington, D.C. 20009
The goal of CSPI is to improve the quality of American diets through research and public education. They have several great posters available. One poster, "Chemical Cuisine," is a handy guide to food additives. Another, "Nutrition Scoreboard," grades many foods according to their nutritional value. They also publish *Nutrition Action Magazine*.

The Feingold Association of New York
56 Winston Drive
Smithtown, N.Y. 11787
This organization publishes a list of medications free of artificial color and flavor.

The Feingold Association of the United States (FAUS)
759 National Press Building
Washington, D.C. 20045
The Feingold Association is a great volunteer group of parents trying to help other parents of hyperactive and learning disabled children through a newsletter, "Pure Facts," and local Feingold groups. They publish helpful lists of "safe" products.

The Huxley Institute for Biosocial Research
1114 First Avenue
New York, N.Y. 10021
The Huxley Institute is dedicated to educating the public and professionals about biochemical causes of mental illness.

LaLeche League International, Inc.
9616 Minneapolis Avenue
Franklin Park, Ill. 60131
LaLeche League is a non-profit organization dedicated to good mothering through breastfeeding. Local groups offer information, books, support, and encouragement for nursing mothers.

New York Institute for Child Development
205 Lexington Avenue
New York, N.Y. 10016

The New York Institute for Child Development publishes an informative newsletter "Reaching Children" about diet, behavior, and learning disabilities. They have some fascinating cassette tapes available.

Prevention Magazine
33 East Minor Street
Emmaus, Pa. 18049
Prevention magazine is a monthly publication devoted to better health through proper diet.

INDEX